Ericksonian Hypnotherapeutic Group Inductions

HILDEGARD KLIPPSTEIN

Translated by
TWINKY J. STEPPACHER-RAY, Ph.D.

BRUNNER/MAZEL PUBLISHERS • NEW YORK

Royalties from all but one chapter
of this book are being donated to Greenpeace.

Library of Congress Cataloging-in-Publication Data
Ericksonian hypnotherapeutic group inductions / [edited by] Hildegard
Klippstein ; translated by Twinky J. Steppacher-Ray.
p. cm.
Some contributions are translated from German.
Includes bibliographical references.
ISBN 0-87630-588-5
1. Hypnotism—Therapeutic use. 2. Group psychotherapy.
3. Erickson, Milton H. I. Klippstein, Hildegard.
[DNLM: 1. Erickson, Milton H. 2. Hypnosis—methods. WM 415
E68526]
RC497.E74 1991
616.89'162—dc20
DNLM/DLC
for Library of Congress

90-2531
CIP

We gratefully acknowledge Avanta Network Inc. for permission to reprint *Community Building Experience* and *Morning Meditation* by Virginia Satir.

Published by
BRUNNER/MAZEL, INC.
19 Union Square West
New York, New York 10003

Manufactured in the United States of America

10 9 8 7 6 5 4 3 2 1

I dedicate this book to
my friends and teachers
in hypnotherapy

Contents

V. Resources

VI. Therapy

VII. Integration

VIII. Future-Pace and Consolidation of Learning

IX. Re-Orienting

Foreword

Perhaps Hildegard Klippstein should have departed from the vernacular in creating the title for this book; perhaps she should have called it "Ericksonian Hypnotherapeutic Group *Climates*," rather than "*Inductions*." However, she cannot be faulted: tradition among both lay and professional circles dictates that "hypnosis" be defined as a procedure whereby a trance state is *induced* in a person. However, in recent years, the hypnotic work of Milton Erickson, as elaborated by his followers such as Ernest Rossi (Erickson & Rossi, 1979), Stephen and Carol Lankton (Lankton & Lankton, 1983), Stephen Gilligan (Gilligan, 1987), and Michael Yapko (Yapko, 1990), has redefined hypnosis as an experience that is *elicited* from within, not induced from without. Erickson wisely quipped that therapists mainly establish a climate for change to happen—both hypnotically and therapeutically. Motive force comes from the patient; the therapist only establishes an experiential environment in which the patient can affect enduring change.

The operational word in the last sentence is "experiential." Reactions to experiences can be damaging or constructive. So much "neurosis" is the by-product of destructive experiences. If experiences create problems, experiences can be used to resolve them (Zeig, in press). Personally, I study Erickson's work because his is the most interesting model of how constructive therapeutic experiences can be used to catalyze change. And one of the primary methods that Erickson used was hypnosis.

Hypnosis is a ritual that presupposes change by its very nature. The underlying injunction of hypnosis is "by having this (hypnotic) experience, you will be different." It is an intriguing area of study for therapists and those interested in social influence.

There are two primary forms of hypnosis: self-hypnosis and heterohypnosis, depending on whether or not a hypnotist is present. (Although most experts opine that *all* hypnosis is really self-hypnosis.) Hypnosis theories can be divided into traditional and Ericksonian camps. Traditional methods emphasize the use of direct and authoritarian suggestions; the Ericksonian model is more indirect and interpersonal.

Many excellent books have been written about self-hypnosis and about Ericksonian and traditional methods of heterohypnosis. But the literature on group hypnosis is sparse. The present book fills a previously uninhabited niche. No previous volumes on Ericksonian group hypnosis exist, and there are not many investigators in the field of group hypnosis. Therefore, we can be thankful to Hildegard Klippstein for filling this vacuum.

What will the reader encounter in this book? One will find state-of-the-art demonstrations from preeminent practitioners of Ericksonian hypnosis. Also, there is a contribution from Virginia Satir, who was not Ericksonian, but whose therapeutic language merits much study (for example, see *Virginia Satir: The Patterns of Her Magic* (Real People Press, Moab, Utah, by Steve Andreas, in press). Many of the demonstrators are from Germany, Klippstein's native country. They are from the Milton H. Erickson Gesellschaft (MEG), one of the world's premiere Ericksonian organizations. The MEG was one of the first Ericksonian organizations, having been founded in 1978, one year prior to the founding of the Milton H. Erickson Foundation.

Some of the leaders of the German school, Burkhard Peter and Wilhelm Gerl, visited Dr. Erickson in Phoenix. They received his permission to found an Ericksonian organization in Munich, which subsequently developed into the MEG. Other leaders of the MEG include Bernhard Trenkle, Gunther Schmidt, and Dirk Revenstorf.

I am very familiar with the high quality of Ericksonian practice and the advances developed by German colleagues. Since 1979, I have traveled to Germany two or three times per year to conduct training workshops. During these years, most of the German contributors to this volume have become my friends.

It is an honor to write this foreword, not only because this book fills a void, but it also introduces the German school of Ericksonian therapy to the English-speaking world. These German Ericksonians are destined to make their mark on the international therapy scene.

This book contains group *demonstrations:* most of the inductions are taken from training workshops for professionals. Therefore, this volume should be of special interest to trainers and students of Ericksonian methods. Practitioners of group therapy also will benefit. They will find ways to adapt these techniques to patient populations. Therapists from all persuasions can glean new methods by studying the rich, therapy communication forms used by the experts.

The contributors to this volume promote and develop innovations in Ericksonian practice. One of Klippstein's innovations is a return to pristeen Ericksonianism. In his teaching, Erickson was reluctant to discuss and dissect technique. Mainly, he lectured to elicit motivation among students to study hypnosis and strategic methods. His lectures were similar to his therapy—experiential.

Klippstein, with the help of her able translator Twinky Steppacher-Ray, has made this book Ericksonian: academic material is presented in the last chapter as a sort of "dessert." The main course is involvement of the reader in the experience of hypnotherapeutic climates. Thus, the book reads more like poetry than didactic prose.

This technique is bold and fresh. Also, it is hard to accomplish in print. The actual inductions were the product of the words in combination with the personality of the demonstrator, the nonverbal and paraverbal methods employed, and the context in which they were offered. In print, these trappings are absent. Only the words are here.

Still, there is much protein for the reader to digest. The contributors are masters who have developed precision in using words to influence. Erickson also used words carefully: He was like a master builder. Each word was a stone artfully chosen and meticulously placed according to an architecturally sound and aesthetically pleasing plan.

Therefore, this book is not only hypnotherapeutic group climates for those present for the actual demonstrations: it is hypnotherapeutic group climates for the reader. The reading should be, in all senses, an experience.

—JEFFREY K. ZEIG, Ph.D.
Director
The Milton H. Erickson Foundation
Phoenix, Arizona

REFERENCES

Erickson M. H., & Rossi, E. L. (1979). *Hypnotherapy: An exploratory casebook.* New York: Irvington.

Gilligan, S. R. (1987). *Therapeutic trances: The cooperation principle in Ericksonian hypnotherapy.* New York: Brunner/Mazel.

Lankton, S. L. & Lankton C. (1983). *The answer within.* New York: Brunner/Mazel.

Yapko, M. D. (1990). *Trancework: An introduction to the practice of clinical hypnosis.* (2nd ed.). New York: Brunner/Mazel.

Zeig, J. K. (in press). Ericksonian psychotherapy: The recreation of experiences, in *PsycheScapes: The evolution of psychotherapy II*, by Zeig, J.K. (Ed.), New York: Brunner/Mazel.

Introducing Inductions

"Use your mind at the unconscious level, even while you are using it at the conscious level."

—Milton H. Erickson *(Rosen, 1982, p. 64)*

This book is arranged to aid practitioners such as therapists, teachers, social workers, and other mental health professionals who work with groups towards achieving certain goals, for instance, acquiring new knowledge and learning for prophylactic or therapeutic purposes. "Hypnotherapeutic Group Induction" is an emerging scientific method, a hitherto little known or used method of attaining these objectives effectively and relatively rapidly. The inductions presented here by experts working according to the concept of Milton H. Erickson are drawn mainly from workshops and conferences for psychologists, psychiatrists and other doctors and dentists within the last seven years. Therefore they originate from actual practice situations, and the hypnotherapists found their results convincing.

As Group Inductions may be a new concept for many of those reading this text, an explanation is warranted. Basically, Group Inductions are introductions into "altered states of consciousness." In this book Group Inductions are defined in terms of hypnotic or trance states. The reader may already have a preconceived notion of hypnosis that implies the subject loses consciousness but responds to the suggestions of the hypnotist. However, our use of the term "hypnosis" or "trance" denotes an altered state of consciousness when the subject is enabled to develop his or her own unconscious creative potentials.

A distinction between the induction and the "hypnosis proper" is sometimes made, but in actual practice it is difficult to determine exactly where induction ends and hypnosis begins. Thus the common usage has come to represent not only the first part of the process as the "Trance Induction" or "Group Induction" but also, implicitly, the process as a whole, including the re-orientation, i.e., the return journey back to the everyday state.

The inductions in this book were chosen to show how entrancingly varied are the possibilities of trance work with groups. Beyond this the reader will be led to an understanding of the basic structure of a Group Induction. This is why some of the inductions are commented on whereas others are left to the reader to follow the process unaccompanied and free to discover and to invent. This approach allows the reader to become familiar with the subtle verbal tools of the hypnotherapist.

Hypnotherapeutic work with one person demands special care; this is even more important with groups. The wording must be considered very carefully, so that no one will be harmed in the open, sensitive state of trance. This book offers some worthwhile stimulation but the reading in itself does not confer the ability to carry out Group Inductions.

All of us have experienced the state of trance. We enter automatically into another state of consciousness, into trance, when we are concentrating on something, reading an interesting book, listening to music, while dancing—whenever we block out everything else. As I am writing this, I enter into a trance. This already demonstrates how trance consists of very complex phenomena experienced differently by every individual, if we dare to pass the borders of our usual perception and our learnt way of life.

It is also known that it is very easy to go into trance again and again once we have learned how to do so. The trail has already been blazed. Those who have learned to enter trance by the way of catalepsy, for example, arm levitation, can use this device repeatedly.

But what is this, a new way to limit, using the narrow path of the same trance trail? Wouldn't it be better to have available several alternate routes to lead us to very different frontiers? We need ways that are in their own way on the way to be ways well-trodden. We need ways that pass over to seldom-used frontier paths and high passes above and away beyond our usual boundaries. However, even these frontier paths on which we walk much more cautiously and on which we observe all that happens in a very alert way, are ways we have walked before. Otherwise, the grass would not be trampled down, the twigs would not be snapped, the way would not be identifiable as a way. Anyway, even this way must be put away if the way is to lead us away to the virgin fields of new learning where we orient ourselves, find the direction of the goal we are aiming at, mark it in some way so that we can find our way back and eventually take and make a new path.

It is a good exercise for us so-called civilized human beings to look around ourselves in this expanse of new learning, to really look around to gain a general view of things and to catch a sight of the way so far, a sight that in my sight may be called an expansion from short-sightedness into careful farsightedness, where on all sides new sights come into sight.

Where are we? Those who have followed me up to here may shake their heads disapprovingly and think: "Why is all this game with words in an introduction? I want to know what this book is about." Those who have let themselves be influenced by my "technique of induction" may have had a taste and have discovered that in this field it is wise to combine theory and practice. Everything depends on communicating in a really congruent manner at every moment. Only then can we be led by our own or others' blazing of the trail into the pathless, but not untrodden land.

Learn on the Side: Every time you communicate congruently, you can provoke a different state of consciousness in other people on the site. You can also do this when you communicate consciously incongruently. This is actually part of the advanced technique.

Do not become confused by my confusion technique. This, too, is an advanced technique, just like the "intentional mistake" technique. Pay exact attention to what I am doing. Then you can learn consciously by the way here and now and also when reading the presentations of all the authors, step by step, stopping and starting, something your unconscious already grasped a long time ago, and has also been using for a long time.

By the way, it is useful to read the chapters in the printed order, step by step, stopping and starting, for they are arranged in a developing sequence. (Important pieces of information are mentioned casually; that way you can reach your goal far faster.) If, though, you dislike eating meat and prefer the bare bones, the drier theoretical final section may be taken as "starter."

During my first trance induction my teacher led me back after a short time so that he, and also I, could test whether everything was in order. It was good this way. I could take security and trust so that I could go even deeper afterwards.

You, reading this, can test how far your state of consciousness has changed by now. Have you noticed that you have hardly been hearing the noises around you for some time now? Have you noticed that for some time you have been disregarding your body posture? Did you become totally absorbed in reading?

Consciously reflect upon your present feelings and sensations before you continue reading. Use the opportunity to explore where you are now clearly and attentively in order to start with learning right here, the kind of learning this book can offer you. Get totally alert at once! Wake up from your daily trance! Probably you are shocked to hear that you usually live in a trance and need to be dehypnotized from all the acquired and trained behavioral mechanisms in order to be able to see without glasses, to be fully awake for the first time in your life. If you do not reach this direct perception immediately, just imagine what it would be like to see with the eyes of a new-born child, not yet "knowing" that objects keep their sizes, although they look smaller at a distance. What would it be like to hear with the ears of a new-born child, not yet "knowing" what single sounds mean. And what would it be like to feel with the hands of a new-born child, not yet "knowing" the "real" extent of the finger tips.

What have I just done? I have just presented several possibilities and illustrations of induction techniques so that there is something for everybody. Further, I have left open the option of which channel of perception (seeing, hearing, feeling) your experience may be focused on so that there is something for everybody. I have composed my sentences in such a way that some rhythmic elements are repeated, "so that there is something for everybody."

I am now going to offer you some further aids you can accept trustingly. You will have noticed that you can safely abandon some prejudices about hypnosis or about unwelcome strategies of influence for you are the only one to determine what you want to experience while reading these words.

What about looking at your surroundings in a new way! Let yourself become aware of the intensity of the different colors, the shades and hues of the various colors depending on the amount of light falling on them! Look at one color with the eyes of a painter who must decide which tone to use when painting a picture! And then look at these words again and pay attention to the type in which they are written! Listen to the more distant sounds! Make a distinction between these sounds and those that are close! Point a directional microphone in your imagination to different noises as if you wanted to record them! Next, fade out the more distant noises and concentrate on the sounds in your immediate surroundings. If it is totally quiet around you, concentrate on your own noises, your breathing, on the noise of one of your own movements, on the noises within your body! And experience fully the feeling of sitting in one special position or lying, or holding your body in some other attitude, your hands perhaps in a particular position! Feel what your hands are touching, the warmth or the coolness, feel what your feet are touching, what your back is up against!

And while you go on reading you may remain conscious of these body sensations, you may still continue listening to what you can hear right now. You may read slowly and peacefully forming words by adding letter to letter, and sentences by adding words to words. You do it automatically because you learned to do so earlier and have brought this to perfection. You cannot even imagine any longer how much effort this learning process you call "reading" cost you formerly.

And you will recognize that it is possible to widen your perception in a very easy way, widen your horizons of perception. And you can feel very secure doing this, because of course you can stop reading at any time, you can make a pause, take a rest from thinking, in order to orient yourself once again to what is happening to you just now.

Learning in trance is an effective way of learning. Wherever people meet to learn something it is useful for the teacher to create an effective atmosphere for learning, whenever in the mood to support the learning group going into trance. Good teachers do this naturally without even knowing it.

Learning by means of clear and simple images is effective learning. That is why I put the abstract expression of "new learning," for example, in a concrete form at the beginning by speaking of paths and footways on the borders of our habits as if they were real footways and paths along a territorial borderline.

Learning in a relaxed situation means learning effectively. Therefore I have been using some indirect suggestions for relaxation with phrases such as: "accept trustingly," "safely abandon," "still continue listening," "read slowly and peacefully," "do it automatically," "feel very secure," "make a pause," "rest from thinking," which you may or may not have recognized and to which you can now "surrender yourself consciously," for your awareness is being allowed to "stay here peacefully" in this process of relaxed learning, totally incidentally but with latent efficiency.

You know a plumb-line, a lead that sinks deep to the ground where you want to explore the unknown sea. And that's the way you listen to the sounds, deep sounds within yourself. You listen to the sea of thoughts, of dialogues that may be ringing on a rock, one here, one there, when you are really deeply absorbed. You can allow yourself to open your ears to understand yourself more deeply, to understand your self more closely and to experience what is self-evident down there. You know the ropes. Maybe your hands feel a little how the lead sinks deeper to the bottom of the sea evoking echoes. You can still let more line out. Give yourself more scope, loosen the ropes, slacken the fixture holding (sic!) the line and let this lead sink deeper to fathom out more depths. For I am sure that that was a lot of line you let out towards outboard. You may breathe deeply and feel free to let the rope glide through your fingers. It's the immensity of space that waits for you down there. And sometimes from your boat you can observe this procedure like on a screen outward. The ground down there is very clear. Your eyes distinguish things in detail outside of you as well as on your inner screen. And while you may go on to watch with fascination the inner pictures, you may be wondering why the printing now is changing, and how it touches you. In order to find out you may consult yourself: Does this change outside myself give the possibility and the permission to myself to really slow my reading down at last however unusual this may definitely be? Why not decide to try this unusual slower reading now, while letting myself be peacefully led downwards by these outward words and changed forms to a deep inner rest and recreation here while I am reading slowly with this unusual form of printing, changed writing? What am I realizing? And what is impressing me about this way of learning?

How precisely and meaningfully do I understand the sentence: I am reading slowly now. Now I have changed my rhythm of reading.

Retarding the drum	To ask for example
Slowly I hum	How much does some "a"-sound
When I can come	In this sample
Right by the rhythm	Below and above
Down to this calm.	Help me to trust
I wonder and start	Venture to love
Wander around	To open my heart?

While I now continue my reading further I can allow some new ideas to appear. For I am here and I am there. What is so fascinating about trance is the fact that here and there and even where, over there things can occur. and while, or even ere my conscious mind is now right here, solutions sound for some other things have already been found there. it is a long while since i recognized that here's a rhythm playing here. i have noticed too the vanishing of letters which were capitals. maybe i have to read more carefully. what does this small change change? and what do the intentional mistakes do?

And what occurs in you, when you are listening to all your inner dialogues? Exactly that! The very thing that wanted to announce itself just now! For only part of you follows the words and picks them up, responds to what is written, sinks into text, into yourself, into this journey to the land of conscious and unconscious learning. What is it, what comes up there vaguely? Can you allow yourself to let it come as a clear picture, as formulated words, as feeling in your body? Can you allow yourself to let this come together, as if a chord had all the hues of the rainbow?

And how appropriate it is for you to turn right to the question now, of how to use these proven Group Inductions successfully:

- to reduce the initial tension and develop an open atmosphere conducive to learning;
- to focus inwardly and to achieve relaxation, detachment and total calm;
- to prepare new steps of learning and train new perceptual abilities;
- to teach how to open to new experiences;

- to mobilize resources;
- to reach therapeutic goals;
- to integrate the newly acquired learning; and
- to consolidate new learning and provide it with an appropriate future position.

You have surely glanced at the contents pages arranged in sections according to the above objectives. Before you return from the first trance you may possibly have experienced consciously—please note the cautious choice of the phrase, "may possibly," that leaves open every possibility and makes contradiction and/or resistance unnecessary—I would like to call your attention to some basic points:

1. It is important to comply with the expectations of your audience, to respond to the circumstances in which the induction takes place or in other words: to meet people where they are at the moment. Or, for readers conversant with NLP terminology, "pace" your group situation.
2. When you are able to make contact in this way, you can guide or, again NLP terminology, "lead" your audience into a state of increased readiness for learning, i.e., trance, by taking care that they concentrate on something specific. Basic to every pathway into trance is focusing your attention on a single subject.
3. In the case of unaccustomed novel experiences, a sense of security can be established by preparing for and training these new perceptual skills.
4. As soon as an altered state of awareness is reached, it can be used for opening up for new learning experiences.
5. The strongest resources often lurk within the problem area itself.
6. Therapeutic processes can often be initiated in that impulses for new and altered structuring are given.
7. It is extremely important to leave sufficient time for consolidation and integration.
8. It is wise to help group members to work through their learning in the final phases by addressing the question of how to continue in the future with the process now initiated.
9. Only after heeding the preceding eight points do you orient your group to the actual situation.

And so you can be sure that you will keep on learning step by step "stopping and starting" with every new induction you read, with every new chapter. Because learning occurs in stages, and learning needs pauses. And your unconscious will know better than you how much you can absorb and digest at a given moment, so that all you have already absorbed can develop to an organic whole by integrating the single parts and fitting them together.

And now the time has arrived for you to take a deep, relaxed breath; stretch yourself and reach out a little; be fully awake and return once again to everyday life, fit and ready to turn to whatever you feel like doing now.

Acknowledgments

My gratitude is due and duly given now once again to all authors for their friendly support and cooperation on this book. The primary impulse for the compilation I owe to Burkhard Peter and Wilhelm Gerl. I would especially like to thank Jeff Zeig, Ph.D., who gave me decisive help and encouragement in the planning and production phases, and to Manfred Prior, who offered his assistance in reading and reviewing my commentaries.

The most interesting though difficult task was undertaken by Twinky Steppacher-Ray, Ph.D., who, herself hypnotherapist and at home in both languages, went into deep trance for weeks for the German inductions to have an English rebirth. Without her creative midwifery this book would not have seen the light of day. My special thanks are given to Arist von Schlippe for his permission to use the inductions by Virginia Satir, and to the Milton Erickson Foundation for using the transcripts of the Third International Congress on Ericksonian Approaches to Hypnosis and Psychotherapy held in Phoenix, Arizona, Dec. 3-7, 1986.

I also wish to express my appreciation for the spontaneous help of Sylvia Liechti and Scott Dingle for the first translations and for the assistance of the Milton Erickson Institute in Hamburg with various questions.

In particular, I would like to single out my friends Barbara Hickel, and Rose and Lee Richmond for their special advice and hints. It is also a pleasure to mention the careful and considerate editorial work of Natalie Gilman, Editorial Vice President, and to thank her for her enthusiastic nursing and encouragement. My gratitude is due to Ann Alhadeff, Executive Editor, whose tragic death unfortunately nipped our friendly cooperation in the bud. Finally, I wish to thank my youngest son Nils, who helped me become familiar with my computer. Only his understanding and his independence enabled me to undertake this time-consuming task in the first place.

Contributors

James M. Auld, B.D.S., private practice, Inverell, Australia
Joseph Barber, Ph.D., Department of Psychiatry, University of California, Los Angeles, Calif.
Paul M. Carter, Ph.D., private practice, Haiku, Hawaii
David B. Cheek, M.D., private practice, Santa Barbara, Calif.
Ulrich Freund, Dipl. Soz. Päd., Rehaklinik Küppelsmühle, Bad Orb, Germany
Wilhelm Gerl, Dipl. Psych., Milton Erickson Gesellschaft für Klinische Hypnose (M.E.G.), München, Germany
Stephen G. Gilligan, Ph.D., private practice, San Diego, Calif.
Wolfgang Herzog, M.D., Central Institute for Mental Health, Mannheim, Germany
Norman Katz, Ph.D., Milton H. Erickson Institute of Albuquerque, N. Mex.
Hildegard Klippstein, Dr. rer. nat., private practice, Ottendorf bei Kiel, Germany
Carol Lankton, M.A., private practice, Gulf Breeze, Fla.
Stephen Lankton, M.S.W., private practice, Gulf Breeze, Fla.
Wolfgang Lenk, Ph.D., Milton Erickson Gesellschaft für Klinische Hypnose (M.E.G.), branch Berlin, Germany
Ortwin Meiss, Dipl. Psych., Milton Erickson Gesellschaft für Klinische Hypnose (M.E.G.), branch Hamburg, Germany
Burkhard Peter, Dipl. Psych., Milton Erickson Gesellschaft für Klinische Hypnose (M.E.G.), München, Germany
Ernst Petzold, Prof., M.D., Section for Clinical Psychosomatic Medicine, Medical University Clinic, Heidelberg, Germany
Manfred Prior, Dipl. Psych., Milton Erickson Gesellschaft für Klinische Hypnose (M.E.G.), branch Hamburg, Germany
Dirk Revenstorf, Prof. Dr., Psychological Institute, University Tübingen, Germany
Hans Riebensahm, Dipl. Psych., Milton Erickson Gesellschaft für Klinische Hypnose (M.E.G.), branch Göttingen, Germany
Sidney Rosen, M.D., New York Milton H. Erickson Society for Ericksonian Psychotherapy and Hypnosis, New York, N.Y.
Deborah Ross, Ph.D., Los Gatos Institute, Los Gatos, Calif.
Ernest L. Rossi, Ph.D., private practice, Malibu, Calif.

Virginia Satir, Founder, Avanta Network, Palo Alto, Calif.
Gunther Schmidt, M.D., Milton Erickson Gesellschaft für Klinische Hypnose (M.E.G.), branch Heidelberg/Rottweil, Germany
Charles R. Stern, Ph.D., Milton H. Erickson Institute of Michigan, Detroit, Mich.
Sandra M. Sylvester, Ph.D., private practice, Cedar Crest, N. Mex.
Kay F. Thompson, D.D.S., private practice, Pittsburgh, Penn.
Bernhard Trenkle, Dipl. Psych., Milton Erickson Gesellschaft für Klinische Hypnose (M.E.G.), branch Heidelberg/Rottweil, Germany
Jeffrey K. Zeig, Ph.D., The Milton H. Erickson Foundation, Phoenix, Ariz.

— I —
WARMING UP

"Warming up" is the term used here for the first, preparatory phase of a hypnotic induction. It includes initiating or enhancing an attitude of expectancy, obtaining closer contact between therapist and group, eliciting a certain degree of trust and acceptance, and establishing "rapport," in short, as the name itself suggests, the process of getting tuned in ready for a humming start and a good run.

This period may start with choice of room, time setting, seating, method of getting acquainted, and apparently casual comments even before the "official" induction begins. Willingness to listen quietly and concentrate initially on what the speaker says, as well as interest and curiosity are helpful prerequisites for trance work.

In order to warm up the reader for what is to come in this first section, here is what may be awaited there: Four authors show their own individual and different ways of guiding groups towards work performed in a state of altered consciousness. Virginia Satir did not explicitly announce her contribution as trance work, similarly Burkhard Peter speaks only of a "relaxation induction." Yet, in fact, participants of both groups experienced deep trance, as both authors intentionally employ hypnotherapeutic techniques: Virginia Satir by dipping in and out of trance (fractionated trance) and allotting tasks requiring alternate plenary and small group activity, Burkhard Peter by using special hypnotic speech forms that he himself explains during a conversation after his induction. Dirk Revenstorf knows members of his group are expecting trance, so during his induction he repeatedly returns to address the observing, conscious mind of the participants. Joseph Barber even informs the group about what to expect with a few preliminary remarks that simultaneously build up contact and start toward his acknowledged aim of warming up.

1

Virginia Satir: Community Building Experience

COMMENTS

It was at the "Symposion Family Therapy" in Osnabrück in 1986* where I met Virginia Satir personally for the first time. She was the soul of this meeting of about 500 people, creating an atmosphere of natural communication and togetherness right from the beginning. This usually happens only at the end of such a meeting—if it happens at all! I knew nobody when I first joined the Conference. After Virginia Satir's extraordinary "Community Building Experience," the Conference opening event, I had introduced myself to six people and "touched them with eyes, words and hands." The whole atmosphere of the room had changed. Never before have I experienced such a warm-hearted, natural and quick warming up in a totally strange environment. It was her personal power that she gave to the participants of the meeting, her full engagement to make us use fully the time that was given to us, appreciating each other rather than comparing who was better. Virginia Satir taught us her humanistic and cooperative view of life right in the first few minutes and gave us an experience of how to be safe in a strange environment and how to have fun. We learned to meet each other in awareness.

Afterwards, when I commented to Virginia Satir that what she had done was actually a hypnotherapeutic group induction, she smiled and said: "Yes, of course." I am so grateful for her permission to include her contribution here, because even in its written form I hope it will somehow still have the same effect now in opening this book.

Today in 1990, looking back to this meeting, I understand a little better why Virginia Satir felt that urgent need to help people communicate in a more open and human manner than usual. Perhaps she had a presentiment of her leaving us so shortly and, also, it was the time when the first news of the Chernobyl nuclear accident reached us. Virginia Satir immediately understood what that meant as can be seen from her meditation in Chapter VIII and her immediate engagement in demanding the inactivation of all atomic power stations.

The message I get now from Virginia Satir's "introducing experiment" is this: When you who work with people, you who are contributors for many others, gather together, gain time by learning to know each other in a loving way right from the beginning. Feel what you are: "a unique manifestation of life, a miracle. Bring things together!" Give yourself permission "to meet other miracles!"

---

*For further information about this symposium, refer to A. Von Schlippe & J. Kriz (Eds.) (1987)

INDUCTION

Now I want to test it out. Now I can find out, if you are also hearing the German . . . is that so? Easy? Ja? Good.

And I want to say: First of all I am very glad to be here. This is the second experience I have had in the last seven months, where people have come together to look at something with many different eyes. The first one was in Phoenix, Arizona last December when through the Erickson Foundation 7200 people came from 29 countries to look at how far we have come in working with people since 1900. In 14 years it will be the year 2000, and I think it is a very special thing that we are thinking now how to bring things together rather than "who is right." And I have to tell you, my heart feels very bad that I belong to a country that doesn't know how to do anything except drop bombs. [frantic applause] And I want you to know something else: There are many, many, many people in the United States who feel as I do. I have heard since I came to Germany that the media say that everybody in the United States adores what happened. It is not true. And I want you to know that. So that is one piece.

Also I believe that we are in a wonderful time on one level and a terrible time on another level. The wonderful part is that we have now so many ways in understanding and knowledge as Rudolf (Kaufmann) was saying this morning that we can make the world better for people. At the same time, we are in a world that knows so much about destruction—that's the whole world.

And so, with people who are working with people like you and me, to come together to look for new ways to connect with one another is a wonderful step. And as I go all over the world, this is something I want to do. So I was delighted when Rudolf said, "Will you do something to build a community?" Alright, so I want to start off with that. Each one of you knows that you are the only one exactly like you in this whole world; there are no duplicates, you know that. Your fingerprints tell you that. And since you are the only one exactly like you, you are rare. And how can you compare yourself to anybody else? Rare things can't do it, only one painting gets made, only one. So we have to learn how to appreciate each one of us. Okay.

Now, first of all, I want to play a little game. And the game is called civilization. Now, if you follow me carefully and do as—I would love to do it, if you don't do it, so you don't do it, but I will love for you to. The game is civilization. It's what we have been following for years, everywhere. Especially in the Western culture. And the game is how to be safe, so I will show you how to be safe and I'd like you all to do it with me.

First of all, you squeeze yourself in the littlest piece that you can and be sure you are not touching anybody. Right so! Tight! Tight! Tight! Yes! Now I will tell you, you are not going to hurt anybody in this position, but you can't breathe very well either. But let's do what most people do, take a pill, when we feel like this. We are safe, but we don't live very long in the world. Now, I want to, now fix this. We can stand it for a little while, we don't look very pretty, we don't feel very good.

Now, what I'd like you to do, take a big "aahh" breath and let your body fill with air and let your hands come up and your legs and whoever you touch now, it's a contact! Weee! You're good! Hoooh. Alright. Huh! Feel it in here? Hah, ja, gut! Everybody who raised their hands now and did like so and felt the air come in, can begin now to be aware that it's going to be safe here. Safe! And it will also be fun, if it isn't fun, forget it. Alright, so now we have passed the first lesson magnificently.

Now, Rudolf, I want you—what I want to do is, I want to give a little demonstration on meeting a person. You see, anyone of you, now, will be if you want to, in the place where you are going to have one miracle meet another one. And you don't know what goodies you're gonna find out. But first of all to make it possible for you to allow that wonderful investigation to occur. Okay? Now these are some ways in awareness to make a meeting. While you are doing two things, your breath is coming through and you are feeling light and that means that there is a nice energy around you. And at the same time you are willing to connect with somebody.

Right. Gut. Alright. Now I am going to make believe this is a stranger, I never saw him before. Because everybody that we ever have known today was a stranger once. You were a stranger to your mother, she didn't know you before you came, you didn't know her, or your father or your husband or wife—doesn't matter. We forget that we were all strangers once. So we can meet people in a way that can make it possible for us to build with them, or we can meet them in such a way so we protect ourselves from them, or nothing. We can do that. I want to use a way that makes it possible to build.

So now here is a stranger. But he isn't really a stranger to me, because he is a human being, like me. He has a difference though, because he is a male human being and I am a female human being. Makes a difference!

Right? Alright. Now, I keep that in my mind, simply, Rudolf was talking about differentness, that differentness is a gift that we need to learn how to teach each other about. So here I am now, I have that in my mind, I am different, not only because I am a woman, but because I am taller or shorter, fatter or thinner or whatever. I am going to be different from any other person I meet. So are you. Because that is part of our uniqueness. So in my mind I then am giving my mind permission to meet a manifestation of life, a miracle. I am one, he is one, before I even know how he behaves, I know it: Because he manifests life.

So now I then have that feeling inside that I am excited about the idea of meeting another person. I am going to have a celebration, simply because I am going to meet another person. And I am in my inside feeling that feeling and then I am going to prepare myself for that meeting: By putting myself in front of him and then by having all the holes—I am talking about holes—all the holes in such a way that we can put our energy back and forth. Now, I tell you about holes. Rudolf is a good example of (w)hole. I will show you about them.

I want to show you now two holes up here: eye holes. Two nose holes—right here, two ear holes, that's six already. An all-purpose hole right here [mouth], look down and 28 breast holes, men and women. Count them! Then we go down, and we find a navel hole. Very important hole. That was the hole that fed us, that took care of all our alimentation, while we were growing, right. Where is it? There! And if we go further: on women we will find three genital holes, and on men, two. That's how women are superior to men, you understand! Well, in addition to that, all the skin, mine, his, are all covered with little holes, called pores.

Now, all human holes have things going out and things coming in. Without our holes we would be dead. So holes are holy. Got it? Our holes are our link to life. So I then want you to have myself in a position whereby my eyes and the person I am meeting, the eyes are in a connection so we can look at each other. And that we are in a position to each other, so we can feel each other.

Now I'll show you something else. Nature is wonderful. If I put a rod through his head down or mine or yours and I go out to the distance where most people shake hands, I am at the level of what I call the "second skin." This is the first skin and this is the second [a distance of about 50 cm]. My first one, my second one. And what is between this and the first skin is a very important area for each person. Okay. So when I meet someone, I meet them at a place where we ordinarily shake hands, because that's a safe place for an individual. And I can tell you, never mind what your books say on sociology and culture, to every human being that I meet anywhere in the world, this is true. This distance does not change because of the color of the skin, it doesn't, I can tell you that. So I just want you to know that that is what human beings come with.

Alright, so here you are—I am, you are. At this point I then have a chance, if I turn towards this new person with the feeling inside that I am going to meet a miracle, that I am placing myself in such a way so that I can say: "Hello!" No, after this totally free whatever you want to make it. But let me show how many people say: "Hello." Auch: "Guten Tag, Guten Tag, ja, Guten Tag, Guten Tag, ja." And we never meet anybody. Who do we meet? We meet our fantasies.

Alright. So now what I would like you to do as a first step on that. It's not easy for many people, I will tell you that. So I would like you to go inside and connect with your courage.

Now I will tell you how to do that, you can go through your wisdom box if you want. Wisdom box is located, if you stick your fingers into your navel, go up towards your heart, half way between the two is the wisdom box that has all your courage in it. And if you will go to that box and give yourself permission and courage to meet another miracle, another treasure.

Now, don't do this fast, do it in a kind of feeling of wonder. Now all of you at this moment are folded up. I had an eight-year-old boy, who said to me, oh, you know, well I don't know, four years ago, he was watching me and when he was watching, I used to say: Get up—I don't say this any more, I say: Unfold! You see, if you are folded up, now unfold. He said: "Look, you are unfolding, isn't that wonderful!" I said: "Don't you like that better than 'get up'? Unfold!"

So what I'd like you to do, is: give yourself permission first of all to unfold. And then, while you are doing that, to know this, all the wonderful things you do, I mean the knee-bends and the toes-bend, all kind of muscle work and so on for you to unfold. The miracle is already working in you. So you get up and you are unfolding and you are thinking about yourself, then you go and you meet people, people.

And what I'd like you to do, is just to allow yourself to move as far around this room as you can and meet as many people as is possible, not so you get a reward at the end for the most people you meet, no. But that you take it in your stride and you move and you meet people. You have a chance to say: "Hello." And then, if anything else wants to come that's fine: but you will sense a feeling of connectedness and then you can say "Good-bye" and then you can move some place else. And feel yourself doing that and we'll do that for about not more than five minutes. Now that sounds short but it sometimes gets long. But this way of meeting people in awareness using yourself and the other person is in a way that makes you feel and know that you are a manifestation of something wonderful.

Remember, this is not about your behavior, because everybody does terrible things. Now it's the manifestation of the feeling of you. Now, before we start over here, I'd like to ask you what it was like to you to meet me when I was meeting you totally. We just have one microphone and this is being creative.

Rudolf Kaufmann:	Some part is astonishing always to have the feeling of being very close to a person, and that's very astonishing, because it is not very usual. And the other part is: I hope you will keep the real good distance from me. Because sometimes memories emerge.
Virginia:	And then if somebody remembers something?
Rudolf:	There is the possibility of having good experience or bad experience.
Virginia:	And if you are having good experience?
Rudolf:	It's great.
Virginia:	If you have a bad experience?
Rudolf:	It's not great.
Virginia:	Will you recover from the bad experience?
Rudolf:	Yes, I do.
Virginia:	Then you have not to worry. . . . Good. Alright. So let us see what happens, if you give yourself permission to get up and move around this room meeting people. Good. As far and as many as you can. [noise in the room]

Alright! If you can hear my voice, let your own voice get quiet. When you hear my voice, let your own voice get quiet. . . . When you hear my voice, let your own voice be quiet. . . . Don't go away, just if you hear my voice, let your voice get quiet. When you hear my voice, let your own voice be quiet. When you hear my voice, let your own voice be quiet. When you hear my voice, let your own voice be quiet. [Slowly it becomes quiet in the room, but only very slowly.]

Thank you, don't sit down. Hm. When you hear my voice, let your own voice be quiet. Thank you for that. I want to tell you something about what just happened. Many of you did not hear my voice, and I want you to know something, that's not because you are a bad person. That's because the pull of being connected and being in attention to another person is always stronger than anything from the outside. When we were little kids and we didn't come immediately when our parents would call us, often we would be punished, because it was seen that somehow we were disrespecting those parents. Actually, nobody can be pulled away easily from something with which they are involved.

Alright. So now at this moment, I just want to make a comment and then ask a question. At this moment you are standing perhaps in a different place from where you were seated. For how many is that true? . . .

Wonderful, alright . . . Now for how many in this room is it beginning to feel a little bit different than it did when you first came in the beginning? Let me see that . . .

Now you noticed that we didn't say anything about how you should feel different. It comes because we have a freedom to contact and an encouragement to do so. I just think what might have happened, had I said to you, "Now, look, when you get up, first of all you got to meet as many people as possible, because I am going to grade you," and then I said, "And what I want you to do is: Look at anybody for what's wrong with them." You suppose that you would have gotten the same feeling? No. And yet do you know what? This is the way that many of us start out with other people. Certainly it has been something in the whole therapeutic field, the parental field, the educational field, that we start out knowing people with what's wrong with them. I hope that never happens to you again.

Alright. Now! How many of you met people that you'd never met before? . . . Wunderbar! Okay.

Now, what I'd like you to do? I'd like you to go in groups of three. Now right around where you are to somebody preferably that you have never seen before or just met. Those chairs are all to be unhooked. So that you can make yourself a little triad nest. So do that now, and when you all have got your little nest, I'll come back and suggest something for you. Unhook the chairs and make a little triad nest. [noise in the room]

When you have found your two other partners and you are seated, just let your eyes close so I can see how it's working. And if some of you are standing and want to make your triads like that, that's okay, too. Because I notice there are not enough chairs, so . . . alright. Now look to see, count: eins, zwei, drei, see if you have got three of you in a group. Ja. Three. Okay?

Alright. Now, I like you to let your eyes close— and your mouth and just for a few moments . . . to let yourself be aware that you have already created a miracle. You took this crowded room and with really very little difficulty created now a set of three-person groups. And I want you to pause, to be aware of how well you did it. It was wonderful.

Now at this point, I would like you to take a risk that Rudolf talked about. Your eyes are closed and give yourself permission, while your eyes are closed, to take a risk that will benefit you. You don't know that yet, but I hope you will believe me and allow yourself to take that risk. And what I am going to ask you to do, is to find out from each of you, how you are alike and different.

Starting out with noticing what you see, I notice that you have lots of hair and I have little hair for instance. Not judging, just observing out loud. I notice you have a brown jacket on, and I have a brown jacket on. And then, as you talk, you may begin to see other similarities and differences, but I would like you to start with the differentnesses first. Remember that everything that is unique, is always going to have differentnesses from something else. So this time it's like you were a reporter for the world, and you are just noticing the wonderful ways in which you and someone else are different, and you may come up with some very interesting conclusions after that.

Now we will do this for about ten minutes, and you won't have to take care of the time, I will.

Alright. Now, just let yourself with your eyes closed feel what you feel like and giving yourself permission, see if you do, to take this risk, with two people that you may not yet know, that you are going to concentrate on the ways in which you are different and then alike. And see what happens in your insides as you make this for yourself. And if there are little things that say: Ahhch, you shouldn't do that! Well—let yourself notice that, too.

I have never lost anybody in this exercise. In fact almost everybody comes out with shining faces and sparkling eyes. But you don't know that yet. So now, give yourself permission to do this rich, important and original thing with the people with whom you are. So let the beautiful eyes open and let the sharing begin. [A gradually increasing murmur in the room becomes quite loud as all of the voices combine.]

Just let your own voice fade and close your eyes. And now as your eyes are closed, just let yourself feel what you are feeling about yourself right now. What does it feel inside? That beautiful self inside—how is it feeling? And what are you aware of what you have experienced, learned, as you have just allowed yourself to notice differences and samenesses with your partners. Did it so happen, at some point, that what you thought was a difference turned out to be a sameness? It sometimes happens.

Now let yourself come in touch with where you are right now, what you are feeling with the experience of two people that you may never have met before. Would you gently just open your eyes, and just look at your partners. And then close your eyes again. And now, when you have closed your eyes, do your partners look a little different to you?

Now ask yourself if there is anything you would like to share with your partners, any appreciations, a question you would like to know more about, so that you can feel finished at this point with something you've started out to do. Many times we do not put in our appreciations, we only feel them but we don't say them. So maybe one piece of this might be any appreciations that you have that you would like to share in the next two or three minutes with your partners, and then I will come back to you. So let the beautiful eyes open and see if there is anything you want to share and if so, do it. [Growing murmur in the room.]

And now I wonder, when you hear my voice, if you'll just gently let your voice fade and again let your beautiful eyes close. And now that your eyes are closed, if there seems to be anything left over from things that you would like to share with your partners, remember: the conference is just beginning, and there will be time, if you want to follow it up.

Now at this moment, I wonder if you would give yourself permission to make a period at this point and I will tell you about that and then we will add another piece. So at this moment I wonder if you could allow yourself, in whatever way seems fitting for you, to say something to this particular experience, although the three of you won't leave, some kind of way of saying good-bye to what the three of you had together in some kind a nonverbal way, a handshake, a hug, a look, or whatever you feel fits you at this moment. And then I will ask you to do a second piece. So let your eyes open now, let that part of a good-bye take place. [A quiet murmur follows.]

And now, now comes a part that I would encourage you to use your creativity with, I would like you now in the triad that is finished as a triad itself . . . and now to move to another triad, one close by, and then to introduce yourself to each other. So what you'll do now is: you as a triad have had an experience, now you will move to a second triad and that will mean, there will be six. So that you introduce yourself to each other. Let your creativity work to make that happen. We will work a few minutes on that. [Murmur in the room.]

When you hear my voice, would you just let your own voice fade. And then let your eyes close. Now that you have heard my voice, your eyes are closed.

Thank you! It isn't easy to get pulled away from something that you are doing. I am watching the clock. For you—and me. And like so many things, a clock may cut into what we are doing. Sometimes when my voice came in, it could have been for someone of you that it felt like an irritation and you wished I wouldn't be speaking. If that happened to you, please remember that I don't take offence. It's natural. Now at this time you've had a chance to touch many people with your eyes, your words, your hands, and then you had a chance to be very special with two other people in your triad. And then you had an opportunity to make that triad into a bigger experience. Perhaps (and hopefully) with people you had not met before or, if you had, you know them differently.

We're at the beginning of an experience which—as Rudolf put it so beautifully this morning or this afternoon—we have a chance to share with each other in many ways. And maybe the experience that you had talking in depth about your samenesses and your differentnesses could bring you closer to this whole group. And now what I'd like you to do is let yourself go completely inside of you at this moment, giving yourself a message of appreciation for you, feeling your own breathing, loving your own self and perhaps also being aware of what happened for you, what enriched you for this afternoon. [Silence.]

And perhaps at this point you might give yourself permission any time during this conference or any time to come that you could just at a moment close your eyes, give yourself permission to love yourself, and to give yourself permission to let yourself know what you have learned. So now the time has come to take another form and what I'd like you to do now is to open your eyes, look around at your new group, and then to say a good-bye in whatever nonverbal way fits you; and then you come back to the seat you had before we started all this. [Voices in the room.]

When you find your own chair, let yourself sit down. [It's still very noisy in the room.]

Alright, if I can have your attention. How many of you are really aware that you are now sitting in the same seat you had when you came in this afternoon? How many came back to the same seat? Let me see! . . . You found it! Wonderful!

Alright, let me make a comment. I don't know if you know how wonderful you were this afternoon. You did actually almost the impossible. This room is packed, you reshaped with your creativity, with your spirit, with your bodies the whole atmosphere in this room. Are you aware of that? You couldn't have known what a really wonderful thing it was to see it, because you were busy doing what you were doing. How many of you at this moment in time now are aware of feeling even a more close part to the rest of the people in this group? Let's see. And what I hope is even if you haven't met everyone else, the way is open. And in a way, what we did this afternoon for me is a metaphor of life. How I can with my intention, my spirit and what's around me, create a community with just myself. As all we talked of today was just being able to be connected. Hearing and seeing, and touching. And noticing differentness, that's all. Think about it for a bit. For me—I thank you for your attention and your willingness and the good feelings I had as all the human energy began to let itself come out. So, my friend, you want to close this.

Rudolf: I want to close it, yes. [Long applause.] Thank you, Virginia, so much for all. So when we are here inside and have the feeling of a new spring here, outside there is a new feeling in the nature, too. So, we can put it together, and we have wonderful weather outside, so that we can refresh ourselves. I would like to remember you . . . [German announcements.]

2

Burkhard Peter: Some Simple Principles

COMMENTS

Somewhat different from that of Virginia Satir is the concise, pithy induction by Burkhard Peter I heard in my very first Hypnotherapy Seminar in 1982. This induction touched me deeply. I remember not having understood at all what he had done with the group: there was only this inexplicable, fascinating, deep silence and inwardness I had never previously experienced. Having done relaxation inductions for many years, Burkhard Peter needed but a few significant words to lead us to where he stayed himself, teaching, in a trance state. It was as though the trance quality actually adhered to those oft-repeated words. It was a totally new idea for me, too, that someone could be in trance while appearing to be in a normal state. Besides the technical explanations given by Burkhard Peter in the comment immediately following the induction, his own state of consciously being in a trance state was for me the main secret of his being able to lead the group to the same state so quickly and effectively.

For me as an observer, then unfamiliar with the field of hypnosis, it appeared that Burkhard Peter communicated his love to the group so we would be able to communicate with each other in the most efficient way.

INDUCTION

To clarify the paradox with regard to both the linguistic as well as the thematic aspects and to present these more generally, I have considered doing the following: I shall now not make any trance induction, where something like a trance may develop for one person or the other, but I shall do a relaxation induction. And with this I should like to ask you to let your body feel really well, but also try essentially simply to be there present with your conscious mind and pay attention and try to follow and keep up with the various things that I shall undertake in detail during this relaxation induction. This relaxation induction has various similarities to a trance induction, at least as far as certain principles, certain criteria are concerned, also in the kind of language and content. There you can put much more generally and more in particular.

See that you yourselves sit comfortably. It seems obviously to have some significance or a meaning if someone puts his legs apart in this way and also the hands apart, but it seems to make a difference, if someone has his hands together, like this or that, or whether he lays them freely side by side.

All right. So far you are still hearing at the moment the sounds here in the room that single individuals are making while they move about in their chairs and try out how to find a really comfortable seating position, a pleasant, convenient place for their bodies, so that all muscles can lie lightly, easily, loosely. You can hear all this, these external noises, and you hear my voice. You hear out in the street this noise or that, and here in the room you hear my voice. While you listen to me, it is not necessary to listen to me closely, for your unconscious will understand much more what I mean. You are sitting here, everyone on your own chair, and so you are feeling the weight of your body. One or the other change still needed for your body, do it if you feel like it. However, it is no longer necessary to do anything in particular. No need anymore to think of something in particular, to feel something special. You can let go, just let go your body and the muscles, feel the tension here and there and let them lie quite (quiet) as they are, tensed, more or less loosened up. You hear my voice, feel your body, think this, that or the other, and the images come and go, feelings come and go. And so you can let everything happen quite (quiet) as it happens, whether it be pleasant or in particular parts not yet pleasant.

And while you are sitting there and letting your body feel well, you could have a try at recapitulating with your understanding, your brain, the particulars I have mentioned. With your understanding remember the single words, the single pieces of content, the single terms; and take these over with you when you eventually refreshed and wide awake and a feeling well going out from this state of relaxation. Returning now forthwith taking that with you that you can remember now at the moment of what you heard, take over and keep ready for you're conscious of the single, particular linguistic and thematic terms that I have used. (Long pause.)

This work of remembering seems to last long. But do it quite thoroughly, because it is not enough to remember. It is just as necessary to take what is remembered with you over into the waking state, the normal state. I can already wish one or the other of you a wonderfully good morning, for the others I shall repeat this greeting later, even though some good night farewell might fare better with you all here. [Laughter.] All right, at last! I really had to work hard for you to return!

Discussion

Participant:	That was very pleasant.
Burkhard Peter:	Yes, now do you want to say something about yourselves, something that struck you? Or shall I say something?
P.:	I noticed that I was only just about in my body. When I wanted to remember, everything refused to. There was absolutely nothing there.
P.:	I, too, couldn't keep hold of anything. There was still only your voice.
B.:	So we shall have to go through it again. All right then, so this time I shall,

> so to say, do it right for the conscious mind, so please be so good as not to take part once more but only listen. [Laughter!]

So I said something like the following: You hear the sounds here in the room, the sounds out in the street. I mentioned the sounds in the room first, because there were more sounds there than outside. I usually say it the other way round. You hear the noises out in the street *and* my voice here in the room. That is already the first combination between pacing and leading. Pacing is mentioning what actually is, namely sounds out in the street. Leading: listen to what I want. I do not want you to notice the sounds in the street, but I do want you to notice my voice. Yes, that is the goal: Therefore, this completely simple sequence. There it is, you are hearing the sounds out in the street. And now a small connecting word: *and* you hear my voice here in the room. If I then say you are sitting here in a chair, this is a simple fact that you cannot deny; you feel the weight of your body, this already requires you to feel your body at all, go inside and see how far this is true. And you can let go or loosen up. That is the leading statement: what I actually want. Every time completely, simply connected with this simple word: "and." There are also other connecting words, the conjunctions: so, because, just why . . . But this simple connection: "and"—that is the most natural and simple. One can, though, then, in such states, make also entirely apparently causal connections or use real, causal connective words. Real, genuine, causal connections are naturally never present. "Therefore you are sitting on your chair *and so* you sense the weight of your body." That is an apparently causal connection." You are sitting on your chair *and therefore* you feel the weight of your body"—is purely verbally a genuine causal connection but with regard to the actual facts, it is an apparent, sham connection, of course. This genuine causal connection *and therefore* you feel the weight of your body—is usually accepted almost without comment, strangely enough. The explanation why such logical inconsistencies will be accepted is simply that that part or those parts of the conscious, the deeper consciousness or the unconscious—whatever you want to call it—functions according to other logical laws rather than the usual logical-linear, causal laws of our conscious mind, however.

Now that is already what was most important: this connection of a pacing statement—that is mention of "what is"—in connection with a leading statement—with "that what I want." The "is-state" connected to a "shall-state."

Furthermore, you see, already in the sequence of mentioning the single facts, a direction, I begin, so to say, with the external acoustic perception and bring this external acoustic perception outside of the house here into this room within. Here I could have gone still further. I could have said: "You hear my voice here and you may at the same time heed what is going on in your inside now." So that would be then the third and logical leading or furtherance. Again simply connect: "You hear my voice *and* can well heed here what is happening within yourself."

This direction from external to internal is also given in the example: "You are sitting on the chair"—that is so to say an external tactile sensation—"and you can feel the weight of your body"—or "You can let yourselves go to feeling well"—then I'm already going more to the kinesthetic-visceral, to the internal body sensations. So in general the direction is: external to internal. Naturally I can say the entire thing directly, like saying: "Direct your attention from outside away towards the inside." Then what I want would be quite unambiguously and clearly said.

P.: Do you then change the channel from hearing to feeling?

B.: Right, well, that is then a third point I want to mention still. I have forgotten before because many of you had already shut your eyes, to speak about visual perception. Had many still had your eyes open, I would have said that still in the following form: you see—usually indeed I say it really so tritely—you see what you just see. So tritely, and no resistance appears, cannot appear for there it's really quite right—and it may be you may see sooner or later certain pictures in yourself. Again the same, now in the optical channel.

P.: You leave open when it will happen.

B.: I leave open when it will happen. I leave open how exactly it will happen. I mention the single perceptual channels, so to say, the modalities where it can happen. Then I leave everything open, that is left fully up to the single individual personally.

P.: Is that then the technique of apparent alternatives?

B.: No, not here.

P.: Because at the moment when I felt required to look inside myself, it's completely impossible for me, if I see you or if I see my surroundings, because that distracts me terribly. Therefore, nothing else is possible for me there than to shut my eyes. Thus so far a technique of apparent alternatives.

B.: No, if a specialist term has to be, then it would be implication, tacit, silent implication, it is: "You can only look inside yourself when you shut your eyes or when you have your eyes open and put away the external picture," that is, "hallucinate internal images with your eyes open." That is implicit.

P.: It's not requested, shutting one's eyes?

B.: No, it's not requested. The request is contained implicitly. Well, what I have spoken of till now is a demonstration of the indirect method of procedure. Directly, I could have said: "Direct your attention away from outside way inside." I said it indirectly in that I ordered the single objects or parts I mentioned on a line from outside to inside, and with this I gave the direction implicitly.

P.: That is actually more effective, as resistance in that sense does not appear at all.

B.: Yes, usually. That is right. All right. With regard to certain linguistic principles, I have already pointed out the connecting conjunctions: and, so, as, because, then, for. I would like to point out the following points still. Listen to the following sentences consciously, for once: "It is no longer necessary to do something in particular. No need anymore to feel something special, not necessary to change a certain something."—That's all not true, what I say there, that is, that is true on one level, on the other level I say, though: "It is necessary for you to change a certain something. It is necessary for you to feel something special. You do need to do something in particular." For it fits the facts. You certainly do something. You feel something special. I use the negation to reach two goals:

> One, to avoid any possible ambition right from the start: "nothing particular need occur"—the other, through the special emphasis: "not *necessary* to do something in particular. Don't *need* to think of a certain something." If I pronounce the "not," so to say, reduced, then in the foreground the sentence stands out: "need to think of something in particular." Purely acoustically.

If one accepts then still the assumption that is to be regarded right critically, maybe it may be even dubious but nevertheless still valid for certain areas, that is, that the unconscious or the primary process obviously knows no negations, then I may use as many "nots" and "nos" as I like. It will always arrive only in the positive form. All right! Use negations! What I mean with this is mention directly, but put it in the negation: "not feel something special, no need to do a certain something. You need not let go. You need not relax. You need not go deeper." These are all formulations that positively express what I want but are only negative in the wording.

As to the next point the following: I have now and then—not always, but here and there—used nouns, substantives instead of "verbalizing." As an example listen to the difference between these sentences: "You can feel how your body is becoming heavy." Or: "You can feel the heaviness of your body." One time, I use a verb, a process word: how your body is becoming heavy. The other time, it's a substantive. Usually—that can be investigated nowadays more exactly with linguistic methods—a process word, a verb, is intrinsically more specific, individually more exact, and establishes in more detail what happens than a substantive. Or another way to say it: a substantive usually offers a larger projection area for the individual, internal contents than a verb. In this substantially static picture of the substantive, everyone can project his own process, at least more likely than when I use the process word, the verb itself.

Then there is a further point—well, here that's not so important. There are specific verbs and there are also unspecific verbs. During relaxation it is not so important, because almost all the verbs that occur within the frame of an induction of relaxation are unspecific verbs: feel, think, perceive, become conscious, sense, observe and so on. All these verbs designate an action but without establishing concretely how in particular or, furthermore, exactly every single one works. In comparison, as an example, "to hammer." If I say "to hammer," everyone of you has certainly quite a distinct, unambiguous, specific image there: for there someone takes up a hammer in one hand, either the right or the left hand—and moves the hand with the hammer up and down. That is firmly established, well nailed in. Such a concrete picture is not there with "perceive, think, feel," because naturally everyone has somewhere one's own implicit image of "perceive, think, feel, observe," but that is fully open, unspecific. Consequently, unspecific verbs offer an essentially larger projection area than do specific verbs. Every individual can then rediscover in what I say his own or her own specific ways and means of doing this particular something.

All right, that was the main substance. With this you already have formally a small part of the language that is quite favorable for trance inductions:

1. The use of pacing and leading, of picking up what is there and connecting it to the required "shall-state" and addressing this "shall-state";
2. Connecting conjunctions;
3. Addressing the different sensory channels;
4. Generally, the direction from external to internal;
5. Indirect procedure;
6. Paying attention to using substantives for preference; and
7. Using unspecific verbs.

These are quite good hints to bear in the back of your mind.

3

Dirk Revenstorf: Becoming Acquainted with Trance

COMMENTS

The following induction by Dirk Revenstorf is subtle. The language of hypnosis has become so natural to him that, upon the first reading, nothing special might be discovered by someone unfamiliar with this subject. In his introductory workshop, Dirk Revenstorf utilizes curiosity about the significance of the trance for creating the trance phenomenon of dissociation: "Therefore you can begin with sitting comfortably and start to examine how far this separation, this partition is possible for you. So you can take note with one part and make notes inside yourself and with the other you can have experiences that these notes describe." Allowing choices on one level and simultaneously employing the implied directive and a therapeutic double-bind on another is also a linguistic technique typical for the language of hypnosis: "that you perhaps wonder whether you would like to go into trance slowly and carefully or relatively quickly and also for how long." So the listeners can be consciously occupied with deciding, while unconsciously they are already proceeding in a therapeutic direction, because there is no question of whether to enter trance or not.

An ethical question arises here. A double bind is a very powerful tool and even for intelligent people it is difficult to discover. However, in a workshop on therapeutic hypnosis we can take it for granted that the participants gave permission to the leader to help them experience what they want to study.

Dirk Revenstorf also gives an example of how to get along with potentially disturbing external noises. You just weave them into your induction, as if these noises were just the best helping sounds and you are so lucky to notice them just now. This attitude of accepting everything chancing to occur within the group or without and thus seizing every wonderful opportunity for utilization is very necessary for leading into trance. I remember a trance induction during which the nearby church bells suddenly began to peal loudly. The leader let us go deeper with every clang of the bells. It was a wonderful experience, this reframing of the previously disturbing noise.

It is very interesting to notice all those expressions with "you can . . ." in Dirk Revenstorf's induction. You "can" allow yourself to experience special phenomena, but you are also free not to. This is one of the most obvious characteristic features of an indirect Ericksonian induction: avoiding any resistance right from the first. Why should you resist? You are allowed whatever you want; you are just invited to experience the special sensations the therapist is describing. Other fundamental characteristics of an Ericksonian induction used here by Dirk Revenstorf are short analogies and anecdotes affecting us on a deeper level, as wise people have always known they do. And there is also this special technique of confusion, when words are turned around and our conscious mind needs time to unravel the threads. We usually give up when we can't do this quickly enough and that is what is intended in order to allow us to profit from the benefits of an increasing letting-go. The confusion technique can be used to introduce a trance, to deepen a trance, and to terminate a trance. Dirk Revenstorf used it here to terminate the trance, so that under the sheltering cover of amnesia caused by confusion we might benefit from the source of the memories and comfort he suggested we look for.

INDUCTION

As well as in the communication with the conscious as in communication with the unconscious—I am just calling it that without knowing more and without saying exactly what that is, but in any case we know that we have at least these two possibilities in communication—it depends on both well on the way this is formulated because the formulation itself can also include more or few limitations; and that can even hinder your partner from being ready to go into trance. You must, therefore, develop this particular ability to speak with a conscious part so that the formulation itself does not hinder or prevent, but can even actually promote it. If you need to note down the terminology or the phraseology, the simplest thing is to switch on a cassette recorder because that's much more convenient than writing everything at the same time. Especially if you are taking notes you are very busy, although being occupied with one thing is a possible way to go into trance, it is still the more uncomfortable way.

Well, on the way, I'd like to ask perhaps you both to take a little time and peace and quietness first and to see what is the least helpful for you and what does not allow you to go into trance. The fact that you are just sitting here means you have actually come to find or work out what trance work actually is. You will, therefore, realize that at all points in time there are two parts in you, namely one part that observes and wants to inspect certain things and the other part that wishes to experience in what way what is being told is right and proper for you yourself.

Therefore, you can begin with sitting comfortably and start to examine how far this separation, this partition is possible for you. So you can take note with one part make notes inside yourself and with the other you can have experiences that these notes describe. And you can make these notes mentally so that your unconscious or you can perhaps recover them inside your unconscious as far as you become more and more convinced that this part of your thinking is able to notice these things without particular noticeable or noteworthy trouble. But it is a good thing to make sure that you really feel well, that you have the right seating position, the attitude that is most comfortable for you and that you perhaps wonder whether you would like to go into trance slowly and carefully or relatively quickly and also for how long and that you are sure that you could return at any time to that state, that is pleasant and agreeable for you, because many people believe that hypnosis is something where one relinquishes control. Whereas in reality you turn your attention ((loud calls outside)) from the shouting that you have just heard and about which you can still be astonished for a time, to other things.

Therefore, you can see where a part that disturbs you or is not clear to you expresses itself through your body, while the rest of your body can relax just as though you were to take up an attitude of dividing between strain and relaxation. You can have a look to see where that is, whether your feet that seem to be resting on the floor with equal weight or whether your legs are crossed or not, maybe sensing this feeling of relaxation or the weight of your body that you can feel on the chair, the touch of your hands, and the warmth that passes from one hand to the other, and the immobility that is pleasant for you at the moment not having to do anything and, at the same time, notwithstanding being able to change whatever you may not now be able to appreciate.

And while you are observing all these things with one part of your attention, the position of your body and the noises, the sounds—you can follow with the other part the things that are also occupying you. So you can also observe how first on the left or on the right foot a feeling of tickling, or some similar sensation develops in the toes and may extend slowly over the foot, maybe, you may be already forgetful of other parts of your body. Just as you can look at certain things and keep them in mind, you can also begin to let other things leave your attention. And you can now follow how this change of perception extends and spreads over your foot and your calves and shins, you can be sure to ascertain where you receive this feeling of quiet and peace within you and how much attention you still need to be quite sure and certain that you are feeling well-being at this moment in this chair, while both at the same time and in the same way, another part is occupied with things that are outside this space and place.

And you know you have all the time you need and may use this for yourself to obtain the conditions that make it easier for you to work on and follow the things that are important for you personally.

All the sounds you hear, my words and that buzzing . . . noise may show you that you have both parts, both kinds of attention, and one kind—part is there to protect the other—And you can simultaneously stand aside to one side beside yourself and smile at yourself, while you sit on this chair and do nothing and yet feel so full of well-being to the extent of how much you can develop that feeling of well-being, doing nothing, having to do nothing in particular, and you may inwardly distance yourself from the chair and leave the room step-by-step. And you can let your thoughts follow and progress—follow . . . like in a street where you see pictures left and right, memories, sounds, that you can pass by or pause and regard by going inside to another time and another place, you may let the hours this morning pass like the time just before falling asleep.

You can wander through the whole of yesterday and imagine the pictures and the situations you experienced. And you can forget them and continue like an album you are leafing through. And imagine that you have opened this album you are leafing through. And imagine that you have opened this album to a particular page at random, a page that is completely white and as you look more closely at this page you see a certain situation [noises outside]. And as you alternate between the pictures and the sounds, you can revisit the situation and the time when you were full of well-being, feeling you can stay there where you felt that part inside you with which you are in full understanding.

And you know that there is this part that only you know and that you occasionally regard this being in various forms. That this sometimes vanishes but reappears; just as the sun sometimes disappears without really getting lost, changes its form and color and yet it remains the same, in its being very big and red in the morning and then gradually it becomes smaller and is invisible in between and becomes brighter and changes its color in the evening, all in order to disappear.

Although there are situations where you cannot see this part, you can develop the certainty that it exists. And you stay internally with one part of your consciousness at this place and stay here to discover and examine what this part consists of, while the rest of your consciousness returns at your own pace to this room, to take back with it something of the feeling strong and refreshed, when you become completely awake on this chair and without thinking about it more exactly know that you have remembered things and you can also forget things that you remember, and may remember more than you can forget at once, and know (no!) more than you forget. And you have time to decide when you will become completely awake and whether you want to enjoy the stillness of your body still for a time or whether you want to enjoy the unrest and the activity and inhale deeply.

You can clarify for yourself what are the hindrances still holding you back from being able to experience more of what is pleasant and agreeable to you, and decide what presuppositions you need to make that possible for you.

Take a moment's more time for yourself. I would like to ask you whether you could just as you are sitting, in pairs, shortly exchange what makes it more easy for you to reach this state of trance.

4

Joseph Barber: Changing the Relationship

COMMENTS

Making contact with the group is the main theme of Joseph Barber's group induction—or accelerating the process of developing a relationship, as he says in his comment. How does he perform this most difficult and important task? First of all by joking. As I am not going to repeat his jokes here, you will have to read them to enjoy them.

What he does next is involve the group in a conscious task very directly: "Be aware of your breathing! Feel special sensations." For some participants, attending to the body sensations and simultaneously following the increasingly calmly spoken words may result in "overloading"* so they give up and go into trance right away. For others able to function on two levels at the same time, this is an invitation to expand their awareness, thus leading to a different form of trance, the trance of awareness with the suggestion, "Notice!", slipped into the text several times.

Joseph Barber even uses the oft repeated word "notice" also to ratify** the trance, as he tells the group to notice what has already changed after some minutes. To deepen the trance, Joseph Barber uses a very remarkable procedure: He invites us to pretend to be even more comfortable than we are (the "as if" technique). Naturally this pretending leads shortly to really feeling this comfort. He also assists his trance-deepening by soft confusion. Confusion always interrupts the conscious set and the usually used pattern of thinking and so opens up new possibilities and new patterns. The use of "fluff" for gaining time, as unconscious processes usually take a little longer than do conscious ones, and also for distracting conscious attention is nicely demonstrated here, as is also the well-known hypnotic device of repetition.

Turning toward the end of the induction, having opened up to empathy with our colleagues, we find ourselves a part of the group. Joseph Barber gives us in this induction also an example of seeding, another important hypnotic technique. We have been prepared for togetherness by one simple phrase, for "rubbing the nose" has been seeded in the first part and then repeated by Joseph Barber talking about himself rubbing his nose, when he tuned us in

---

*"Overloading"—the simultaneous or sequential presentation of more stimuli in one or more representation systems (visual, auditory, kinesthetic, olfactory, gustatory).

**Ratification—drawing attention to changes and other commonplace, verifiable facts within the person's own experience.

for empathy. Thus he initiated an arm levitation in an indirect way, a familiar movement that is an anchor of comfort for some Ericksonians.

However, there is in Joseph Barber's induction one point with which I disagree. Asking someone to "try not to imagine a piano" is an impossible request (like asking someone to think of rabbits without thinking of foxes on the last day of the month) and, in my opinion, is conducive to provoking a mishap analogous to admonishing a child who is carrying a glass of milk, "Don't fall down the steps!" I had an exchange of letters with Joseph Barber about his recurring phrase "with nothing to bother and nothing to disturb you." If we believe the admittedly still unproved theory that our unconscious does not note the negations, the words "bother" and "disturb" may have an effect opposite to that intended by the author. Joseph Barber told me that he had never observed adverse reactions to such negatively formulated suggestions, so perhaps the meaning is what counts. Nevertheless, as this, too, is still unproven and as in a large group some people may react adversely without the therapist detecting this, to my mind the wording should be chosen with the utmost care. This includes avoiding the mention—even with a negative—of any words likely to provoke troublesome associations, unless this is specifically intended and the therapist is confident of the outcome even in a large group. We are just at the beginning of exploring this new, extensive area of human consciousness. One single word may provoke a lot of reaction in a trance state. That is what hypnotic subjects, including myself, frequently experience.

Dr. Barber has requested I close my commentary with his clarifying words: "The foregoing comments reflect my own understanding and interpretation of Joseph Barber's hypnotic work, and are at significant variance with his own understanding of that same work."

INDUCTION

INTRODUCTION

Hypnosis is typically thought of as a psychotherapeutic tool in one of three ways: as a means of altering symptoms; as a means for exploring unconscious processes; and as a means for changing the therapeutic relationship—that is, of accelerating the development of the relationship between patient and therapist. The following group induction is an example of one way hypnotic suggestions may be used to create just such a change, although, in this case, the relationship is both between the group and the therapist, and members of the group in relation to each other.

Following response to such a group experience, people tend to feel a change in their relation to others in the group. Some people feel closer to the therapist and to others in the group, some people feel more isolated. Some people have sudden recollections of unpleasant moments in their life, or they may suddenly be overwhelmed by anxiety, in which case the experience is not a pleasant one. Alternatively, people may have an unusually pleasant experience of well-being and emotional support. You as the therapist need to be prepared for either eventuality. Whatever experience the patient may have can be a therapeutically useful one—if you are prepared for it. The patient is likely, in any case, to feel that you are largely responsible for the experience, and the emotional response of the patient is at least partially a function of this belief. The essential requirement for you, as the therapist, is to remain aware of whatever may be happening, of whatever may happen, and to be prepared to deal with whatever happens.

INDUCTION

All right. I'm going to offer some suggestions, and you can feel free to participate as fully or as minimally, and as temporarily as you like. And just feel free to respond in whatever way that feels best, feels most natural to you.

So maybe the best way to begin will be . . . just close your eyes and notice . . . where you sit, make sure you are sitting as comfortably as you know how, and just be aware of what it feels like to be sitting here. Notice how comfortable you feel, or how much your nose itches, or how relaxed your legs feel. Just notice what it is that you are feeling right now . . . without any particular requirement that you feel a particular way.

And as you sit here, just noticing what you are feeling, I'm going to offer some suggestions to you for experiences that you may or may not have, and I would like you just to notice in what ways your experience might change, moment by moment. For instance, I would like to suggest to you that you begin attending to the sensations of your own breathing. Just begin to be more fully aware of what it feels like to take each breath. Notice, as you do that, how easily you can continue hearing what I'm saying to you. It's as if you just naturally follow what it is that I'm saying. As if your imagination in fact creates some reality almost automatically out of the suggestions that I offer. And notice with each breath you take that there are different sensations associated with breathing in and breathing out. Notice that when you breathe in, for instance, the muscles in your chest feel different than when you breathe out. Notice that the skin across your muscles feels different when you breathe in than when you breathe out. You might even notice the change in the tension of the material of your clothing as you breathe in and as you breathe out. Notice that the air, as it enters your body, is cool, perhaps even cold, in the back of your nose, in the back of your throat, and notice that, when you breathe out, the air is warm . . . and of course it has been warmed by the very process of your life. And as you continue allowing yourself to become more and more centrally aware of just this perfectly natural process of breathing . . . notice how many other processes have already begun automatically. Just notice that there are areas of your body that feel more relaxed than they did a few minutes ago. Just notice how much more oriented your mind is to the fact that you are just being here.

And I would like you even to pretend something, if you will. In addition to pretending, notice that I'm speaking only to you, and that it is very easy for you to understand and identify with what I'm saying. In addition to that, I would like you to pretend that you are even more comfortable than you already are. I would like you just to pretend that you are feeling even greater ease, that your body feels even more relaxed, even more fully balanced, as if for right now there is a "time-out" for all the cares and concerns and considerations of the world, almost as if you and I have lifted off the earth and have begun to soar out and away . . . out and away from all cares and concerns and considerations left on earth, so that for the next while, you can just allow yourself the sense of resting quietly and easily . . . and in fact I wonder if you'll be surprised to discover, if you haven't already . . . that the sounds around you, all the sounds you can hear . . . near sounds, and far sounds . . . and high sounds, and low sounds . . . sharp sounds and soft sounds . . . all the sounds you can hear . . . are sounds that can become more and more a part of your experience of comfort and well-being . . . with nothing to bother you, and nothing to disturb you. So that in fact . . . every sensation you can feel . . . every feeling you can notice . . . can become more and more a part of your experience of comfort and well-being . . . with nothing to bother you and nothing to disturb you.

You might also be aware of interesting physical sensations. Perhaps aware of a sense of tingling in your fingers . . . perhaps aware of a sense of a curious sensation of weightlessness in your hand. And yet, you know that I have not given you a suggestion for weightlessness in your hand. Perhaps it is due to prior experience that you feel an inclination for your hand to lift into the air . . . because I have not offered that suggestion.

You might also have a sense of turning . . . almost as if your body is somehow floating, slowly and easily, into the air . . . and turning . . . round and round. Or perhaps you may have a curious sensation of leaning from one side to the other. A curious sensation, because as you lean, you never move. As the angle of leaning increases, you somehow never fall. It's almost as if you are discovering a wide range of your own comfort and your own well-being, and as if you are discovering automatically and finally that . . . right now and right here, everything is fine.

I also want to suggest to you that your capacity for empathy, your ability to empathize with someone else's experience . . . is a capacity that is important to you. But I wonder if you realize that it has personal importance to you. For instance if you see someone looking very comfortable, very self-confident . . . wouldn't it be terrific to suddenly notice in yourself what that feels like, at that moment. If you see someone looking very relaxed and at ease, wouldn't it be fantastic, just to know what that feels like yourself, at that moment . . . with nothing to bother you and nothing to disturb you. It might even happen in what seems like trivial ways . . . even in respect to me. For instance, if you see me, say . . . rub my nose . . . it's perfectly natural that you notice that I'm rubbing my nose . . . and it's perfectly natural that you know what that feels like at that moment without even having discussed or considered the concept of empathy or what value that might be to you.

I would also like you to know that this experience, whatever it may be like for you at this moment . . . is your experience, not mine . . . and that the capacity to create this experience . . . is your capacity, not mine. But you might enjoy feeling more confident about your capacity to develop this experience, whenever you need to. So I offer you this suggestion: Any time that you need to feel more comfortable than you do . . . whenever you would like to feel a relief from tension, whenever you would like to feel greater relaxation, all you have to do is . . . settle back in a chair or sofa or bed, and take a very deep, very satisfying breath . . . and hold it for a moment . . . and then, when you let it all the way out . . . these feelings of comfort and well-being will just automatically wash over you . . . like water in a hot tub . . . with nothing to bother you and nothing to disturb you.

And now, from wherever you are, I would like you to begin noticing that, as you allow this very pleasing comfort to increase in intensity, I would like you to become aware, without disturbing this experience . . . I would like you to become aware of the presence of your friends or colleagues nearby. I would like you to become aware of yourself as a part of this group . . . become aware of the fact that we here have begun to form a community of colleagues, some of whom you know, and some of whom you do not yet know. And I wonder if you are going to be surprised, perhaps more pleased than surprised . . . but I wonder if you are going to be surprised at how quickly you feel an inexplicable sense of comfort and ease, and an inexplicable but pleasant feeling of belonging . . . and an explicable but delightful sense . . . almost of fondness . . . for others in the group . . . and also a sense that that is a feeling that we also have for you.

Now it isn't necessary for you to develop complete amnesia for the things that I have said to you. I haven't said anything to you that you haven't thought, yourself, anyway. It isn't necessary that you memorize the things that I'm saying to you, because, as I say, you know it anyway from your own experiencing. You might enjoy . . . you might just enjoy the feeling of being completely "amnestic" for a while in order to experience the delight, as the memories come back to you, or you may prefer to feel a continuing sense of inflexible control over your memory. That of course is entirely up to you. But just notice . . . just notice what happens . . . when you have a feeling almost as if you are being somehow suddenly brought back to full and complete awareness. But it's a slightly different angle . . . almost as if you have reentered your body, almost perfectly . . . but with just one fraction of a millimeter's disparity from the way in which you resided in your body before we began. So, as your eyes open . . . just notice what it is that you feel.

_ II _

ABSORPTION IN AN INTERNAL EXPERIENCE

Absorption is increased concentration. If attention is focused on something, concentration commences. Thus the process of altering the state of consciousness can lead to absorption through focusing attention and increasing concentration step by step. When fully absorbed in something, experience is automatic and absolutely no effort is required. Indeed, on the contrary, complete relaxation occurs. Trance is more than just relaxation, of course. Relaxation may be understood as being a particular phase or special form of trance, a state at the very beginning of the trance process.

In this section the reader will find inductions that aim mainly at relaxation and are particularly concretely, tangibly inviting to have internal experiences full of feeling. With Ortwin Meiss the rhythmical elements of his bedtime story are predominant, thus addressing those who are primarily auditorily disposed, i.e., people who rely first and foremost on what they hear. Norman Katz adds the kinesthetic approach in his use of Autogenic Training, while Ulrich Freund employs his hypnotherapeutic knowledge in both of his inductions, to which he gives his own most careful comments, to enable patients in his Cardiac Clinic to experience an unusual form of Autogenic Training. The fourth induction, by Deborah Ross, is a very good example of a learning trance for beginners. She employs the hypnotherapeutic method of story-telling, a technique of leading inwards long familiar to us as children. The images she conjures up are—particularly for the visually orientated—brilliantly painted pictures that remain vividly imprinted in the memory.

5

Ortwin Meiss: The Seven Sleeper Dormice

COMMENTS

This induction, which aims at aiding listeners to find inner peace and relaxation, is available on tape in German and works primarily with the auditive channel, although kinesthetic and visual sensations are addressed as well. Utilizing the natural rhythms when we calm down for sleep, Meiss weaves irresistible rolling patterns of rhythmic words. Quasi-logical connections between the sentences, comparisons and metaphors alternate with each other so naturally and convincingly, that usually we do not become aware of the grammatical incorrectness of some figures of speech required by Ortwin Meiss for the sake of embedded commands. It is only soft confusion, when he does not finish his sentences as you expect. It is harder confusion when he utilizes negations, for example, to "elicit" rather than to "induce" (Zeig, 1987) heaviness: "therefore it isn't necessary to notice consciously how gradually—somewhere in the body—a pleasant heaviness—a nice weight develops . . ." Often more convincing still than any metaphors and pictures is when the author talks about his own experiences, actual happenings. We can learn this from literature for group inductions. It's a technique when we just pretend to be telling our own story. It's totally convincing when we really relate our own experiences. Some authors, e.g., Ernest Rossi, prefer to tell true stories only, because from their own experience they believe clients notice if we lie. Other authors are not that strict, e.g., Gordon, 1986,. Ortwin Meiss told me that the sleepy bedtime story of his Seven Sleeper Dormice induction originated from his own experience, a story he loved as a child.

There is another convincing moment that seems to increase the pull into trance: the content of the story. It again deals with sleeping. So there is "sleeping" embedded in the go-to-sleep story, a trick all parents use in order to help their children to fall asleep. I believe that all good "Good-night" stories we tell our children are hypnotic inductions. Ortwin Meiss draws from this well, utilizing age regression as well of course at the same time, his dear little dormice serving as cuddly toys. He also uses a technique from orthodox hypnosis: counting in connection with a command. But here he weaves his numbers into the text so that the listener usually will not be aware of this. Counting to seven makes this group induction coherent, and it is specially nice when we are woken up with a final joke.

INDUCTION

You have sought out a pleasant place, where you have all the room and all the time to yourself, where you have room to stretch out fully . . . and to make yourself comfortable, cozy and snug, perhaps to sleep or simply to rest after the events of the day . . .

So you may allow yourself to relax and regain your composure . . . and rediscover your inner peace and quietness . . . to feel how you are lying on a comfortable underlay so you feel fine and well now . . . how you can adjust yourself a little more . . . how your body jerks and twitches when it's asleep all by itself to give itself more comfort . . . and notice so simply how your body is supported without it having to do anything at all . . . in the background this soothing music . . . so that you can take the words and sentences more like warm waves you let flow through . . . and it isn't necessary to listen consciously . . . for the unconscious understands and takes . . . what you used to need and need to use . . .

Therefore it isn't necessary to notice consciously how . . . gradually . . . somewhere in the body . . . a pleasant heaviness . . . a nice weight (wait) . . . develops all ready . . .

which spreads out which you can utilize
which gradually without your noticing need further
and it isn't necessary to know how you relax
how it's not necessary to know how you fall asleep
for people sleep before they can think
with open or closed eyes and so enjoy this inner peace (piece)
something that really works to achieve detachment at a distance
and from farther away like everything becomes smaller
and in a way in its meaning insignificant or unimportant
like thoughts and images come, go and dance Drift past
like white clouds passed across a fine blue summer sky
In the way past and future melt into the present,
why how nice to feel how breath can flow
In this up and down and back and fro
Soft light waves that come and go
Soothing waves lapping receding
smoothing on fine sandy beach
To smoothen contours soon for each
As past dunes and downs sleep comes, as well, in waves, billows, (pillows) swell surges
a-swell urges soft gentle drift off
a peace full floating up a piece

then sinking a while deeper down a
while not knowing yet discovering as well
this rhythm ripples by itself
and humans sleep since beings be

there since olden times they have told, will tell
Tales to fall asleep by the way
Like those bye-bye stories, the good-night tales
I heard as a child still dream about
today when I feel comfy, safe, well-snug
Remember (a member) maybe grand-mother's hug
I don't remember which story I always fall asleep by
Like I never knew by which story I had already fall (sic!) asleep
but I remember anew the pleasant relaxation and coziness
in all ways while listening to the voice I knew and like
How to peep out of half or wholly shut eyes and have that
special feel that all beings have a while
Feeling full of that well being waiting
downy, drowsy feeling in arms and legs
While begin to sink down inter-nal (into) images
So I remember this story, this special tale
Of a very special dormouse type with a nice long tail
That live and also on the main sleep
near the River Severn but also on the Maine
So may be called like some old saints the Seven Sleepers
For the favorite pastime there is sleep to pass the time
And in time past, hence called Seven Sleepers
Who liked to sleep so much he (sic!) knew how to use
every suitable situation like count only seven sheep
And knew how to . . . slip off to sleep anew
to dream a new piece full further back and retire
to roost and rest kinda doze off or take a nap peace fully
feeling just fine how seven sleepers are . . . Well,
Being very sociable animals so

being well able to sleep alone
as well as with others and in this case
know full well how their eyes
shut all alone or all by themselves
Whether they are standing up or lying down or wandering off
To rest just a moment and not think of anything special
Like comfortably all ready for sleeping
full of well already being sleepy
and being well able to become sleepier

these seven sleepers get so sleepy
and just obey the need to rest fully

and slumber deeply so easily so delightfully
so light music to dream by
Strewing sweet chords
the seven sleepers in true accord
accordingly in full harmony
Enjoy the slumber sweet so fully
so pleasantly so delightfully
a comfy way to enjoy a lay
In that the little seven sleepers
would attend the wood-school like
all the rest of all
the little wood-beings would be
restfully learning in beautiful sleep
already the readiness to fall asleep
whenever liking to begin to cuddle down
cuddle down and curl up in that nice long tail
and feel how the warmth like the sleepiness spreads out in
such delightful ways and trails
and means such comfort now entails
for the seven sleepers are such soft cuddly animals
So they can already sleep
Seven sleepers learn how to count in the wood-school
How much they can count
Do count—of course—up to seven
Their special subject is that by seven they've long fallen asleep
but every seven sleeper can count right even to seventy
but they count while asleep as well
being already deeply well asleep in their unconsciousness
they can well ask their unconscious for an unconscionably pleasant dream
for to count to seven and simultaneously fall asleep
Is really well and truly deeply a speciality for seven sleepers
one is especially nice for them
these special dormice in their dormitory well-engrossed and enveloped in the long comforting tails
So listen to stories, bed-time stories,
and store them well in the well-kept deep well of their memory store-room
become very sleepy and begin to dream
sometimes consciously sometimes unconsciously
of pleasant things well being aware
how important it is to count well and like how to count
while so beautifully listening
to stories and so deeply dreaming

which is why at two already almost fast asleep

and sleep is called by the seven sleepers "slumbling"
and seven sleepers slumble at all times and
in all places at every opportunity
even while cleaning their teeth they slumble
well away and cuddle down within
well inside the soft downy skin the fluffy fur
(like Fuzzy-wuzzy was a bear

Fuzzy-wuzzy had straight hair
so Fuzzy-wuzzy was not fuzzy, was he?!)

So pleasant and so relaxing to lie there
and seven sleepers like you know how well
sleep three seasons long in autumn or fall deep winter sleep
anew in the first season of a new year and being seasoned sleepers
in summer somemore (sic!) nap daily and
hold that relaxing comfort well
being most deeply and comfortably night sleepers
dream how to like gliding down, floating away on a warm deep feather bed
drifting off softly, weightless (wait less!) to the middle of nowhere
Without any wait securely suspended in a fourth dimension
so safe and snug taking care of yourself
Let's let peace and quietness ease
rest the body, give it what it please
to keep while sound asleep
Well-balanced in a beautysleep
Ever better floating freely fine
Like letting all five senses wander
Off free from time and space
Flowing freely in together into another
Being carried by these pleasant waves
Well as well as well (a swell)
Knowing how likeable to like being carried and go to the middle of nowhere
like to be one above all able to know
the sixth sense of the seven sleepers is the unconscious knowledge
of what you really need and is truly good for you
like how to find the proper rhythm
You're finding the proper direction well inside
Like how to tread the proper path and be in a special way
peacefully, safely and surely taking care of yourself
in harmony with one-self

Well be like the seven sleepers seven times a week
like being able to sleep in all the utmost well being
to an inward accompaniment
Like being accompanied on the way by sound tones and well-tuned sounds
Like music lets (let's) be carried by all the harmony unanimous
For us of how well the waves go deeper and deeper
Quiet naturally with the inward need to sleep
well relaxed deeply dreaming with dream pictures descending
well on your own way like to know the way

how like the seven sleepers now
having dreamt in this pleasant way
well being sure to feel how much power and energy
you are beginning to collect yourself
after this pleasant experience how to feel
now this all begins to grow and works
further in you awakening a new
well being to begin to become wider
awake and seven sleepers have this special way
how to wake up

They let the'selves (sic!) be surprised . . .
how the body decides for itself whether . . .
first the lower half of the body will wake up . . .
or first the upper half can appreciate this relaxed wakefulness . . .
like the waking up happens in waves or . . . gradually . . . or fits
and starts some feeling more awake with a little more weight (wait) . . .

For when I was a child and always after hearing these tales of the Seven Sleeper Dormice, there was a pillow on my grandmother's couch with real writing (righting), stretching across and up, saying, "Only a quarter of an hour still," . . . and sometimes a quarter of an hour was like our five minutes; and sometimes five long minutes were like a quarter of an hour; and I well remember the feeling returning that followed and the need to stretch that every member that we all have . . . that everyone has when he has slept so well relaxed . . . restored and refreshed, recuperated and well be enjoying . . . using this good feeling for a new awakening with a new wakefulness refreshing . . . intake of air breathing in and . . . thus returning to this room with us coming back as though from a journey.

Some are all ready to wake and some are already awake and some others are showing how to begin to be completely and thoroughly awake and to start gradually looking up and forward to stretching and looking around to see . . . all the little seven sleepers.

Translator's Note: "Seven sleepers" means "dormice" in German, therefore, considerable but considerate alterations were necessary.

— 6 —

Norman Katz: Hypno-Autogenics

COMMENTS

We now come to the interesting topic of how hypnotherapeutic methods and Autogenic Training can merge and profit from each other. Norman Katz has developed such an approach he calls "*Hypno-Autogenics.*" For making contact in a natural way he uses his humor. This gives the Autogenic Training a most necessary additional quality, because usually these exercises are a very serious affair, a doctor often having sent his patients to Autogenic Training courses because of serious problems. Norman Katz, however, after having had us focus on the kinesthetic sensation of how our clothes feel, plays a game with us, a game with the funny name: "catch-up game," which is a kinesthetic trance induction in itself.

Dealing with the exercises of the Autogenic Training in a more particular sense, it can be said that he has changed the levels of hypnotic experience in eliciting the warmth before the heaviness. We had a debate about this, but we agreed there need not be a rigid schema. He told me that it worked well this way round. Previously it had been my experience that it is more difficult for most people to develop warmth in their bodies than to develop heaviness. Maybe part of this difficulty is because we have suggested it ourselves!

"Seeding" is a hypnotherapeutic technique Norman Katz likes to play with. He seeds the advice to hear our own music by telling us about the music he uses at home. He seeds the catch-up-game by using this word before. He seeds the breathing exercise by mentioning it already during the catch-up game. He seeds the journey through the body via the catch-up game. He finally seeds going through the experience of the conference by promising to do so at the beginning and by proposing to look around at other seminars. To deepen the trance he also uses time distortion, confusion caused through deliberate mispronunciation, other "mistakes" and frequent repetitions of the same words; and dissociation of the whole body with the proposal of going to other rooms. He combines suggestive labels like "hypnotic doorway" with impressive pictures—e.g., the hypnotic bubble—convincing stories and an Indian prayer as well as the wisdom of Yoga science.

However, there is one little story that I personally would not tell, and that is the story of the client who practiced Autogenics by putting ice cubes on his forehead. J. H. Schultz taught that one should never use the words "the forehead is cold," but only: "the forehead is comfortably cool," because when too much blood leaves the head we may cause fainting or a migraine attack. When the vasoconstriction and the resulting diminished blood circulation in the forehead takes place too quickly, a headache may be the result, because the nerves in the vascular walls react very sensitively to sudden changes in blood pressure (Peter & Gerl, 1977; Hoffmann, 1981). Other authors would not be as daring here as is Norman Katz. For people who suffer from headaches, coolness of the forehead may be wrong in any case and induced warmth might be indicated instead. This is a point to be clarified individually. I usually talk about the head as "free and clear" in groups, having talked about the possibility of coolness before the exercise.

INDUCTION

Thank you for coming so early to share this hour of group hypnosis. One person in the audience is already hypnotized, totally entranced, look around, could it be you?

I'm Norman Katz, and I'm director of the Erickson Institute of New Mexico. This is the second time I've done an 8:30 a.m. group induction. What I want to do this morning is just share with the whole group some interesting hypnotic exercises which I like to teach clients in my office. One difference working here (since everything is being taped) I can't use the usual music that I do while working in New Mexico. I like to play music as kind of a second more beautiful voice to listen to.

So what I would like you to do, is, after your eyes close, whenever that may be, is to let yourself hear whatever music you'll find most enjoyable this morning. And if you would like to sing to yourself, that's fine.

I'm going to be working later on a panel on humor, and I'm thinking about that, so funny little things, funny funny images might come into our induction this morning, just a little contamination from everything, from about what I've been thinking about, and there are several people I know who might be here, who have asked me for some special advice during the trance, some special images. You may hear something that answers your needs, as we go along.

It's nice to wake up this morning, get to something earlier like this, so you can have the opportunity to go away again very fast. There are special nice things about this hypnosis conference, such as: you don't need much sleep, because you can always catch up during the workshops. So I want you to stretch a little bit comfortable, I like to start up working with people by just paying attention to how your clothes feel. I think that's a good place to begin hypnotic inductions. You just might notice how your shoes feel, and please leave your clothes on for this part of the induction, notice, how your shirt feels, your hands, your dress, whatever you are wearing, just notice, which shoe is more comfortable, your right or your left? And see, if you can let be the other one just as comfortable. And you might notice, if you have any jewelry on, it's tight or it's loose. Sound of the air conditioning, sound of my voice, sound of other people coming in, sound of your breathing, notice, how the chairs support your back, notice, how the hair feels on your head, notice, if you are ahead of me, that's all right. Notice how the right side of your body feels, what part on the right is most comfortable, what part is most comfortable on your left? What part is the most left out?

And I would like to play a little game with you, that I call the Catch-Up Game. It's all different from the Mustard game. In the Mustard-game you have to do something. In the catch-up game we find out which parts of your body are the most comfortable, and let the other parts catch up. I would like you to find a place on your right hand or in one of your fingers that's the most comfortable inside. And then let some other finger of the right hand catch up with it, as if you could share that hypnotic feeling. And maybe you could find another place on your right hand, that would like to catch up to the most relaxed spot. And let that part catch up. And maybe there's a place on your arm now, that would like to catch up. And you may find, as I talk and you listen, or you listen, you talk, I listen, that there are different places that can serve as a reference of the most comfortable place in your body. Any body can find at least one place to share there in, that's the most comfortable in the room for you. And find a place in your left hand, that would like to catch up, in your right hand, right shoulder.

And every time you breathe I wonder, if you could feel that wonderful breath behind your eyes inside of your skull, the one that helps you feel like you do right when your alarm clock goes off and the sun goes in the window and you think: If I only had ten minutes more! And then give yourself that ten minutes, or twenty minutes, or maybe even half an hour today. And you might want this at various times, touch various places on your body, find places that would enjoy staying still. And you might find a place in your foot that would like to catch up, a place in your leg. And as you go through your whole body and allow various areas to catch up, you are comfortable.

I would like to share with you a series of hypnotic reference points that I recently developed, that I call Hypno-Autogenics. Hypno-Autogenics is a system of self-hypnosis that is very interesting, because it is based on a physiological system of relaxation. It has six or seven parts to it. I would like to start off with your hands:

And what I would like you to do is in some way allow your hands to get very warm, as if the sun is shining through the window, or you had nice warm gloves on. You might however think of another way you could allow your hands to get as warm as possible. I was just holding a cup of nice hot coffee before I came in here; I can still remember that nice feeling. And you might prefer to hold tea or something else.

And perhaps you could let your feet get warm too, (two) feet. And there might be other areas of your body where you could begin to just begin to allow a warm feeling begin to radiate. And some people feel it as a kind of a pink feeling or red, others more like . . . or you might feel during massage or right afterwards. A nice, warm, safe feeling. And that may allow muscles in your neck to slowly let go, so you don't have to hold your head so high up. And as your body begins to feel warm, you can move on to a second level of Hypno-Autogenics. And as I move on, you might find however that the cloth you are wearing still begins to feel the same or perhaps change. Maybe the other shoe becomes more comfortable by now, and perhaps in your mind you might enjoy going for a walk to one of the other presentations or you just let your body continue working with me. That's one of the nice things about hypnosis, being able to be at three or four places at the same time. So as your body gets warm, now let it begin to get heavy. It's as if there was a phenomenon in your mind, where you could just turn up gravity. If you have already turned up the heat in your body a little bit, now I wonder, if you might allow your body to feel heavy. Find a place in your right hand, where you could let your whole hand feel heavy. And at another place you could let your left hand feel heavy. Interesting how you might feel light with warmth, but heavy with the gravity. And your right hand can get heavier, and then your left hand get heavier, maybe one finger at a time always in the bones. And then you might find some other place in the body, that could feel heavy. Let the weight of your body sink into that chair. You don't need to support yourself at all. Just let my words and that chair support you.

And by now you might enjoy your hypnotic bubble, as if you were in a wonderful clear bubble, that could give you the feeling of total protection and yet connection with whatever you want it to come into your bubble, whatever you would like to leave out, could stay out. Your bubble could float at the same time you got heavy. And there is this wonderful movie called: "Fantastic Planet," with people, who learned to meditate from another galaxy, and they could meditate and let their minds form bubbles and go into the bubble and just float somewhere outside the planet. And in your bubble you could let your whole body feel very heavy, because the bubble could feel light enough to support and float with the rest of you. And some people, when their bodies feel heavy, feel like they are melting, as if you are a piece of other material or something that was just melting in the sun. So you could just form kind of padding in your chair, if you want to, as if you haven't any bones at all. And let your body continue to get warm and heavy as your *breathing* begins to breathe itself. You could just begin to watch your breathing and notice how it begins to breathe itself. When your breathing begins to breathe itself, so that you don't have to even pay attention to it, notice how your breathing breathes itself. And when your breathing breathes itself, every time you breathe out, you might notice how the warm heavy feelings get a little stronger, more comfortable. And every time you breathe out, you might notice some other interesting things. And there is a pause right before you breathe out, and in that pause, after you breathe in, before you breathe out, it's almost like time stops. I call that pause the *hypnotic doorway*. And in that pause you might find, you could just let yourself go deeper into trance each time that you come to that pause, that place, where you are suspended between breathing out and breathing in. And enjoy that pause and let it get just a little longer, as your breathing breathes itself. And as your breathing breathes itself, if my words wander somewhere else, you might enjoy, wherever you are wandering, whatever color, whatever music, whatever memories.

A little later after we complete this comfort in our bodies, we are going to explore some of the conference in order to help our memories remember what needs to be remembered about what you have learned already. That you might find even before then some of the interesting phenomena you have experienced in the workshops, presentations, presenting themselves, here and there is some piece of information floating through your awareness. And as your breathing breathes itself, you might just begin to focus on your forehead.

And let your *forehead* become *cool* and comfortable, as if there is a band of blue color or a cool washcloth on your forehead. Let your forehead become cool and comfortable. I had a client once who went home and took an ice cube and would practice this part of the autogenics with a nice big ice cube on the forehead. But you might prefer something else. And as that breath behind your eyes breathes itself, every time you breathe that breath keeps your forehead cool on the inside, even as your hands are warm and your whole body continues to be heavy as your breathing breathes itself. And as your forehead gets cool, comfortable, just as all the muscles in your eyes and your face can let go. People store so much tension on their face. So nice to just let your jaw hang down, and behind your ears the neck, as your forehead continues to become cool. And as your forehead gets cool, I would like you to begin to enjoy a nice *warm feeling* right behind your stomach in your *solar plexus*, the place that Yogis call the Hari, right behind your tummy, where you feel all the warm fuzzies, when you feel warm fuzzies, where you feel, when you feel really loved and someone gives you care, when you have just got a present or given a present that you or someone else enjoys, where you really like to feel full, filled (fulfilled) with feelings of comfort instead of food, and that's why it is not in your stomach, but behind your stomach, deeper than your stomach, a place where all those nerves connect, so that in the very center of your being you feel warm, connecting all those feelings, taking place, as you feel the comfort of the warm fuzzy feeling in that area.

And as your Hari begins to feel comfortable and warm and time begins to slow down, so that we have all the time we need to enjoy this half hour that remains. You can begin to feel how this all adds up to a feeling of peacefulness inside of you. And there is an old Indian prayer; peace inside me; peace to my right; peace to my left; peace below me; peace above me; I am peace. And in all those directions and in any other directions or whatever directions might help you, add whatever else might add to your enjoyment of a peaceful feeling, knowing, that all this well right now let this peacefulness spread all through you.

And I would like you to take a little journey through your body, an old Yoga exercise, about three thousand years old. It didn't get named as "Hypnosis" until only recently. And starting off in the little finger on your right hand, I would like you to take a little journey through your body, as if your bloodstream was a little system of rivers and you are a little canoe, let yourself walk along the shore, and where you do go, I would like you to place a little candle, a light, whatever kind and whatever colors would make you feel the most enlightened inside, starting off in the little finger of your right hand. Take about five minutes to go through your whole body and light up your experience from the inside. And if there is any areas that need extra attention, you could add a few extra lights, perhaps of different colors, perhaps different shapes, and breathe into those areas and add those lights, so that, when you breathe in, then the lights grow stronger. In New Mexico, where I live, at night, because the air is so thin, because it's so high, everything flickers. And I like the lights in my body to flicker like that, like the stars. But you might prefer steady light. And whenever you have completed your whole body, notice how you feel in the state that you are in, and know that you have just completed a hypnotic exercise called Hypno-Autogenics, that has the physiological effect of about ten to fifteen milligrams of your favorite tranquilizer or the effect of a nice, long walk. And you can also learn to do this while walking or doing things. Whenever you finish your whole body, you might notice how quiet you have become except for the vibrations under the floor, vibrations coming through the floor. Whenever you finish going through your whole body, you might enjoy touching your nose just to make sure it's still there or your ears or your face in some way, being ready to go on to the next hypnotic adventure this morning.

You might enjoy opening your eyes and closing them five times very quickly, one second open, one second closed or perhaps not. I would like you to remember after you have touched your face, about when you first heard about this conference. I don't know if you read about it in a brochure or heard on the Ericksonian Television Station or if Milton spoke to you directly in a dream. I don't know, when you decided to first come here. And perhaps you can remember, when you sent in your registration and first began to really tell people, you wanted to come to this conference. And then it seemed so far away, half a year, six months. Who would have ever thought, that it would be December in 1986 that quickly, and you began to pack, get ready to come here, wondering, how many people you would know, what you would experience. And I know, whenever I go to conferences, there is always one favorite piece of clothing I pack, a couple of interesting things that help me feel like I'm really going to be ready, whether it's a favorite pencil or a magic wand. And then, when you get there and you look at the actual program, it's hard to decide which things to go to, and eventually you choose one and you go to it. And you hear a lot of things, the first day is always such an exciting and confusing situation, looking for what you want to learn, certain questions you brought with you, others that develop. And perhaps you take written notes or mental notes or just notes, certain pieces of information, store as you want to remember. And by that (buy that!) it's almost the afternoon of the first day, and there is more, interesting ideas, information. And even, if you write it down, it seems like there must be much more you should have written down and remembered. There is almost too much your conscious mind can remember, so the rest gets rested in your unconscious mind. And by then, it's almost Tuesday, waking up on Thursday, perhaps in a new place, wondering what you learned the first day.

Now one of the interesting things about working with Dr. Erickson was you never quite knew until the next day, what you discovered the first day. Sometimes it took two days to find out what you learned the first day. Sometimes it took two weeks, even if you wrote down what you thought was the most important learnings. It could be something else, that often came out of the pattern of images and discoveries, that was more important at a later time.

I was going through my desk the other day, and I came across some notes from a time I was in Phoenix a number of years ago. And I had written in my notes: What is hypnosis? Take out the garbage. And I was trying to figure out, what that meant. And I remembered Dr. Erickson telling a colleague of mine if he would mind taking out the garbage, and when he agreed to do that, Erickson asked him if he would be hypnotized in order to agree to such a request. And he said, he thought he was. And Erickson replied: "Is that what hypnosis is for, getting someone to take out the garbage? You probably would have done that anyway, if I just asked you." I found that note in my notes and other notes about animals and festivals and Mrs. Erickson. And some new patterns came to me, and that was four or five years later. And on Wednesday, Thursday afternoon, things I'm sure had become slightly run together: different colors, different speakers' voices, beginning to wonder what you would take home with you from this conference.

And was it all clear, precise, all those books, enough to make you give up reading. All those papers! I once heard that a person can only remember really three or four things from any hour presentation, so the rest will be entertaining, fun. I don't know what you want to remember out of all those things from Wednesday and Thursday. You could only remember one an hour, that would be yours. And I experienced this morning perhaps, it will be four or five things that might come to you later, perhaps you could reach into your unconscious mind and ask Elvis what you should remember, because Elvis often remembers things you don't. He has his guitar, lots of songs to play, perhaps he could play you a song that would help you remember something you would like to remember about this morning, perhaps not. And so I understand some others might prefer to ask Lassie. So you would probably better rather ask Lassie or Elvis. And by tonight there are going to be thousands and thousands of words, patterns and facts, ideas filtering through your brain. Perhaps you could assign a certain song, a color to one of those memories, that is very important. And be thankful for all the ones you forget. Think about how horrible it would be, if you remembered everything in this conference, every word, every phrase. There is a story by the Argentinian writer Borges about a man who falls off his donkey and hits his head on a rock and loses the ability to forget. And he remembers everything, the shape of his donkey, the rock, the hit, the path he was on. He slowly becomes more and more confused, and begs for his forgetfulness to return. How nice that is, to only remember those things that are really important: like the feeling in your chair as you begin to return your attention to the room: or which part of your body got the most relaxed in which trance or which voice will go with you; which book are you really going to read; which pattern of trance you are really carrying with you. Whenever you are ready to just begin to let the light come back into your eyes and taking a few deep breaths, let yourself begin to be back in the room and notice how you feel differently than when we started. Hallo!

Comment

Did Elvis give anybody any good advice?

Participant: Don't step on my blue suede shoes!"

That's always good advice.

What I shared with you this morning was just to give your conscious mind a couple of interesting self-hypnosis games. These are really nice self-hypnosis tools. I shared them with you in the form of an induction this morning. But these are very easy to do without anyone else leading you. And the catch-up game is something you can do anywhere. I like to do it standing in lines, waiting. It's a nice time to just find out which part of you is the most comfortable and share it with other parts of you. Autogenics is a wonderful system of physiological self-control, that produces clear-cut changes in sympathetic arousal, and the components of Autogenics we use in behavioral medicine to treat many different disorders, that have a sympathetic and stress component to them.

With slight variations it can be used as a primary psychological treatment for things like high blood pressure, heart conditions, any kind of physical problem that has a stress component to it. And you can learn to do that very quickly, in five minutes or so. You can learn to create that kind of tranquil feeling by going through those six images. I call it Hypno-Autogenics, because the hypnotic aspect of it is allowing the different images and unconscious processes to enhance the six physiological steps of Autogenics.

This has been used for many years in Europe and was only recently picked up by biofeedback people in the United States. And it's interesting that the biofeedback people use Autogenics to train people on how to respond to the biofeedback machines. But you might as well use it to learn how to respond to yourselves.

— 7 —

Ulrich Freund: Do What You Want and When Wishing Was Still Helpful

COMMENTS

There is another critical point in Autogenic Training we should be very careful with when working with groups—work with the heart-formula. Norman Katz omitted this, and that is what I do. But let us see how Ulrich Freund, a specialist, solves this problem when he does his hypnotherapeutic Autogenic Training in his own cardiological clinic. The second induction is founded on the first and is held a week later.

Ulrich Freund keeps to the Autogenic Training formula more strictly than does Norman Katz, using them as anchors for the relaxation the patients have had during the induction and so helping them with their task of repeating the exercises on their own. In the induction the formulae are embedded in the context. Ulrich Freund has elaborated formulations to utilize the hypnotherapeutic techniques: working with resistance, which is extremely necessary with psychosomatic patients, using confusion, implications, direct and indirect suggestions as embedded commands or as interspersal technique. In detail he explains this procedure in his informative comment.

But how does he solve the problem with risky parts of Autogenic Training for groups? In dealing with the coolness of the forehead, an old adage helps him to suggest just the right balance between the warm body and the cooler forehead, the balance of healthiness. The coolness is addressed as that caused by evaporation and the picture that helps the imagination is: a light summer breeze cools your forehead as you lie in a green meadow.

The still more exciting part is working with the heart formula with heart-patients, which many colleagues leave out, as Ulrich Freund knows. He, however, does not want to lose this chance of working with this most critical part. In the holistic conviction that the symptoms are our friends and the highest potential for healing is within the symptoms themselves, he gives the group in an advanced state of the trance the powerful story of integration, the story of a hearty friendship between the giant and the dwarf. With this he gives his patients what they need most: confidence. When they use the heart formula afterwards, they will be reminded of this confidence.

INDUCTION
Do What You Want

FORMULAE OF AUTOGENIC TRAINING I

Hallo! Good day to you!

It isn't very difficult to see who is here for the first time. If you are a newcomer it is natural to have for what is going on here . . . VERY GREAT INTEREST. And then it is naturally also a legitimate interest to take a good look first of all and SEE WHAT IS GOING ON.

And that all takes time till . . . YOU KNOW THERE'S NOTHING SPECIAL GOING ON HERE. And if you want to go . . . and if it gets to be too much or too little for you then . . . JUST DO IT QUIETLY. And this does really go for all without saying that all the people here are actually, I mean with that indeed in actual fact . . . EVERYONE DOES WHAT S/HE WANTS.: i.e. DO WHAT YOU WANT. This can scarcely be . . . always the same . . . Therefore it is very important for you to know: please do only what is AGREEABLE, PLEASANT for you. And therefore it is very important to know that you only . . . REALLY FEEL WELL, really feel well, if you do ABSOLUTELY NOT, ABSOLUTELY NOT force yourself to anything.

Because first of all then if you . . . REALLY LET EVERYTHING GO ON, as it's going on anyhow then, then you can relax. Then you can relax. When you LET EVERYTHING GO on as it's going on anyhow—now, for a while, this time.

And you know that in Autogenic Training (AT) there are set formulae, certain special affirmations or statements. And I shall give you at the end of this hour—if you haven't already got it—a sheet of notes about these, a memo-sheet for your attentions, this means in effect that you now need NOT NOTE, NOT NOTICE, ANYTHING at all . . . For you will certainly have everything at the end in writing.

Now you only need to . . . WELL . . . FEEL FINE . . . LET YOURSELF GO WELL . . . HAVE A GOOD TIME . . . If you really do that in that you DO NOTHING, then you can . . . RELAX. Then you can after some time LEAN YOUR HEAD BACK ALL BY ITSELF—now . . . or later on . . . into the head-rest. And you can also, if you like . . . CLOSE YOUR EYES. Or you can also . . . WAIT TILL YOU NOTICE . . . YOUR EYES ARE CLOSING ALL BY THEMSELVES—now or later—just as it happens to happen.

It can well be that with some of you now . . . THE EYES ARE CLOSING not yet but later for a little bit of SHUT-EYE does you so good having . . . THE EYES CLOSE while, what is actually at the beginning of every relaxation training: I am already quite quiet. Or at least: I am becoming quieter and quite a piece calmer.

Then you can if you like at the same time . . . TURN YOUR GAZE INSIDE . . . COME TO ONESELF . . . LEAVE me IN PEACE. And because I leave my self in peace, I can always

---

Editor's Note: Within this chapter, words in capital letters are meant to be spoken louder than normal, and italicized words are meant to be spoken softly.

. . . BECOME QUITE CALM AND PEACEFULLY COMPOSED . . . always becoming more calm and more composed.

Be a lot able to . . . SIMPLY LET THINGS AS THEY ARE . . . so LET IT BE . . . let it be as it is and knowing I am resting on a restful deck chair and . . . IT IS COMFORTABLE.*

For when you . . . LEAVE YOURSELF AS YOU ARE . . . then you can . . . BECOME CALM AND COMPOSED . . . and will notice that you . . . FIND MORE AND MORE REST. For rest you can only find. None of us can—however—not at all make rest. But rest we can find. For the REST COMES ALL BY ITSELF.

You can, if you like, this feeling—more and more rest—fully attach it to a formula that you . . . SAY TO YOURSELF WITH YOUR INNER VOICE. Every person has an outer and an inner voice, an inner restful quiet voice. And we speak to ourselves the whole day, we think, but actually we are speaking. We can EXPRESS OUR THOUGHTS INSIDE, "I am already quite quiet. I am already completely calm." Is there a way, a formula, a sentence, that you can SAY TO YOURSELF? I am already quiet. I am already calm

If of course you are *not* QUIET AND CALM, then you cannot say the sentence. Then you just say then: "I am not QUIET AND CALM. I am not at ALL QUIET AND CALM." Good, that's all right, also in order.

Just as it is, whether you can be QUIET AND CALM or *not* ABLE TO BE QUIET AND CALM and PEACEFULLY COMPOSED, just as it happens to be for you. Then take only what is really there. No demands whatever, only what is there—now, at this very moment.

And if I now ask you to say, to say "I am quite quiet and completely calm," then I mean only those of you who . . . can REALLY BE QUITE QUIET AND COMPLETELY CALM ALSO. Only they.

And you can as often as you like . . . REPEAT INWARDLY . . . this formula from AT in that you say to yourself . . . "I AM QUITE QUIET AND COMPLETELY CALM." Then you see, some of you are really in effect—that means realistically effectively quiet and calm and the calm affects you really well. And here everyone can do what is necessary, blow your nose, everything belongs here. Do what is good for you. For, well, I cannot know as all really what is good for you. I am already quite quiet and completely calm.

Simply repeat this formula as often as you like to. Feel . . . THE QUIET CALM IS GROWING, BECOMING MORE . . . it will even then become more, the quiet calm when you have the feeling that you are not yet quiet, calm and restfully composed. Even then it becomes more: the quiet calm.

I am already quite quiet, completely calm.

You are all here on a deck chair and you know a deck chair is a chair where one can . . . BE PARTICULARLY COMFORTABLE . . . Because a deck chair is a chair where the heaviness, the weight of the body is well borne and taken up certainly comfortably. For every body is heavy. You know that when you get weighted. The body is heavy, you know. But in a deck-chair you can particularly well . . . FEEL THAT THE BODY IS HEAVY.

*Here in German there is wordplay around "lying in a lying-chair"—resting chair, deck chair, reclining chair.

Because a deck-chair is built for that: it can take the weight, bear it well in a particularly agreeable way.

If you therefore TURN YOUR ATTENTION INSIDE . . . FEELING YOUR WAY INTO YOUR OWN BODY, then you will be able to feel my legs are on a leg-rest because . . . my legs are heavy. My legs are heavy. My arms are laid on my lap, or on the arm-rests, or wherever they are laid, touching, for my arms are heavy. My back is leaning against the back of the chair, heavy. And the entire weight of the body is pressing with its seat (bottom, buttocks) onto the seat surface (bottom part) of the chair, because my body is just heavy. If you . . . REALLY RELAX THE MUSCLES OF YOUR BODY, a feeling of weight, of heaviness ensues.

When you were still a child and your mother, your mother said "Don't make yourself so heavy," when she wanted to pick you up. What do we children do to MAKE OURSELVES HEAVY? . . . LET ALL THE MUSCLES LOOSEN . . . for then . . . we shall BECOME HEAVY . . . difficult for mothers to pick us up. And such a FEELING OF WEIGHT IS REALLY OF NO WEIGHT. More and more weight. Then we cannot say to ourselves lightly: At a pleasant rate, the body feels more weight. And, meanwhile, some are falling asleep already. But naturally if it is for you im- . . . POSSIBLE TO STAY AWAKE, you can no (know) . . . longer experience that calm feeling of peace, of rest. But live experience is so important in life. Some people must look out for the LIVING EXPERIENCE ALL IN DETAIL, so exactly that they never get around to having a real outlook on life, when detailed to COME TO LIFE. And some have to snore. And it's also something entirely natural. For I did say, indeed, I did, everyone of you may here DO WHAT YOU WANT. And I mean this seriously. So you may also snore here or go out there, do what you want. For only then when I CAN LEAVE EVERYTHING JUST SO . . . like it is, then I can FIND CALM, RESTFUL QUIET, PEACE. And then I can say to myself with my inner voice: At a pleasant rate, the body feels more weight. As often as you like repeat this second formula: At a pleasant rate, the body feels more weight. I don't know where you . . . FEEL THE WEIGHT, THE HEAVINESS MOST—arms, legs. I also don't know whether you can now hear the dining trolley roll past. If you hear all that outside you can all the more—ATTEND TO HOW YOU TURN YOUR ATTENTION INWARDLY. For it is no weighty matter to feel THE BODY IS HEAVY. Drifting heavily, a floating weight, if you perhaps don't FEEL THE head-REST, the chair, the foot-REST MORE . . . Not feel it more . . . That, too, may be. Also coughing, anything at all may happen. And meanwhile I feel it is an enormously pleasant feeling to notice more and more:

At a pleasant rate, the body feels more weight.
Body heavy.

Simply like this . . . REPEATING: body heavy—there where you . . . FEEL THE HEAVINESS DIRECT YOUR ATTENTION TOWARDS THAT . . . there where you feel the heaviness. The formula is: body heavy. Body heavy. When you notice how the relaxation due to the heaviness takes place more and more, then you can also imagine a relaxed muscle is a muscle through which the blood can flow more easily. And when the blood can flow into the musculature better, then there's this there: more blood, more warmth. More blood in the musculature, more warmth in the body. Now it can be that you . . . FEEL THE WARMTH AT FIRST ONLY IN YOUR HANDS, . . . or it comes then, too, with the warmth. In your hands, I don't know whether you . . . FEEL it in your hands more, or more . . . ONLY IN YOUR FEET THAT FEELING. Some of you will certainly experience—the warmth, the circulation, the increased blood supply, the enlargement—FEELING IN YOUR ABDOMEN. There, where you feel the warmth, you can . . . DIRECT YOUR ATTENTION TOWARD IT. TO THE PLACE, WHERE YOU FEEL THE WARMTH. Feel the warmth. And then you can use the formula: Body warm. And by "body" I mean the part of the body where you FEEL THE WARMTH MOST DISTINCTLY. If you do (you'd) first sooner . . . FEEL THE WARMTH IN YOUR HANDS, then simply now if you like, when you want to leave everything as it is. You need not . . . FEEL THE WARMTH in the left hand, in the right hand, if you do not . . . FEEL THE WARMTH . . . then there it still has time till later until you . . . FEEL THE WARMTH, then it can be that you less than . . . FEEL THE WARMTH . . . or perhaps again then it is like that . . . you can . . . BE ABLE TO FEEL THE WARMTH . . . perhaps for the first time may be next time. Then, too: simply leave it like it is. Just let it be. Then you can say to yourself: body warm. As often as you like. Simply repeating with the inner restful, peaceful calm voice: body warm—now. And if it is not true, say quite quietly and completely calmly: body not warm, not warm, not warm if it should become warm. And then you can also quite naturally hear when somebody falls asleep.—Now—. Peace, calm, rest, quiet is present then when everything around me may be LIKE IT is. Including the snoring. May be LIKE IT is. And unrest, unquiet is present when things are not allowed to be like they are.

Body warm, or *not* warm
Arm warm.
Hand warm, or *not* warm.
Foot warm.
Abdomen (belly) warm or also *not* warm.
I don't know where, but: body warm.

Always then at the same time also the . . . FOREHEAD IS COOLER THAN THE BODY. Therefore, that is the reason, why the human being, because the . . . FOREHEAD IS COOL—perspires or sweats there earliest. For coolness—that is the coolness of evaporation. A light summer breeze blows, when you are lying on a green meadow, over . . . the FOREHEAD COOLING IT. Therefore the forehead becomes slightly moist when perspiring, so that is . . . KEEPS COOL—stays cool . . . for you to . . . KEEP COOL. Thus you can always feel: body warm, forehead cool; feet warm. Hands warm and forehead a bit cooler.

Is there always this gradient, this fall? There is an old farmer's lore that says: Feet warm, forehead cool, make the best doctor look a fool. For that means: healthiness: Forehead cool, feet warm. And then the forehead is cool and the head is clear and free. And it is very pleasant.

Forehead cool, head clear and free.

Then you can also repeat this formula: the forehead is cool, the head is clear and free. I believe as often as you want to repeat it. And notice how the calmness and composure increase further more.

Forehead is cool, head is clear and free.

Now, well inside with your own inner peaceful, quiet, restfully calm voice with which YOU also . . . ARE ABLE TO TALK TO YOURSELF, . . . with the particular peaceful, calm voice . . . SPEAK TO MYSELF . . . The forehead is cool, the head is clear and free . . . now.

The forehead is cool, the head is clear and free.

Sometimes one can also . . . LAY A MOIST CLOTH ON THE FOREHEAD . . . That is also very pleasant, the forehead is cooled well.

The forehead is cool, the head is clear and free.

That is a practicing procedure. That means, it should practically really . . . BE PLEASANT . . . so that once or twice a day you can simply sit down there or lie down there somewhere else, in your room, at home and there for yourself . . . LEAVE YOURSELF TIME . . . and TAKE TIME FOR YOURSELF . . . to DO THESE EXERCISES. And always, when you repeat these formulae, you can regain, bring back again these feelings of quiet calm, of warmth, of forehead coolness, that means in that you CAN REPEAT THE FORMULAE AGAIN for you . . . to BRING THEM BACK AGAIN. It is truly important, the fact that YOU CAN DO IT YOURSELF. DO IT YOURSELF.

Now, well, in order for you then when you . . . DO IT ON YOUR OWN with the formula—I am already quite quiet and completely calm—or, as long as you are quite unquiet, say calmly: I am still unquiet and fully begin with the rest of the unrest quite calmly because it is so important for you when it's truly all ready, all in order for you to be instead quite quiet or only a rest fully quiet and a piece fully calm, and then it's truly all ready in order: the peace, the quiet calm increase further more.

And you can choose from the formulae those that ARE SPECIALLY EFFECTIVE, PARTICULARLY EFFECTIVE for you, for you therefore need not . . . TAKE WHAT I AM TAKING HERE. Choose, select critically and pick out what is . . . EFFECTIVE FOR YOU, REALLY EFFECTIVE.

At a pleasant rate the body feels more weight.
Simply repeat it like that.
I am still unQUIET.
I am already quite quiet and completely calm.
Body heavy.
Body warm. The body warm.
The forehead cool. Forehead cool.
The body warm. Body heavy.

Outside snow is lying. It is very pleasant and cold at the same time. Not only that: the forehead is cool. Forehead cool. Perhaps you would still like to go for a walk this afternoon. Then you can while the others who are sleeping . . . WAKE UP . . . BE ALREADY THINKING A BIT OF TAKING THE WALK, while the others who are asleep are AWAKENing. I mean now first all those sleeping. They can NOW WAKE UP NOW. And only then when after all

SLEEPERS ARE FULLY AWAKE Now (awaken now) can we begin to slowly stretch a bit and yawn and then . . . EYES OPEN. Some don't want to WAKE UP. Oh yes, NOW they all want to . . . DO WAKE UP, all . . . ready? It was a mistake. And some are glad that it's over and they could tell us how terrible it is not to do anything for a whole half-hour?

INDUCTION
When Wishing Was Still Helpful

FORMULAE OF AUTOGENIC TRAINING II

Yesterday it was still cold, today everything is thawing. Ice—when ice thaws, it becomes soft. But then it's all so good here . . . to SIT HERE IN THE WARMTH AND DRYNESS and to know here I CAN DO WHAT I WANT TO . . . and ABSOLUTELY NOTHING disturbs us. Here everyone may snore, go outside, whatever. DO WHAT IS GOOD FOR YOU. Check and control ABSOLUTELY NOTHING AT ALL . . . everything is well now . . . LET EVERYTHING HAPPEN just LIKE IT happens.

Just like outside one raindrop falls after the other and yet one individual drop does not know anything about the others. One drop's simply able to fall. Their (they're) dropping is sooner or later . . . SIMPLY LETTING IT HAPPEN AS IT DOES. NOW, well now.

And always when you . . . LET THINGS GO AS REQUIRED, DESIRED IN ANY CASE . . . absolutely WITHOUT INFLUENCING THEM, then you can—if you LIKE—find RESTful PEACE AND QUIETNESS. And the longer you simply quite quietly and peacefully . . . GIVE COMPLETE CALM ROOM APIECE AND THUS SPACE TIME GIVEN ROOM FREELY . . . the more you will notice THE RESTFUL PEACE WILL STILL INCREASE. Quite gradually, entirely unnoticeable but yet still EFFECTIVE. RESTFUL PEACE WILL STILL INCREASE.

I am already much quieter and calmer. Actually calm comes completely regularly, peace comes perfectly periodically. That is really nothing special that RESTFUL PEACE WILL STILL INCREASE. When you happen completely gradually to feel quite quiet and completely calm and really take your time and give yourself time for then you will also notice that peace and quiet is what we also FIND IN THE BODY. For instance . . . A QUIET BREATH.

Always, whenever the chest expands and the abdominal wall rises then you feel, "I'm breathing in (inhaling)." And always whenever the chest lowers to relax again and the abdominal wall will loosen and relax, you feel, "I'm breathing out (exhaling) . . ." (so hale and hearty)

And when I breathe in quite calmly and completely regularly, I take in oxygen. This oxygen I need to live. And when breathing out the superfluous carbon dioxide can be LET OUT AGAIN.

Taking in, letting out, oxygen, carbon dioxide.

Completely calm and regularly I feel: this vital life-giving breathing function calmly and regularly HAPPENS ALL BY ITSELF.

The trees in the forest (woods) breathe the carbon dioxide in and LET OUT FOR US, GIVE US the oxygen again.* And so it can be that it is so LIKE IT is that TO EVERY ONE HUMAN BEING THERE BELONGS ONE tree, too, and this exactly opposite to and unlike the human being breathes in carbon dioxide and breathes out oxygen. And the human being breathes in oxygen and breathes out the carbon dioxide. So they are—all the trees and the human beings—are all—YOU ARE LIKEWISE ALLIED WITH NATURE. Your allied confederates united in solidarity with Nature! One part of the whole entity and yet alone also a whole entity. Says our breathing to us thus . . . when we observe how it quietly calmly restfully flows and all by itself does what it knows we need to live.

The breath flows calmly and regularly.
It breathes me.
Breath, calm and regular.
It breathes me.

Then you can CONNECT WITH THE BREATHING everything that is so important, and ENJOY THE QUIET CALM, and in internal dialogue with your own inner calm, still voice still SAY TO YOURSELF, "Breath, calm and regular. It breathes me." That is the next formula from AT.

Breath, calm and regular. It breathes me. And this formula from AT you can as often as YOU WANT TO REPEAT with the inner calm still voice still: Breath, calm and regular. It breathes me. Repeat—now.

Calm and regular. It breathes me.

DIRECT THE ENTIRE ATTENTION INWARDS and FEEL YOUR OWN BREATHING ACCORDINGLY and USE THE FORMULA: Breath, calm and regular. It breathes me—now. There are indeed many organs in the body that completely restfully calm and regularly DO THE WORK, COMPLETELY QUIETLY as a matter of course, taking it for granted. No one can, for example, feel the kidneys, although they incessantly cleanse the blood from all superfluous matter, of fact (sic!) they are constantly calm and keep quiet peacefully doing their job. Also the liver, that is constantly processing sugar you cannot feel. But YOU CAN FEEL YOUR BREATH, and SIMULTANEOUSLY SAY THE BREATH EXERCISE TO YOURSELF.

And just as the organs keep quiet within the body, so is that often also thus for us: When you imagine that you are walking through the silent, deep forest and the oxygen that the trees have breathed out there, exhaled for you, inhale the oxygen. When you feel like that, then go through the deep forest, hale and hearty. Once upon a time—already long ago—when you were a child and fairy tales were for you very lovely and important. Once upon a time—already long ago—in olden times—when wishing was still helpful.

Once upon a time—in olden times, when wishing was still helpful, through this dense forest, so rich in oxygen, deep and wide, a dwarf was wandering. And he knew the world . . . well, how to see with the eyes of a dwarf, the ferns just as they were up to his eyes. And sometimes he got hung up with his red cap on a fern. When a dwarf walks through the forest he can see lizards, have spotted salamanders and new newts before his eyes, . . . observe blind-worms. Sometimes he could rest on the soft cushion, . . . it was made of moss and he could . . . see how a squirrel flashed past with a nut in its mouth. For squirrels it's a pleasure to crack a hard nut, that's great fun when it goes "crack" and look there . . . the problem is solved.

And so the dwarf went through the forest and could . . . enjoy his life utterly. Being how-ever sad not to find anybody, some body some being who would accompany him. Because he was alone. And when he was eating the blueberries that stood right ready in front of his hands—and for him large fruits—then he thought: "How marvelous it is, though, to imagine: SOMEONE IS ALWAYS WITH ME." And one day as he was on his way and came to a crossing in a clearing, he saw, though, that there really was a giant coming from the other side. And the giant, of course, did not see the dwarf at once, for the giant was up and above the clearing, his head up high in the tree-tops. But at the crossing, though, the giant did then look for the right way, and there down beneath him stood the dwarf. The giant said, "Who are you, now?" The dwarf said that he was a dwarf and asked, "And who are you?" "I AM A GIANT." The dwarf said, "May I . . . GO WITH YOU?" The giant said, "You don't like be-ing alone either, do you?" "No, I don't," said the dwarf. "I would LIKE TO ACCOMPANY YOU, but you are so gigantic and you could . . . PROTECT ME A LITTLE." "But how shall I GET AN ADVANTAGE FROM THAT?" asked the giant. The dwarf replied, "I'll show you that sometime later still."

Well then they went further, to go together quietly and further deeper and deeper and still deeper into the forest and spoke very little—because—each one could . . . ENJOY THE PEACE AND QUIETNESS THE DEEPER THE FURTHER THE MORE THE ENTERING INTO . . . the EVER DEEPER . . . STILL DEEPER . . .

But all at once they came then, though, to a wide, green meadow and the dwarf said, "IT IS LOVELY, the green meadow." "No," said the giant, "it's a yellow meadow." Because it was covered all over with yellow flowers. And the giant was so tall and far up that he could only see the yellow. The dwarf down low though could see much more green. And the dwarf asked, "Can you SMELL THE FLOWERS like I can?" "What's that, smell?" "Can't you SMELL FLOWERS?" "No, I don't know what you mean." "Then you must PUT YOUR HEAD RIGHT DOWN HERE." And so the giant bent right down and the dwarf was then able to BE SO FULL OF JOY AND HAPPINESS and he said to himself every so often with his in-ner voice, "THE GIANT IS AS SMALL AS I AM . . . ALL GIANTS ARE AS SMALL AS I AM." And when the giant lay so flat he smelt for the first time the juicy yellow flowers and stroked the lush grass with his big hands and could laugh WITH THE DWARF. Because IT'S LOVELY.

Then the giant said: "While I'm already down here, I'LL just stretch out a while on the meadow, and smell things, and JUST LET MYSELF HAVE A NICE ENJOYABLE TIME." And the dwarf laid his head on the giant's hand. And so they really were able to ENJOY BE-ING ABLE TO REST TOGETHER, HALE AND HEARTY. And they had a really HEARTY relationship. It was completely HEART-FELT HAPPINESS for both. And THE

PEACE IN EACH HEART GREW EVER MORE. Because it was so calm and peaceful, and the giant enjoyed it exactly like the dwarf being able to lie there quietly and listen to the silence and smell the flowers when calmly and regularly breathing in and breathing out. Then all hearts were full of joy and happiness.

All the peace and quiet of the earth is within the hearts. The hearts of both are very calm and satisfied just like their breaths calm . . . and regularly flows, all by itself.

And so you can while lying here also if YOU WANT TO, say the last formula from AT to yourself, "heart calm and reliable." As reliable as the friendship of those two. And it's so quiet and peaceful in the deep forest. Really pleasant, when you are able to say to yourself: Heart, calm and reliable. As often as when you are awake . . . YOU WANT TO simply repeat this formula: Heart, calm and reliable. Repeat as often as YOU WANT TO—now.

Heart, calm and reliable. [Pause]

Still with your inner voice as often as you like repeating. With the quiet still voice. Still with the quiet inner voice—now. [Pause] It is of great importance that you CHOOSE THE FORMULAE YOURSELF, those with which you . . . also HAVE SUCCESS YOURSELF. That you, when lying, resting alone, morning, noon and evening—leave yourself time—take time for yourself at leisure. And therefore I shall once more go through with you together all the formulae that we have done yesterday and today, so that in this way the choice for you will be easier for you to . . . FIND THE FORMULAE YOU WANT TO PRACTICE.

I am already quiet. I am already calm.
Restful peace will still increase.
Body—arms, legs—heavy.
Body—hands, feet, abdomen—warm.
Forehead is cool.
Breath calm and regular.
Breath calm and regular. It breathes me.
Heart, calm and reliable.
Heart, calm and reliable.

And you can really TAKE TIME FOR YOURSELF two or three times a day for these exercises or one or more of these exercises and REPEAT them for like wise (sic) YOU to bring back repeatedly all the pleasant feelings . . . like wise you to bring back repeatedly all the pleasant feelings. So it is really for you yourself indeed PERMANENTLY PLEASANT . . . LASTING REALLY COMFORTABLY and enduring easily. EXERCISE TWO OR THREE TIMES daily.

And now you can remain resting where you are lying down now, well, we'll have to first WAKE UP those who have fallen asleep. And only after they have been AWAKENed, the ones that are asleep, can the others BECOME REACTIVATED, BECOME ACTIVE AGAIN.

I see that some are not yet AWAKE. Some perhaps do not at all want to WAKE UP. But sometime somewhere everyone WAKES UP to BE AWAKE to BE AWARE of AWAKENing. Even the one(s) so fast asleep AWAKEN(s) also to WAKE UP, too. No, (to know) it really is in my opinion not right to WAKE UP without having slept before. And if one has been sleeping, then one can WAKE UP AGAIN . . . NOW.

Well, NOW, I see, to BE FULLY AWARE, you do not want to WAKE UP!

Well, then we must all stay here till this evening so we do not disturb you. Or DO you perhaps . . . still want to WAKE UP AT LAST? [As a rule this last piece will get even the deepest sleeper awake.]

It is a fairly false assumption that when asleep one doesn't hear anything, as you see. One can listen to everything very well.

Right, how were the difficulties?

And what else is there still to report that went easily?

EXPLANATIONS FOR UNDERSTANDING THE MANUSCRIPT IN AN ERICKSONIAN CONTEXT

The formulae of Autogenic Training (AT) were developed in Berlin during the twenties and thirties of this century by J. H. Schultz. Corresponding to the then usual directive and authoritarian style of hypnosis, which Schultz also practiced, he conceived AT also as a directive, authoritarian system of self-hypnosis.

Where German is spoken, AT has speedily spread and the conscious resistance to learning this method is low, the unconscious resistance on the contrary is that much higher. It is striking that many patients report that they "cannot feel what is said at all." Direct confrontation with the formulae did not take into account the patient's resistance. The formulae that Schultz had developed were appropriate for patients with nervous organic complaints or vegetative troubles. However, those methods for teaching these formulae did not take the phenomenon of resistance into consideration at all. Correspondingly large in such directive groups is then the number of participants dropping out prematurely.

Two things are of import to me in my approach: One is I want to utilize the fact that patients have a high acceptance of AT for a group trance. The other is I want to use the formulae developed by Schultz as an anchor, for which use they are very suitable.

The pleasant physical sensations the patients had in the group sessions should be retrievable, "bring-back able" when bringing back the formulae to mind. To achieve this and thus increase the efficacy. I included Ericksonian techniques in AT, as I had already learned from Burkhard Peter. These techniques will now, in the following, be described in more detail:

1. *Working with Resistance*

This means concretely allowing everything a patient in a resistant position could do. Then it becomes superfluous. An example: For many patients it is an anxiety-provoking image "having to sit still" for a good half-hour. Therefore, right at the beginning is the remark: "And if you want to go, and if it gets too much or too little for you then . . . just do it quietly." Of importance here is the interspersed "too much or too little" in this sentence, for this introduces confusion into the sentence and this disturbs the action-sequence sufficiently for action to become impossible.

Of equal importance, however, is the immediate incorporation of the word "go" into another context: "It really does go for all without saying that . . . everyone does what s/he wants."

2. *Implications with Paradoxical Confusion*

"If you really do that in that you do nothing, then you can relax." Nobody can do doing nothing, but the sentence is effective and only that is why it is really so that "you relax." It is not clear whether the sentence is logical or only apparently logical, but the suggestion "relax" works within the framework of the implication.

3. *Suggestion*

I employ direct as well as indirect suggestions. Many of these suggestions are hidden imperatives. If they are emphasized by a change in the voice, they work unconsciously as an imperative. This remains, by reason of this embedding, without the resistance that is normally aroused by the use of commands. For instance: "Then you can after a time lean your head back all by itself." "You can also if you like . . . close your eyes." An interspersed suggestion, strewn in—as opposed to an embedded command—is on the other hand the closing formulation: "or you can also wait until you notice: Your eyes are closing all by themselves." The preliminary resistance at the beginning—in the form of conscious, attentive curiosity—may be reduced also by the phrase, "there's nothing special going on here." This implies that the patient expects something special. According to the emphasis at an unconscious level is given the message: there is nevertheless something special.

About the Formulae

The opening formula used by Schultz is: "I am completely calm." This formula if used without preliminary preparatory work, triggers off massive resistance, because this formula can only sound to an excited tense patient as though one wanted to push something down his throat that's not at all true. This is bound to strengthen resistance. For this reason the formula "quiet or unquiet" plays an important role. The emphasis is made so that the syllable "un" is emphasized progressively less and in a deeper voice, although still remaining audible, so that the word "quiet" remains left twice, doubly effective, but at the same time resistance is avoided.

The feeling of relaxation proper lies within the first formula used by Schultz: "My body is heavy," for the muscle relaxation is always perceptible as a feeling of bodily heaviness. The pacing is here: "The fact that the body is heavy is already known to you," and the leading: "But in a deckchair you can particularly well . . . feel that the body is heavy. Because a deck chair is built for that: it can take the weight in a particularly agreeable way."

The cognitive approach, knowing about the heaviness, is so general that it has to be affirmed. This leads to kinesthetic feeling via the embedded command "feel how heavy your body is," which is then confirmed by the apparent logic using the structure of a deck chair. The description of the body surfaces lying on the chair makes the feeling of the body concrete, whereby the formulations must be vague enough not to disturb and suppress the experiential state already present for the participants but rather to advance it associatively. The feeling of heaviness is promoted metaphorically by the phrasing, "When you were still a child and your mother. . . ." The metaphor constantly encourages and uses regressive tendencies already existing. Present here, too, is the use of the right hemisphere with body feeling fantasies while simultaneously obviating left-hemispheric resistance by using the expression: "The feeling of weight is really not of weight." Here and the double meaning of the word "weight" is used.*

Giving permission to perceive all sounds in the vicinity is necessary. Concurrently it is important to utilize them for a dissociation: "outside/inside." To steer from this dissociation over to perceiving the weight of the body implies utilization of prevailing external sounds. This should always be inserted when outside noises are obviously present and cannot be ignored.

On the basis of what has been achieved and with the aid of apparent logic, sham-logic, a relaxed muscle "necessarily" becomes a muscle with dilated blood vessels. Then follows the next formula from AT, the exercise "the body is warm." Here, too, body parts that could be warm are cited concretely but also so vaguely that feelings of bodily warmth already present can be turned to account.

In my work it has proved advantageous to insert here an exercise from muscle relaxation according to Jacobson, one that promotes hand warmth in a special way and that can reduce the tingling, the pins and needles, in the hands that often crops up during the warmth practice in AT.

The sensation of coolness in the forehead, the last exercise in the classical AT of Schultz, can follow immediately after the warmth part, as a dissociation. If there are parts of the body that are particularly warm, there must also be others that are cooler than all the rest. Thus the coolness of the forehead founts out of the warmth of the body, and a peasant's proverb proves positively that this signifies health. Also, afterwards, the dissociating feeling of forehead coolness after body warmth is anchored with the aid of an AT formula so that these feelings become permanently re-accessible, assisted by the anchoring formula.

The last part of the exercise is concerned with suggesting that after these positive experiences AT will have a firm place in life and the participants will continue to practice. To this end, all the formulae are repeated once again and it is emphasized that the individual participant should practice only those formulae that have afforded positive experiences. Here the emphasis on single passages should be particularly regarded so that the interspersed suggestions can become effective.

It should be noted here that participants who are fast asleep must already be wakened *before* a general recall to return succeeds. It should be explained concretely why first only those who are sleeping "wake up, for those who are awake cannot wake up." In saying this, "awake" and "wake up" are emphasized so that all the sleepers are roused.

With an ensuing discussion concerning the experiences, the first training session with four AT formulae ends. A further hour is dedicated to the other two formulae. In the second ses-

*The German word "schwer" means both "heavy" and "difficult." Analogous in English would be: "Being hard is really not hard."

sion the permission "Do what you want" is joined to the familiar permission while utilizing the raindrops falling hard onto the glass roof: "They're (the raindrops or the participants) . . . simply letting it happen, and "are able to fall."

The fact that from now on only peace, quiet and restfulness is spoken of and lack of calm, restlessness, etc., are no longer mentioned is founded solely upon the individual participant's having taken part in the first training and therefore already having had a definite personal experience of calm. This definition of actually experiencing calm (as soon as all are breathing calmly) is thus a pacing-step in order to generalize via the breath to experiencing calm throughout the entire body as a leading step. The holistic concept of the unity of mankind and nature in experiencing breathing is the important metaphor for this step. Here the metabolic exchange of oxygen and carbon dioxide as the cognitive start of the happenings is utilized to describe the dynamically flowing unity of human being and tree, person and nature. In the description I proceed so that the remarks (with "sie" in german) can refer to persons as well as trees. This slight soft confusion can cause direct perplexity of the "you." Confidence in the body and its functions, trust in the holistic nature of untouched nature is the starting-point.

It is well-known from AT practice according to Schultz that the heart exercise often leads to alarming states in cases of heart-neurosis. I work in a cardiological clinic where many of my colleagues simply omit the heart exercise for safety's sake. This entails, though, that simultaneously all chance of change through desensitization is relinquished. This is why I add stories as metaphors for the transition from breath to heart exercises. The example cited here is one of the many tales about giants and dwarfs. This metaphor contains the message that all great things become smaller and all small things become larger. There are quite a quantity of embedded commands and indirect suggestions thrown in besides. I have marked these so it is clear how to say them so they are effective.

A further structural element is that whatever pertains to the dwarf, i.e., to the fairy tale, is in the Perfect tense, whereas commands and suggestions are always in the Present tense. Thus, the present situation can be conceived of as a leading step, while the past return into the world of fairy tales contains continually new pacing steps that join up with the familiar feelings of childhood from past days and render further pacing steps possible.

A manifest group trance is necessary for using the heart exercise with a heart patient group without unpleasant side-effects. This is actually true, though, for all groups, as heart patients could also be in any group. The forest is in this passage a metaphor for the unconscious, and the suggestion of going "deeper and deeper into the forest" is indeed very trance inducing in actual practice, as is the rather more direct instruction to go "deeper and deeper into trance." Once a medium depth of trance has been reached, the heart can be addressed, at first indirectly, as a hearty, heartfelt relationship and then also directly with a heart exercise. The recourse to the preceding breathing exercise, to the calm breathing, should be joined like an anchor onto the vegetative homeostasis then present. Only then can the heart exercise be carried out with success in a version different from, though derived from, that of Schultz.

The last part of this training is concerned with prescribing behavior promoting further meaningful, independent practice by the patients themselves. The balance in the vegetative nervous system should thus be ensured to be thoroughly successful and sustained; whereby it is of minor importance whether this ability is for self-relaxation or for auto-suggestive induction of a trance.

An explicit prescription of amnesia seems to me unnecessary. The simple activating return is sufficient. I can accept with composure the fact that always some patients fall asleep during the training. They must be let sleep. If not, the "Do what you want" would prove to be a double-bind. It is more important to utilize all external sounds meaningfully and to feed back to the group immediately, reframed in the form of an announcement of success, the fact that all stay calm although someone is snoring.

8

Deborah Ross: Story Telling

INDUCTION

I want to teach you a highly reproducible method of self-hypnosis, and then, what we'll do is all go into trance together, and I'll use some story telling and I'll try to leave some time at the end, so that if any of you wants to ask questions we can dialogue a little bit about what we did, that there is time for that. O.K.? Any special requests on story telling? Kinds of things you would like? That you can use for your practices, for that's what I'm concerned about? O.K. How about if we would use something useful for empowering and raising self-esteem? What I'm going to do is do an induction with you very much the way I do with my patients in my private practice. By the way I'm Deborah Ross and I'm Director of the Los Gatos Institute, a residential training center for hypnosis in Los Gatos, California.

When I'm working in my own practice I will do a formal induction exactly once, because I start with the whole empowerment idea right from the start, and the trance will strongly belong to the patient, not to the therapist. So what I will do is teach you what I like to call trance IA. And once you know it, you know it. And then what I will do in my practice is fractionate patients three or four times, let them go in and out of trance state, so that it is very clear by the time they leave my office, that the trance is theirs and has nothing to do with the setting or the therapist. O.K.?

Well, I would like to start with just asking inside yourself a very simple question, which is: Is there anything I can do right now to allow myself to be a little more comfortable? And let your bodies answer for you too, because what you are getting in touch with is body brain, if you like, as well as thinking brain. And you might feel like loosening a button, uncrossing your legs, putting down your writing materials. You learn much better from being in trance than from taking notes. Unbuttoning the top button, anything at all that is going to add to your comfort. It helps, when you are in your first learning trance, to have your hands and your feet separated; after that, it really doesn't matter. At the very beginning it's useful.

And then I would like you to check out some points where therapists in particular hold tension, the jaw and the shoulders. And if you just make a little sound as you exhale (Dr. Ross demonstrates here herself with a sound), you will find that that helps you to release your jaws and get a nice kind of long and loose feeling, your teeth slightly separated. And then I would like you to also notice that as you take an inhalation your shoulders tend to rise, and as you exhale, that they lower. And I would like you to really exaggerate that exhalation and that descent of your shoulders as you exhale. And just let your shoulders come all the way down. It's kind of like a reverse bicycle pump just breathing up and down. And then, thirdly, allow your breathing to be very natural, easy breathing, the way little babies breathe or an animal breathes, stomach rounding and emptying, so that you are giving yourself that nice full support of oxygen.

And then I would like you to just pick a spot a little bit above eye level to fix your eyes in a very soft focus. And by soft focus I mean gazing without really trying to see anything at all, just looking in one direction. The first time you do this it helps to have it a little bit above eye level; afterwards it doesn't matter. And what you begin to notice as you are continuing to breathe, allowing your shoulders to be nice and relaxed, what you begin to notice are visual distortions, you may notice blurring, double vision, or things losing their thingness, kind of a visual equivalent of saying a word over and over and over and forgetting what it means. You may notice that your peripheral vision begins to diminish, almost as if you are looking down a mailing tube. You may notice changes in light and dark interplay or texture. Or even the pulsation as if where you're looking begins to have its own respiration and is breathing very much in rhythm with your own breathing. And just nod to me as you begin to notice any of the various visual changes as when you are softly gazing at sunlight on water, or patterns of rainfall: blurring, double vision, superimposition of image. Good. And keep watching, because that is very interesting.

And also put your attention in your hands. Now what you are feeling for is a tingling or a warming. You feel it most easily in the fingers. And what's happening is that as you relax and oxygenate fully, you are encouraging some vasodilation in your hands, just a slight increase in blood-flow. You feel that as a warming or tingling, some of you feel it as heaviness or lightness, most often it is that very agreeable warming and tingling feeling. That is your hand signal, and that means that any time you want to you can just allow an exhalation to close your eyes for you, almost as though you are breathing them closed, knowing any time that you want to, you can breathe them open again, get the visuals back even more quickly, and then breathe them closed with an exhalation, and every time you open and close you go a little deeper inside, and you allow body brain and thinking brain to form a very, very good synergistic team, each one potentiating the other. And that very agreeable feeling in your hands can begin to spread. And as it spreads up towards your shoulders you can allow all the muscles and ligaments and tendons to go very long, loose, smooth just like cooked spaghetti and just breathe out any tension. Good.

Releasing your upper back, shoulders, muscles of the throat widening just that little bit, some of you are already getting an impediment in your swallow reflex which is one of your body's ways of telling you that you are already in a very nice level of trance, releasing your jaws and letting them get very comfortably heavy, facial muscles relaxing, releasing, all the little tiny muscles round your eyes, smallest muscles in your body relaxing, forehead, scalp just as smooth as the surface of a pond on a very calm summer day, smooth as a mirror, doubling, reflecting downward into the body a very comfortable warm flow of good energy. Relaxing upper back, chest, lower back, stomach, buttocks and anus, pelvis and genitals, lower legs, ankles, feet, toes, continuing to allow your exhalations to take you more and more inside, beginning to experience on all levels of your mind and body how much you know about opening to that pleasure that is your birthright, all those things that you know that you don't know you know, opening, teaching you about your own very good abilities.

And I'm going to count from 5 to 1, and you can double the quality and comfort of the trance state with each number. Five, and while you're enjoying the pleasure of the trance state, trance is a very pleasurable state, the deeper part of your mind gets a chance to do a lot of very important physiological change for you without your having to think about it at all. Your respiration has slowed and deepened, your pulse rate has slowed, your blood pressure has lowered, four, your heart muscle is working with the most possible efficiency, the very least expenditure of energy, a very personal energy conservation program, three, half way there, going even deeper, even more comfortably inside with every exhalation, muscle tonus has very greatly altered, and that deeper part of your brain gets a chance to store an incredible amount of energy, all the energy that normally you lose in chronic muscle tension is now freed up, has been collected and can be used in so many good ways, two, to balance all the different systems of the body, muscle skeleton system, endocrine system, neurological and vascular systems, digestive-eliminative systems, all the different systems working in a very perfect balanced state with the whole body just like a very finely tuned Ferrari before a Grand Prix race, everything on hum, and that synergy and that balancing adds to the comfort, the peacefulness of the trance state, one, totally relaxed and comfortable, continuing to allow your own unconscious mind to teach you how much you know, opening you to the very finest teacher you will ever know, your own unconscious mind. That energy can also be used to allow new answers to old puzzles, to kind of float up all on their own, or again just for the pleasure which is your birthright, which is God-given, which is always there.

And you can continue to just allow breath to follow breath just like waves of the ocean, flowing one after the other. It's not really important, if you listen to my voice. You can let one row of neurons do that very nicely, while you begin to connect with your own internal teacher, your very personal sanctuary. It's kind of like finding a secret garden that has been there all these years; you just forgot for a while where the gate was. And now you are inside, and there is every imaginable color and fragrance of flower, and the grass is that kind of sweet summer grass, that feels so cool and velvety on your bare toes, just the right amount of sun, just the right amount of breeze, and find you a place to sit or lie down, and enjoy that sweet smell of the grass under your body and the buzzing of summer insects, maybe just the motion of the butterfly half-seen in the periphery of your eye, the red of a ladybug on a green blade of grass, and it's so easy to just sink into that warm grass under you, the warm sun over you. And I think that all you need to be happy is just to allow yourself for some moments in time to become absorbed in something so much bigger than you are, and infinitely supportive . . .

And you can allow your unconscious mind to begin to give you many, many gifts, the right to this kind of pleasure, knowing that your eyes—by going soft-focused—and that very agreeable tingling feeling in your hands can take you back inside to just the right level of trance any time you want them to, because everything you learn in trance you learn forever, because you are learning with that ideomotoric part of the brain just like when you learn to swim or drive a car or ride a bicycle. Once you know, you know and the body will remember for you, taking you always to a very comfortable, agreeable, pleasurable sanctuary. Then you can allow your unconscious mind to begin to create a very personal safe place for you. And I don't know if that will begin as a color or a memory, a sound of water, the wind, a picture, a feeling.

When I was a little girl, growing up in Boston, one of the things I liked to do after a big snow storm was to go out in the back yard and find where the snow had drifted very high above my head, and I would hollow out a little cave and line it with newspaper so it would be warm and dry. And I would crawl inside with a book, sometimes a stuffed animal, and I made a hole so some light could come in. And outside the snowcave it could be storming and windy and sleeting and one of the older kids could be looking to hit me with a snowball and my mummy could be yelling for me to come home for lunch. But inside the snowcave it was so warm and so quiet with the most incredible quality of light that all the walls looked just like diamonds, and I didn't have to listen to any of them at all.

And just take some moments of clock time, it's all the time in the world for your unconscious mind to begin to create this very special safe place where you can go in to touch with yourself, with your own internal teacher. And meanwhile your body is balancing and healing, sorting new solutions and all without your having to think about it at all. And that sanctuary can be the first of many, many places that open to you in the trance state, teaching you about trance, teaching you about the resources you had forgotten, about your own wholeness, so that you can become a very clear mirror for others to find their whole within. And while you are enjoying these happy, pleasurable feelings, I'm going to tell you another story about an Indian woman who lived a long time ago in Arizona. She was out on the high mountain desert one day when she came across a band of wild horses. And on the edge of the band was the most magnificent stallion she had ever seen. And she just stopped and stared, and inside herself she knew that this was no ordinary horse. This horse was very much a gift of magic from the Indian Gods to her and through her to her people. She had never seen such a magnificent animal. He was strong and he was muscled and he carried his neck arched and his tail bone straight up in the air, he was so proud. His coat was so shiny that where the sun touched it, little blue lights flew up. His hoofs were the color of ebony, into which someone had very lovingly rubbed oil, but the most amazing thing about him was his eyes, which were blue, the color of an Arizona summer sky. And you could travel forever into that eternity of blue. And she listened deep inside her. And she knew that her task was somehow to learn to ride that animal, to merge with its power, so well, that the Indian Gods looking down would nod in satisfaction, that they had given such an incredible gift to a woman worthy of it. And she was plenty scared, she didn't even know how to begin. So she looked around her. She noticed a place where the earth had a little rise to it. And she waited there very patiently until the stallion was grazing nearby and then she sprang with all her might onto his back. She was there for only seconds, and found herself bruised and breathless back on the ground, tears in her eyes. She gathered up all her strength and she tried again and again and again, and I don't know how many times she found herself back on the ground, bruised, breath knocked out of her, tears in her eyes, until one day her legs found just the right way to grab that stallion's flanks and her hands found just the right way to tangle in his mane and they were galloping.

And if you could have been there watching, you would have sworn that the horse's blood was running in the girl's veins and her blood in his, so much were they one thing.

Now a magic horse can do a lot of different things; he can gallop all day after buffalo without getting tired; he can leap right across an entire canyon, gallop to the top of the highest mesa. But the day that this woman really knew that she had completed her task was a very different kind of day; it was one morning very early before dawn when she rode so quietly into the Indian village, that not one dog barked. And she came to a halt in the center of the teepees, sat very quietly on the horse, and the people felt the magic and gathered silently around the woman seated on the horse, and without saying one word she gave out all that magic, all that power to her people.

And just keep going down, really enjoying, just how easily breath follows breath, with that tingling all through your body, reminding you that you are all very much star-stuff, the atoms and molecules of your body have made the trip from here to the sun and back again some eleven to twelve times, allowing yourself to connect with your own internal knowing on a level much deeper than words, almost as if you leave the words, the thoughts floating on the top of the pond, attached with a strong cord to a tree root so that you can get them back again when you want them, and just let yourself sink very comfortably below the words, below the thoughts to a different level of your mind to very much your own knowing-place opening to the pleasure that is your birthright, gathering it like big armfuls of wild flowers.

Then, when you are ready, and only when you are ready, float back up to this time, to this place. And if you like, you can experiment with first just awakening from the neck up, allowing an inhalation to open your eyes for you, letting your body stay put in the trance, continuing to store energy for you and know that you can extend the pleasure of that trance state just as long as you want to. When you do decide to allow an inhalation to open your eyes for you, your body is going to be there and not there. And all that energy that used to go into muscle tension is freed up for very clear conscious mind processing, the colors are very bright, your mind is very clear and rested, try that very strange feeling, if you have not felt trance dissociation before, of your body being there and not there. And then just for your own knowing go into soft-focus again, getting the tingling back and going all the way back down, so that you know that the trance state is yours and is there whenever you want it. And that your body will remember it for you. That's right. It's just like going down a playground slide, it's so easy, you already know the way. Again touching the pleasure, knowing that it's your birthright. [Pause]

And then, when you are ready, using your inhalations to bring you back to this room, this time taking a nice big cat stretch and wakening all over.

COMMENTS

Story Telling is the main technique used by Deborah Ross in her group induction. Notice how she seeds the goal of the induction (raising self-esteem) right at the beginning during the phase of making contact with the group by asking questions. Asking questions is her skillful transition to orient the group inwardly.

For visual people Deborah Ross offers all the distortions that can happen during eye fixation as a signal that the state of consciousness is changing, for kinesthetic people she describes the possible sensations in the hands as the "hand signal." Notice also how she makes us close our eyes, passing back and forth between the visual and the kinesthetic signals, thus pacing possible eye blinking. At this level of the trance she also involves breathing, combining the opposites "thinking brain" and "body brain" mentioned before and making them form a team. Step-by-step the trance is deepened. From muscle relaxation she leads over with a confusing passage to the counting technique, a passage in which the trance is ratified. Only then, when she has made several suggestions where to feel totally comfortable, when everybody has found a "safe place" and is connected with "something greater than we are," she begins her story telling about her safe place, her "sanctuary." Notice how in this way words flow in ways that are usually used in a religious context. What we are dealing with here is not the unconscious Sigmund Freud helped us to recognize. It is the potent, positive and resources-offering unconscious Milton H. Erickson taught us about. For him it is the vast potential of all our learning experiences we have ever made (Peter, 1988, p. 52). For closer consideration of the concept "unconscious" please refer to the publication: "Hypnose und das Unbewußte" (Peter & Kraiker, eds., 1989). Hearing those words like "internal teacher," "birthright of pleasure," "infinitely supportive" and "the most incredible quality of light," we would be better off talking about the superconscious to avoid misunderstandings (compare Scharfetter, 1986; Wilber, 1987). The story of the Indian woman and the magic horse the Indian Gods have sent is the heart of this induction on raising self-esteem. It connects us with our birthright of having access to the superconscious realms. Maybe it is the secret of Erickson's successes that he connected people with these regions, where the main changes occur. Here, as in the moving stories of all religious traditions, the problem of having too little self-esteem is solved.

III

PREPARATION OF CONCRETE LEARNING STEPS

This section contains a selection of inductions that demonstrate preparation of the actual hypnotherapeutic work in trance and also afford practice in basic skills such as entering into a trance with open eyes (induction by Wilhelm Gerl), identification with a tree (induction by Paul Carter with his own comments), and developing warmth in various parts of the body (my own induction). The mystical Indian tale by Wolfgang Lenk suggests that learning about trance can be like an initiation process.

Initially I had planned to include here an induction done by Burkhard Peter in Kiel in 1983: "Self Hypnosis as a Group Induction." The group hypnosis had developed spontaneously when Burkhard Peter wanted to show the group how he intentionally entered a trance state. Unfortunately the tape has been lost, but this is a good idea to pass on for others to use in a learning situation. Two further inductions by Wilhelm Gerl had to be sacrificed to keep this book a reasonable size. The aim of one is to sensitize us to the language in which the patient represents his or her own world, and the purpose of the other is to induce hypnotic hand levitation.

9

Wilhelm Gerl: The Externally Oriented Trance of the Therapist

COMMENTS

Learning about the different types of trance requires a mental set in which you emotionally experience a group induction. It also requires an awareness of what happens in trance. A therapist working with clients in altered states of consciousness must be aware of what is going on and must be in control of the situation although still able to let go simultaneously. Jeffrey Zeig speaks of the "self-conscious trance" in this sense. This is the type of trance introduced by Wilhelm Gerl in his group induction: "The Externally Oriented Trance of the Therapist."

We have become acquainted with this awareness-demanding type of trance before in Joseph Barber's introductory "Changing the Relationship." What was only one of the sidelights there is explicitly the main goal in Wilhelm Gerl's induction here: We are encouraged to experience the changes in our perception while remaining in trance, open to all types of perception, with eyes, ears, body . . . During this we train abilities basic to any work with patients, whether singly or in groups.

The trance of the therapist is the trance of awareness. And when are we more aware of what's going on around us than when the environment is new! Here a new environment is created by looking at a familiar one in a new way, using new or seldom realized possibilities of our senses. Wilhelm Gerl leads us to expand our visual, auditory and kinesthetic perceptions, weaving them together by using words from all perceptual channels and by combining this opening of the senses with a description of Milton Erickson's attitude during therapy. Thus, this induction is a basic multi-level example for therapists as it teaches externally oriented trance and, indirectly, Erickson's enchanting way of doing therapy, while extending use of the individual's sensory and perceptual possibilities. I want to draw your attention to a simple statement by which the trance—as far as it has developed—is ratified: "You are able to perceive more fully with all your senses." When I first came into contact with this hypnotherapeutic technique, having come from Autogenic Training, I thought: "That's impudent! How dare he state that certain reactions have taken place!" But he can and he does! This is very effective but only, of course, if he uses these statements at the right moment when he observes these re-

---

Editor's Note: A breathing pause in the delivery is indicated by (—) in the text.

actions and this development has actually taken place. This ratification somehow stabilizes the steps already taken and also helps to convince the listener that he has already reached a special goal.

INDUCTION

I don't quite (quiet) remember any more to whom I owe this idea—perhaps Paul Carter or Stephen Gilligan, well, that's the same either way—this idea, this phrase "the externally oriented trance of the therapist."

Well now, how can we understand that and begin with it? As you sit here and listen to me, all sorts of possible thoughts and images, associations about that may be there . . . you may let any thought come . . . may be with in your regard it may be—and then let it go again, just as with every breath you can get what is new (—) and then may let go what has been had . . . that happens all on its own . . .

And while you use one or the other thoughts to grasp the meaning of the single words, you may already, otherwise already have some wise inkling of what that is: to go into an externally oriented trance . . .

Well now, for clients and all people who are learning to begin with, to become reacquainted with, their inner reality, the being within, it is helpful to orient internally in trance . . .

To get into contact with internal experience more easily, one may begin to fade out the surroundings, where-to shut the eyes may be left . . . the inner eye be left let open for everything that lets itself be perceived . . . sense how it feels . . . feel the sensations . . . and notice what there is to hear there. And if you look around here you find that just thinking of this process alone is enough left on its own to have let some of these pleasant experiences happen . . .

Everyone who wants to accompany another person confidently and reliably must have already learnt that oneself; a therapist must ken (can) that to (do) be really familiar with it. On this basis it is then possible to take a further step (—) and in trance to (do) open your eyes again—or with open eyes enter trance again—and also to be orientated to the outside . . . Perhaps that reminds you of something you know from ZEN meditation: here you learn to meditate with open eyes (—) and be fully in contact (—) both inside and outside . . . You simply sit there, make sure your posture is not only pleasant but really well-balanced . . . if not, you adjust it (—) until it's just right for you . . .

Then you choose a point nicely in front of you, let your gaze rest on it . . . nice and easy, take a deep breath again and let go . . . and feel how you are simply right here . . . in the center of the space—all around all in its own proper place—and you are at the center.

And shouldn't it really once be so really let it be: simply sitting there (—) to feel how one's in contact at the moment . . . simply look . . . and listen . . . and respect what it's like now . . . and altogether get a feel for what it feels like all together . . . like a complete entity . . .

And so you can study the things in detail . . . and then again the complete total . . . just use just as you like . . . Just like a telescope or a camera (—) with a zoom-lens you can narrow your field of vision (—) and concentrate on this or that . . . Which detail can you recognize? . . . perhaps also a colorful note . . . or a harmonizing color—as soon as we let ourselves attend to fine details . . .

With somewhat more distance you can distinguish more easily: What is clearer?—what more vivid? What is still?—and where is something moving? . . . if your objective or telescope is held steady, it stands out more easily.

As your gaze rests so peacefully, you can be open all round to all sides . . . and perceive even the most minute change—for the peripheral regions of your retina are extremely sensitive . . . and, furthermore, you can experience how much further more extensively widened your visual field is than you think . . . if you let your eyes rest like this, it shows up (—) all round, to the left and to the right . . . further, more than you were conscious of till now—seeing, with this "defocused gaze" just like it was described by Carlos Castaneda, too (do). This is a deep or profound way to go into trance and to be in contact with what you experience outside . . .

Many people who want to help others undertake something in particular . . . set their sights and envisage something, then search their client's terrain for it. Their sight and their mind are fixed on something whose existence they want to prove to the client. Should this succeed, this be rendered visible to him, he has actually gained absolutely nothing—just got one more extra "Ah" experience.

A therapist, though, knows that for changes a bit more is needed, namely, "Aha" experiences. We do not obtain these if we work towards the confirmation of preconceptions, as though whether such a something is such and such a thing.

On the contrary, we are optimally receptive and also reliant on using our senses to the utmost, fully filling out with up-to-date data, when we do not imagine we already know.

For when we allow ourselves not to know, we are a w a k e—and really ready to discover something . . . and to learn . . . with your wits all about you. . . .

There is also a third, astonishing surprise: the "Haha" experience (—) when you discover the joke of the whole matter.

When you go with a camera through a piece of country to make a picture, for example, of a plant, then you search until you have found the right specimen—and leave everything else on one side. . .When, on the contrary, you want to know what life is here and you consider that there are many things that via their types and relationships create the phenomena, then you have to be open (—) and mobile. With your attention, you may wander all over to focus on this or that—and then let go again . . . in order to find each time the best distance and the most suitable frame that lets you recognize essentials . . .

If you now let your gaze, only your eyes, roam about a bit, then something new, some new things enter your vision—new details—regard them now simply . . .

They were already (all ready) there: you had already picked them up in the peripheral zones of your retina—and they have contributed in a general way and yet completely specifically to the vividness of your perception (—) here (—) as you experience it . . .

You are able to perceive more fully with all your senses . . . it pivots really (—) on allowing yourself actively (act-deeply) to remind yourself consciously and intuitively (into-it-deeply)—and let yourself be reminded, at the right time there where you need it . . . to remember (—)

and become aware of these multiple potentialities (—) to notice and to take more advantage of the many you simply already carry within you . . .

For you can, for instance, pay regard to colors and tones and react—you may enjoy more color-ful-living . . . and how intensive (—) does a certain color in all its shades appear to you . . . in contrast to another . . . and you notice the tense, strained relationship . . .

We are also speaking of the dissonance and the harmony of certain colors, of a harsh or clashing color, or warm and cold color tones. The transitions may be flowing—and the mood flux that the colors set off . . . You can go with your attention into all regions . . . and acknowledge this wealth of experience . . . and you need not know, how you will use it all . . . It is simple to learn (—) in this state (—) to orient oneself (—) and then orient back again (—) to what you are actually seeing . . . We can see things in the foreground . . . and things in the background . . . and all together (—) in a survey, an overview . . . and then again deeper—perhaps once from a surprising perspective . . . discover something that had been overlooked till now . . . notice what had not been able to present itself in the right light till now . . . Why not simply leave sufficient space?—some time can still pass by—and there something can find a willing ear, perhaps something that speaks only in a very still small voice . . . [one minute pause]

Milton Erickson once said: I always trust my unconscious. Many helpers plan in advance what they will say, what they will do, instead of going into the situation open to all the signals and stimuli to which they should now respond and react—in the most appropriate way for the present. Now, I do not try to structure the therapy—except in a vague general way. Whereby it is the patient who structures it—in harmony with the patient's (patience) own needs. Within this flexible frame-work frame, the patient can move about and make individual discoveries. Milton then added: Trust your unconscious. It is a happy way of life, a very enjoyable way of perfecting and finishing things.

Well now, this unconscious has at its disposal all that gigantic store of all the learning experiences you have ever made. The way, the quality, the coding and the organization of this knowledge will be codetermined by the way, the quality and the organization of your learning.

Milton's way of learning was characterized by openness for what was directly and concretely sensorially comprehensible. Bandler and Grinder call this outwardly directed attention "uptime"—this means that after you have clarified your own state, you direct your whole attention towards the client. To tune yourself completely to him, you interrupt your own pattern—for instance your usual posture—and you also attune and adjust your own rhythm, e.g., your breathing, completely towards the client. You use all your senses to orient yourself totally towards the outside—to "where the band's playing," as we say in Bavaria.

With your attention, fully absorbed in the client, you are completely there where the things are happening—and at the same time in trance.

Milton's way of learning was, furthermore, characterized by his being open for the possibilities of unconscious learning and functioning. On the basis of solid, sensory data, reliable and verifiable, learning can further develop; and moreover you may effectively get well into contact with yourself—on all levels—learn (—) to react in the most appropriate way—with hitherto consciously unplanned interventions—learn (—) to move freely within this close contact—trust yourself—to learn (—) to trust confidently. And your behavior will then be repeatedly congruent, harmonious (—) and creative . . . Your speech will be sound (—) and your movements will be flowing and rhythmic—in unison . . . with your partner, trustworthy, you use with empathy everything that comes from your partner as fertile ground for trust and further cooperation . . .

In this state, freely mobile and open to everything that may appear, the attention of your client shifts into a more experiential state—and this aids the development of further progressive possibilities to obtain important experiences in trance . . . you are in the process of grasping the internal structure of the present processes— and discover how you can proceed with your clients . . .

Much appears with a new countenance, sounds different. When we consciously note what a person says, the timber, the depth of tone often recedes into the background. But, when reminded about it, we can again pay attention to the sound of a voice (—) and track the breathing. You may remember how once you were at the seaside (—) and soon, after a short time, had blotted out the roaring of the sea (—) the regular coming—and going of the waves . . . until you suddenly became aware of it again and knew, simultaneously, that it was there the whole time (—) taking part—and you can bid this welcome, in your own way . . . In your own way, you may begin to take up contact again with the way you are sitting here, with your whole body . . . learning—and where you feel that more plainly, now, the weight (—) with ease and lightness, perhaps if you notice the difference it makes, when you breathe in . . .

Have you already noticed what your right hand is feeling like?—also in detail?—what about your finger tips?—and, different from that, the back of your hand?—the temperature compared with that of the palm . . . the temperature there where you feel your seat . . . and on your cheek, your forehead (—) the temperature of the room (—) you can feel how your foot is placed or your back is touching—just those places where you are in contact even more distinctly . . . and it is extremely simple, although we do it very little consciously, to notice the taste (—) and the smell . . . Sometimes only little attention is paid to something that only changes slowly. Therefore you may be curious to see how it may well feel if you move somewhat . . . you can move even more(!) . . .

And hear the noises—your own and the others' . . . becoming more aware . . . And perhaps become a little curious about where the others may well be? Right, then take a minute for yourself (—) time to take a look around—inside and outside: how are you at the moment? . . . And: what would you like to pay more attention to next time, so that it will be an experience for you that you may be even more satisfied with?

10

Paul Carter: Tree Meditation

INTRODUCTION

Today we will work with those ideas (written on the blackboard), four ideas for developing parts or any experience you work with. Yesterday we focused on safety, developing safety. And we can work with all kinds of parts/experiences. But there are some general tools that I want us to work with, so that you can get used to them and so that you can get an idea, when I'm doing a demonstration with someone or when you work with each other of what's going on. For me these are four basic ideas, and there are lots of ways you might use them.

The first one is the *sensory awareness*, we have worked with yesterday. Whenever you have an experience, you develop the sensory awareness of it. O.K.? The "what do you actually see, feel, hear, smell, taste."

The next one is a little bit different. It's taking the awareness and putting it outside you, that's *expression*. So there are lots of possibilities: it's in words, it's in movement of your body, it's in the tone and sound of your voice, you can make your experience into a picture and draw it. There are all kinds of possibilities of putting it out to the world, outside yourself.

And the next level I call *communication*. We will work with it a little bit this evening so that you can feel the difference between expression and communication. Communication is, when you take an expression, you take the picture you painted, or you take the words you spoke and you connect them to another part of your world, so you connect it to another person, for instance, or you connect it to another part of yourself, so that a conversation begins, so that you get now a response, which is a whole different thing, when you develop an experience. Do you understand that difference?

And the last level I call *meaning*. As you develop a part/experience, something happens, that I call meaning, which has to do with its relationship to everything else. So when we think of meaning, it's the value that experience has for you. How is it important to you? What value does it have? Another way of understanding meaning is as the intention of the experience. What is its goal? What's it leading to? That's another way of thinking about meaning. There are different sorts of avenues to understand the meaning of a part. The most basic idea of meaning is to understand its relationship, of how a part's relationship is to every other part, to the whole.

What gives meaning to a daughter is the mother, the father, the sister, the brother, right? That's what makes a daughter meaningful. Otherwise a *daughter* has no meaning. You understand? And it is the same with opposites. That's the simplest kind of meaning. What gives meaning to black is white. Without black, white has no meaning at all and vice versa. So that's one of the most basic ideas, the most basic ways of understanding meaning, finding the meaning of a part. The meaning is very important for a human being. It seems to be one of the most important things. So to really fully develop a part you usually need to discover the meaning, its relationship to the whole. And in many ways, when you do that, what happens is: a part becomes whole again. That's like a solution. It's now seen as a part of the whole, of the whole world. If it's a human being, you are working with, it's the human being. So you come from the narrow to the whole. This is the idea of family therapy. If you look at certain things people did—there may be somebody, who is going like that (shows, beating on the head) and sitting in the chair of your office, it had no meaning. You couldn't understand: What is this? But when you watch the person in the family, this makes a complete sense. The father was doing it on his leg or something—there are some relations that you would have done this too, it would have made sense. Maybe mother starting getting very angry or something. Or father is beating his children and wife. And then the mother and the father look at the child, and then this whole drama fear happens. And it all fits together. It has a sequence. That's how family therapy started. People were saying: well, it makes more sense now. I can see it in more of a whole. And that's what you are doing with this idea of taking a part and starting to discover, what its meaning is, what its connection is. Now you find out, what a part wants, O.K.

If you take a part that is very scared, shaking, seeing dead bodies everywhere, you find out: what do you want? And the most simple answer is something like: I want to be safe, I want to feel alive. And what's happening is, it's connected with the opposite. Fear evidently connects with safety through what it wants, through its intention. We have a circle that we talked about yesterday. You feel afraid. Until you really feel afraid, you don't even have a sense of what you need to become safe. When you really feel afraid, you start to get more of a complete sense of what you want, what you need physically, what you need to have in your surrounding to be safe. It's through the intention, through the wish of some part that you come back to the whole, and therefore the meaning of a part. So, let's do something, just to work with these ideas. You have a question so far? O.K.

INDUCTION

What I'm going to ask of you then is this: I would like you to close your eyes for a moment. Let us work with developing a part. Let's start with an idea. You could start with anything. What I ask you to do is: start with the idea of a tree. Let's start with a tree. O.K. And just pick a tree that you know. Some tree that you know well. Maybe it stands by your house, a

Editor's Note: This induction is meant to be read slowly, with pauses at each punctuation.

tree that you have looked at, maybe you have watched for a while. You know its branches, you know the shape of its leaves.

And if there is no tree that you paid attention to, then pick a different part of the world, of nature. You can pick a mountain, a bird that you like. But if there is a tree now, take a tree. And just take a moment to remember that tree, how it looks to you, its shape, tall, short, wide, narrow, spread out, triangular, round. Notice its shape.

And as you do that, slowly start to feel your own body as the tree, so that your own body begins to become this tree's body. And you begin to extend through the branches of this tree. And you rise and grow to the height of this tree, whatever it is. And your feet travel down into the earth and extend into the earth as the roots of this tree. And then you start to notice a gentle movement of yourself, as the wind blows gently. And just feel the movement of your body, of your branches, of your trunk, responding to the wind, a gentle wind. And notice, how it feels, how you respond, that gentle movement, perhaps more on top or out to the sides with your small branches, smaller in the middle. And as you do that, notice, what happens inside you in your tree body, your roots in the ground, your branches extending out into the sky. Notice what happens inside you. [Pause]

And slowly I ask you to let yourself grow. You are a growing tree. And let your arms become branches of this tree. And let your arms begin to extend slowly, so that, if you meet another growing tree, like trees do, they will adjust. So find the space to let yourself extend a little bit. It doesn't have to be much, maybe two centimeters, five centimeters. If you feel like it, maybe a whole meter. Sense your own growth and let yourself grow slowly as a tree grows, a little bit each day. And just take a moment to know, what that's like, where you are. [Pause]

And as you are here, your roots in the earth, your branches growing outward into the sky, get a sense of what your purpose is. You can just ask this question inside: Who am I? What is my purpose here? What do I do? And you can answer it personally as the tree that you are. How do you connect with the rest of the world? And you can also ask yourself: What do I need as a tree? [Pause] Everything you need. Just become aware of that, what you need. And that will also tell you something about your relationship to the world around you, the elements, the nutrients that you will absorb, that you will take into you as you grow.

And then just relax and let that go, you can let your branches drift back down, your arms relaxing, even when your whole body relaxes, kind of sinking into the earth, as if your tree structure was leaving you. And all that's left of you is water. You are water. [Pause]

And as water you sink back down into the earth. And let yourself go deeply, deeply into the earth, as water travelling down into the earth, down into the soil, down into the rocks, further and further into the earth, until you meet other water. And take a moment just to notice, what happens, when you meet the water inside the earth, the rivers, the pools deep inside the earth. [Pause]

And maybe you find yourself moving here, maybe you sense yourself expanding, when you meet a larger water. Maybe you'll find yourself floating, drifting. And even let yourself move into the currents of that water, small or big, and move into the currents of that water, inside the currents, moving, moving, moving. And continue moving, until you find yourself back at the surface of the earth, rising up perhaps in a spring, bubbling up to a spring or rising up to the ocean and coming back up to the surface of this earth again. And like some old creature sense yourself emerging from the water, like many many years ago the amphibians did, you emerging from water and returning slowly to your human form, coming back to the human structure. So once again you are a human being, a living being in human form. And take a moment just to sense yourself as a human being, human body, human embodiment of living being, of life. And take a moment to just notice what you sense of being a human being, your body, two arms, two legs, two eyes, in the middle, one spine, one mouth for the most of you, one nose, one heart, one belly. [Pause]

And again you may simply ask yourself at this time as a human being: What is my purpose? And just notice whatever you notice, not the final answer, just the answer you receive at this time, what you are aware of, what you sense your purpose is at this moment as you feel yourself as a human being. Or one of your purposes. And also take a moment to sense, what your need is, what your needs are as a human being at this moment in time. What is it you need from the world around you to grow as a human being. And just sense that for a moment. [Pause] And know that all growth requires nutrients, support, no matter what the form of life. The tree has its needs to grow, the bird has its needs, and they are different, and a human being has human needs to grow. They are not bad, they are not good, just a part of the nature of life, of growing. It is good to know what you sense of your own needs at this time.

And then just let yourself return to your own breath, feel your breath, feel the movement of your breath inside you again. There is no need to force your breath, just sense your breath, notice your breathing inside you, what happens with you. For some of you may be holding your breathing, it's fine, just notice that, notice where your breathing stops, where you hold it, where there may be tension, a stop, a block. And like the water in your breath you can continue to grow and expand. Even just let yourself feel it inside you and notice, where it goes and what parts of you have moved with the growth further inside you.

And when you are ready, let yourself orient again back to this room over the next few minutes of clock time at your own rate, comfortably become aware again of sitting in the room on a chair and let your eyes open.

COMMENTS

Paul Carter in his introduction to "Tree Meditation" gives a short history of family therapy. Then, in the induction, we worked with a visual image he had chosen for us, a tree. I think everyone present chose a tree, as he had proposed. How did he manage this? After he had proposed this image he said: "And if there is no tree that you paid attention to, then pick a different part of the world, of nature. You can pick a mountain, a bird that you like. But if there is a tree now, take a tree."

At first there is the direct invitation to imagine a special picture. To avoid resistance he allows anything else to be taken, but only in a few words. Then he goes back to his first idea and works with it. It is not attractive to take it upon oneself to transfer his words to another picture. This proceeding is an answer to the question: Do we have to be only general in group inductions or can we also work with special ideas without losing somebody?

Paul Carter utilizes the opportunity to give imperceptible posthypnotic suggestions for our growth. One of them is staying with the tree image: "Sense your own growth and let yourself grow slowly as a tree grows a little bit each day." Later he talks about water expanding, and finally, leading us back, there is a last possibility to utilize our breath, helping us with expanding, growing. So this whole induction is an indirect suggestion to grow, while in the foreground you may take it as an exercise to imagine special things in trance.

— 11 —

Hildegard Klippstein: A Learning Step of Integrated Relaxation

COMMENTS

My own group induction in this chapter is from a course for relaxation and Autogenic Training in 10 stages. The participants were varied as to age and social status. The sessions were structured so that there was a separate relaxation phase at both the beginning and the end of each session; thus the former prepared the different learning steps to be taught in the latter. During the first five meetings group members learned muscle relaxation according to Jacobson. Then, on the basis of this accomplishment of relaxing the skeletal muscles, exercises for vegetative or autogenic relaxation were introduced during the last five meetings. I owe this concept of slowly building up the ability to relax step by step to Burkhard Peter and Wilhelm Gerl. Published in 1977, their book "Entspannung" has helped many people to learn Autogenic Training more easily. As shown in the previous chapter, this concept can be still further improved. I attempted this by seeding each learning step in a group induction, the relaxation phase already mentioned, at the beginning of the session.

The example chosen for inclusion here is taken from the seventh meeting, the goal being the development of warmth in the body. In the sixth meeting the heaviness formula of Autogenic Training had been taught, consequently this seventh session provides the heaviness—and warmth—formulae of Autogenic Training. In preparation for this, the group induction aims at muscular and vegetative relaxation of the whole body with the emphasis on sensations of warmth.

I endeavored to attain this goal using various methods: following the ceremony of tensing and relaxing in a special way the group is used to, using words that suggest warmth like "cuddly, nest, warm hole, warm red light, warm air from breathing, contrast bath, warm blood, warm colors," giving examples of how to get warm, and painting pictures that suggest warmth. This induction is an example of how to follow a program and give strict directives even in a direct way while still weaving in elements of hypnotic language to improve effectiveness.

INDUCTION

After you have been able to lie down pleasantly and properly and find a really comfortable position, you can progressively guide your attention more and more from outside to inside. Presently the noises outside are becoming uninteresting, boring. You can listen to my voice here (hear) in this room. You have surely already closed your eyes so you can obtain for yourself a better view of the general state of your body.

Ball up your hands now to fists, press the lower arms against the upper arms and tense both hands and arms intensively. Observe this tension intently!

And: 5–4–3–2–1–let go, relax!

If we have cold hands, we rub them frequently to make them warm up again. Perhaps you may now notice that the tensing of hands and arms can have the same effect, and how already this pleasant warming-up is readily prepared for by a tingling and flowing feeling present inside the parts of the body you have just tensed.

Now turn your attention towards your right hand. Creep, so to say, in a certain way into your hand and make yourself pleasantly comfortable and snug there, like in a warm and cosy cave. If you feel every finger singly, you can let your hand glow and shine out in a certain way, from within to without. On the way, assure yourself and ascertain that the warm reddish light of your lamp penetrates into the further-most corners, right to your very fingertips. And this hand can certainly well remember all the feelings of relaxation that it has already learnt, the lightness, the weight, the pleasant pulsing in the fingertips. Just as when you play the piano, a piece (peace) may stay inside the fingers, your hand knows this letting go, this relaxation. And you need do absolutely nothing. Your hand knows its way certainly, for it has the most practice. It knows how to become cosily warm and pleasantly comfortable.

And when you are satisfied and content with your right hand, you can continue to the next station and feel inside the left hand. How much further has it so far accomplished automatically, because it is simply so pleasant for a hand can full well have a certain feeling of well-being? How much further will it follow the right hand with letting go and relaxing, so that this left hand gets into balance with the right? And now let the left hand decide for you to let go and relax, letting this happen, loosened, letting up and liberated, free and easy, more and more, left to do this all by itself. And while you stroll along further and notice your heavy, loose relaxed arms loosely lying there, you may let go a bit more and let the tingling and flowing make your arms warm.

Now wander up to your face and feel a way in there. Tense all face muscles equally. Think of the sour lemon then and feel the tension all over your face in full detail.

And: 5–4–3–2–1–let go, relax!

Your face smoothens out again and will become regular, lovely, well-rested and rejuvenated. All the many small muscles of the face, those that are responsible for our individual expression receive, so to say, in a certain way a warm bath from within, the best beauty treatment. And within your face is movement, a breath of movement, the movement of breath. Notice how warm the air is as it leaves your nose. And this warm air can wrap round you snugly, and each breath out lets you spread this warm wrap out around your face and then flows out further over the whole body, more and more.

Continue with your attention inside the neck, nape, shoulder region. Tense your neck muscles by lifting your head first forwards, then slowly dropping it over to the right, then rolling it backwards and then over the left shoulder back again to face the front. After rolling your head to the right a few times, you can roll it round to the left. Feel the constant change of tension in the single muscles.

And: 5–4–3–2–1–let go, relax!

Your head finds its resting position exactly in the middle where it need not be held any further. Notice now what these alternating baths of alternate tension and letting go gives leave to go, let's (lets) go! First let the large skeletal muscles loosen and relax, and you can feel the heaviness of your body as it lets itself laxly hold the reins more and more loosely, giving free rein to what occurs all on its own all right, more and more comfortable, cosily relaxed. Then let the small circular muscles around the blood vessels loosen. The arteries swell well and dilate so the lovely warm blood can flow all over your body and warm you.

Now you have already warmed up, and to keep you in fine fettle, I would like to ask you to tense tightly the whole upper body. To do this, breathe in deeply, hold your breath, press your shoulder-blades back together and harden your abdomen (stomach, belly).

And: 5–4–3–2–1–let go, relax!

And what a relief it is after this heavy work to be able to let yourself become completely heavy again! Sink back into a snug, comfy, soft, warm bed, the bed of relaxation. What a wonderful relief, indeed, to be able to breathe completely freely again! And every time you breathe out the warm air, you can make it still a piece more pleasantly comfortable.

Knit a piece more onto the air blanket, let it become thicker and cosier, warmer and still more pleasantly comfy. And some of you have wrapped yourselves in a real blanket to have a really comfortably warm time. Others are, so to say, covering themselves up outside from the inside and warming themselves with the knowledge that they only need to relax their muscles to become right warm from right inside. Some of you have already experienced this and can draw on this experience. Others may be helped to this new experience by these alternating baths.

And notice how your chest helps to prepare the warm air ready for the blanket, how it furthermore becomes free and easy when the air flows in and out tranquilly. And how your abdomen helps, too, with its comfortable up and down, rising and falling. And when you have dedicated yourself to the flux of liberating sensations in your abdomen-wall, which can fully spread out here, the pleasant warmth can gradually sink deeper into the lax abdomen. The abdomen rises and falls completely loosely with the breathing. The breathing happens all on its own.

And then turn your attention to the lower part of the body for the last strenuous part. Legs and seat are tensed best by lifting your legs somewhat with knees pressed well back and straight legs. Your toes are turned up towards your face.

And: 5–4–3–2–1–let go, relax!

Now you've managed it. Now, too, legs and feet receive your full attention and show their gratitude by well being healthy right well. Now all parts have been worked through and can recover, take time off for recreation, have a rest, take a holiday. Lie in the warm sand in the sun or wherever you would like to spend your holidays. Every one has individual favorites and own single preferences. And you can paint this in the warmest colors to warm yourself on this so that your relaxation becomes ever increasingly extensive, all inclusive, and you can deliver yourself up to the comfortably cosy feeling further, more and more, spinning and weaving yourself from head to foot, with every breath, more and more, in your imagination and in this soft, warm, cosy breath-like being completely wrapped (rapt) inside a cocoon. [Pause]

Until it's then time to return. And if you want to go on holiday again, you needn't wait for next summer. It is really entirely simple and becomes simpler from time to time, to visit these isles of peace and quietness and the real holiday paradise within ourselves where we can tank sun and recuperation. And so you also now quite easily and lightly say goodbye, for you will surely return again, certainly come back again. Go now, as always, with your attention into your hands; every one of you at your own rate, make fists, draw in a deep breath and open your eyes again to be completely awake and refreshed again, here.

12

Wolfgang Lenk: The Story of Blackcrest*

INDUCTION

. . . you can make yourself comfortable on your blanket and wander through your body again, before you enter into a longer and pleasantly deep trance—yes, you can lie down back there to rest—and should I perhaps become quite quiet—too quiet while telling this story, simply lift your arm—it is quite all right after such a busy day to laugh and giggle for a while like at a youth hostel in the evening before becoming completely relaxed—and I think you have done a lot today and know this and so be certain you have well-earned this feeling of well-being, sure you may have real bodily recreation—perhaps you have already discovered the two, three places where your body has the best contact to the floor: perhaps your feet, perhaps your pelvis, perhaps your shoulders, feel there—and while you do that, you can be closing your eyes slowly or quickly, if you haven't already done this to let yourself relax deeply—if you like take your own path, or you take note of your own breathing without changing it: perceive how deeply it may go into the pelvic region—where you feel it all over as a light and easy movement—simply flow with it while you let my words accompany you—and when you are settled so comfortably so then I shall tell you a story to end the day—and this story begins like all stories with "once upon a time"—so then:

Once upon a time a young Native Indian boy—and this story could similarly have happened to a Native Indian girl, but being a man I am telling this tale about a little boy—whose father was a hunter and fisher like the other Indians from the village on the edge of the Great Sea where the little Native Indian boy lived and who was called Blackcrest by his mother, for his hair was blacker and denser than the blackest night.

Blackcrest loved to dream—day dreams—and his mother had trouble with him for, instead of mending nets, gathering firewood from the forest or tanning furs, he would often lay on the beach. He like (sic) to listen absorbed in the ever changing songs of the sea and its waves, which followed their own rhythm. He could sink in this more and more deeply so he did not notice how the time passed. And while the soft wind stroked him, he let himself be taken by the salty smell of the sea on ever new voyages. And in the night he lay in his gently swinging hammock and held conversations with the stars. "What is beyond the stars?" he thought,

---

Editor's Note: This induction had to be shortened considerably. The original contains more stories.

*Drawing upon ideas from Gundl Kutschera and Georg Schäfer.

"and where does the realm of the gods begin and where does it end?" And while he listened to the wind whispering in the tree tops, he sometimes asked himself "Why are we alive?" And so it came about that usually the sun stood many hours in the sky before Blackcrest heard his mother calling, "Wake up, Blackcrest, it is high time for you to wake up!" and he greeted the new day with curiosity and sleepy eyes.

Growing Up

One day his mother asked the old medicine man for advice, as she was worried whether Blackcrest would ever grow up and become an adult. He had Blackcrest come to him. "Be patient," said the wise man, "I know your wishes. Come to me again after the moon has thrice shown her full face."

Blackcrest had long known that every one grows in his own manner and has on his way various tasks to perform to become full-grown and adult. Some Indians of his village had sometimes spoken around the fire in the evenings about how one must be very brave and full of courage, for customarily these were wont to be adventures that could not be compared with anything in the whole world. (So Blackcrest visited the medicine man repeatedly and each time was given various tasks whereby he obtained many new experiences and insights and learned many skills that would be useful to him.)

Then he went for the last time to the Great Medicine Man, who came out of his hut bearing in his hand a wonderful gourd—or calabash—embellished with many kinds of decoration. "Here, Blackcrest, take this calabash," he spoke, "but take good care of its contents. When the moon shows her full face again, go forth into the thick, dense, pathless forest. Follow your heart. It will lead you. But take care that your head does not say "Follow me and forget that silly heart!" for then you will lose your way and no one will be able to say whether you will ever again get out of the woods. On the Path of the Heart you will find the old temple ruins on the Sacred Place in the middle of the forest. And when you are looking for your place there, then search until your heart and head speak of one accord. Stay there so the dreams from the realms of the Gods can find you. The next day before the sun sets, take the calabash and drink out. Then you will find what you are actually seeking for in your life."

Follow the Path of the Heart

When the moon had once more rounded fully, Blackcrest took as he was bid the painted calabash, bowed before his parents long deep in slumber, and sallied forth. As he was more stumbling than walking into the pitch black forest and he heard the monkeys calling, his head warned, "Blackcrest, turn back, there is still time, turn back, Blackcrest!"—"Think of your plan," admonished his heart, "Nothing will happen to you if you are unafraid; don't turn back, for now you cannot return." Blackcrest hesitated a while before he continued and noticed to his surprise that his progress in the unknown territory became ever easier although he saw almost nothing. "Stop!" his heart suddenly exclaimed, "Stay still, Blackcrest!" Before him, only a stone's throw away, an enormous constrictor was sliding along. "Run," said his head, "run for your life and as fast as you can!"—"Stay still," exhorted his heart, "The snake won't touch you; but if you run away, it will notice you." The giant snake slithered by and disappeared without discovering him.

He did not know how many hours may (sic) have passed before he finally made out the dark silhouette of the Great Temple ruins in the forest clearing. He had arrived at the hallowed place the medicine man had described. His heart rejoiced, "Now you are home!"—"Isn't all that dangerous?" questioned his head still hesitantly. Despite the darkness, Blackcrest patiently sought his place where his body may feel completely safe and full of well-being. "Here!" exclaimed heart and head simultaneously. He was before the entrance to the Great Temple. It seemed as though he could discern an almost imperceptible golden shimmer of light that seemed to issue from the temple interior. He became very curious, but both head and heart reminded him of the medicine man's words, and he lay down. Again he conversed with the stars. All the time he had felt in his heart that they were accompanying him, even though he couldn't see them in the thick forest. "Were there sometimes things the eye could not see but the heart could well perceive?" With this thought he fell asleep. [Here in the German original is the story of his dreams, experiencing life outside of the Holy Temple, and embedded in that, is the story of Tatufeju, an old wise medicineman.]

EMPTYING THE CALABASH

He had to blink and looked up into the dazzling clear light, the bright light of the sun, that already stood high in the sky. Then heart and head said, "Blackcrest, the moment has come!" Blackcrest looked at the calabash that lay beside him down on the ground. He set it to his lips and drank the bitter liquid out right down to the last drops. "You have courage," rejoiced heart and head together. In the distance a jaguar called, the howler monkeys sprang screeching from branch to branch. For a split second Blackcrest was afraid. Then something happened that made him forget all the fear. The very rocks, the trees and the bushes began to dance merrily and the animals sang an accompaniment according to kind. Then his legs began to grow. They grew longer and longer. Once it was his hand that glowed with a rosy sheen, then again it was a foot that, dipped in shining gold like the sun, hastened through forests and sped over steppes. Then something jerked inside his middle. He tumbled down and fell ever deeper and deeper and couldn't do a thing about it. He grabbed at something that could give him a firm hold but there was nothing there. He wanted to scream, but his lips formed no word. "Heee," it said and he gazed spell-bound up over him. Wasn't that a luminous fireball that had just sprung out of his own mouth? Now it bounced upwards and flew through a golden gate. And while he was staring after it with open mouth, the Plumed Serpent slithered out of his mouth and slid along a stone wall, coiling up to take a seat there.

Blackcrest said to himself: "I'm no longer afraid of new experiences!" and, full of curiosity, approached it. "Who are you?" he asked. "The time," it answered. "And where am I?" he continued. "In the realm of Thought."—"So there is no tomorrow for me any longer?"—"No." He enquired again: "So there is also for me no yesterday?"—"Right deep down in you there is no time!" replied the Plumed Serpent and opened its jaws wide to reveal its mighty maw (more) and looking out of this, the Great Medicine Man. He was wearing the colors of the glitter-lizard, shades of turquoise, and his eyes were blacker that the night. "Blackcrest," quoth he, "you will learn the right answer in the right time and in time in that you now go your way self-forgetfully, for all is on the wayside, all ready on the way. Let it come to you and it will really belong to you, certainly be yours!" The Medicine Man disappeared into the gaping gullet, the snake shut its jaws.

"Tell me, O Plumed Serpent, how shall I reach the place where there are no questions more?"—"Wait till the fall of the first rain that from the Diamond Sea Moor (more) rise up and wash yourself pure and clean."

Blackcrest was alone once more. In front of him, though, there were four roads transecting to separate out and lead off to the four corners of the earth, and from every direction there came: "You must go here, Blackcrest!" "No, this is the way to success, come along here." "Oh no, here is the true road to happiness!" It made him completely confused. He sat down and conversed with Heart and Head. They told him he must search for and make his own path within the impassable territory away off the frequented highways, and the way would develop while walking on the way when going. For a while Blackcrest hesitated, for it would have been so comfortable to go there where already many before him had trodden the ground and beaten the paths. But he set out and went across country. Thus he discovered marvelous flowers, sky-blue, that stretched their delicate, petalled goblets towards the sun and, when touched, gave forth wonderful, ringing chimes. And when he looked back, it was to him as though a path had appeared, there where he had passed.

(Here follows an encounter between Blackcrest and a grotesque little man, the Emperor of Cares and Worries, whose constant warnings were of possible future catastrophes and his admonition was, "Think of tomorrow.")

At last he came to a wide river. "I'll swim across," he said to himself. Scarcely had he stuck his big toe into the water, though, then it began to seethe and boil. There was no possibility of getting across. Somewhat discouraged, he sat down on a large boulder at the edge of a bank. "Blackcrest," whispered a tiny, soft, little voice. He startled up, but couldn't see anyone. "Blackcrest," it called again. "Where are you then?"—"Here, under your foot." Carefully he lifted his foot and a tiny ant crept out." "I wish you a good age." "Oh, it's you," exclaimed Blackcrest, disappointed. "Yes, do you think only because I'm so small," said the ant, "that I can little help you?" Blackcrest listened to heart and head, who assured him he could trust the ant. "Wait for me," it told him, "and when darkness falls, await me on the top of that palm!" (At sunset the ant, now transformed into the eagle, flew with Blackcrest to his goal, the "Isle of No More Questions," a wonderful islet in the Diamond Sea.)

Blackcrest gazed up into the sky, the heavenly blue passed, clouds rose up glittering out of the Diamond Sea and became iridescent with all the colors of the rainbow. "Ling," and a drop fell onto his back. "Lang," this time a drop fell onto his hand. As he watched, the waterdrop became bigger and bigger, rose up and drifted up floating over him like a balloon. Then it fell down over him. Now he knew he was sitting in a drop that washed him clean and pure. When the drop then ran off him like rain, the Mother of Life came towards him, and in her eyes he read the question: "Will you dare that ever and ever again?" He went behind her to melt with her to a "Yes." It swept out rushing and sounding and filled the entire universe with one single will, with the "Yes" to the dance of eternally returning life. Blackcrest listened without fear to the eternal music of the spheres. Suns emerged and faded. What was lost here continued somewhere else and carried on there. An eternal shuttling to and fro. Blackcrest heard a thousand songs, each mote of dust spoke of eternities, of the creation and destruction of worlds, that had developed and now long gone with the wind, had existed otherwise. There were no questions any more.

Return Home

When in the mild evening light of the setting sun he saw the outlines of a large eagle or heard the call of the jaguar in the distance, he became somewhat sad, because he knew how difficult it is to tell of the journey into timelessness, there where there are no questions more. He bade welcome to his heart and head, who had also experienced all that, while the Quetzel Bird croaked "Who self-forgetfully goes into love cannot stop a single claw!" He said farewell to his place on the site of the Holy Temple, that had sheltered him the whole time, and set out to return to the humans. He wandered the whole night through, rested and confident, and the next morning when he could greet the sun with its promising light, the animals called out: "He's coming, someone richly bestowed with many presents soon will return home." They escorted him and pushed the matted boughs and undergrowth aside to smooth his path. The treetops murmured. "There goes someone to whom the secrets of life have been imparted."

The father was sitting in front of his hut repairing nets, the mother weaving and singing a song as before. "I am back again!" announced Blackcrest. Then there was boundless joy and happiness, and all the people of the village met together in front of his father's house. "How was it?" one wanted to know. "What happened, what have you learnt?" asked another. "Are there spirits?" pressed a third. And then there were so many voices that he couldn't tell one from the other. "I don't want to talk yet," said Blackcrest, "I need to take time to think about everything over the next few days in peace and to have some dialogues with the stars." But Blackcrest saw the Mother of Life dancing in the sky and heard the sound of the universe when it was creating new worlds. He learnt to understand the hater and appease his rage. He could look deep into the envious heart and make its owner ashamed. And when people were sad and darkness and desperation wrapped around them, then he showed them the light up high in the sky and taught them to find the source, the spring of love within them and to dance with the Mother of Life. Although he possessed nothing, people called him the wealthiest, the richest person they had ever seen.

With this the story ends—and it can begin anew every day just as you can always decide anew—you can now decide either to go within your body again more and feel, how it is lying, resting, how it is breathing—all the thoughts and feelings that you had during this story are only possible because you have a body, because you are in your body. There are people who speak of the body as being something like the temple for the soul—and it is good to treat one's body lovingly—and therefore, slowly, just as is suitable and right for you, come back, return gradually, becoming always more clearly conscious of the fact that you are lying here on the evening of a long and busy day—that you can move your body, that so many magnificent movements of your body are possible, certainly far more than you consciously know—and you need not know everything, when you return from your trance back here—but you may know that you may give yourself a good evening, like a present, as a gift, alone or with others, you will feel what is right, in order for you—and whoever would already like to leave, go carefully, take care, so that the others can still be quiet—and you may be curious and open your eyes again to look at the dusk through the twilight—to see the others in this group again—I wish you a pleasant night full of dreams.

COMMENTS

Wolfgang Lenk tells fairy stories, one at the end of every day at a seminar lasting several days. When regarded as a whole, the stories surrounding the central story of this induction may be perceived as the petals of a blossom unfolding. Wolfgang Lenk uses the introductory story of a dreamy Indian boy to introduce trance and then the words of the medicine man to leave us time for deepening. When the way into the woods begins, the way on which the boy follows his heart, the journey proper has still not yet begun. This happens first in a dream, after he has fallen asleep. Thus we are taken down, step by step, becoming gradually deeply curious. Only then come more tales, stories within the story. This is an example of the "multiple embedded metaphor" method, a powerful technique developed and perfected by the Lanktons (1983, p. 247).

Wolfgang Lenk utilizes the story in the story to mark the different trance stories of work in this living building. Embedded in this we get the message, e.g., Respect the smallest! On the next level await new experiences. The fantastic language invites us to dive into timelessness and then on the "Isle of No More Questions" lets us share the mystical experience of the young Indian brave. Telling myths and stories with their own special atmosphere is surely the oldest way of transporting experienced truths and transmitting true experiences.

IV

OPENING UP FOR NEW EXPERIENCES

In this section there would be some surprising adventures for you, if only you were able to actually experience these inductions. Hans Riebensahm shows how it is possible to forget pain. Wilhelm Gerl has us dance with each leg in a different language. My commentary follows his induction. Kay Thompson teaches us to have strange, indeed hitherto unknown body sensations during hand levitation, and, finally, Kay Thompson and James Auld in their Double Induction let us listen to the harmony of two voices speaking simultaneously.

The Double Induction or Dual Induction, where two people lead a group (or an individual) into trance, was invented by Bob Pearson, Ray LaScola, and Kay Thompson, though, completely independently, Paul Carter and Stephen Gilligan were developing their own version of this technique. As so often happens when something new is in the air, special people are able to grasp it at the same time but in different places. In her comment on her double induction with James Auld, Kay Thompson vividly describes how this invention evolved. Gilligan (1987) states that he found a double induction "to be one of the most effective confusion techniques available: not only does it interrupt the ingrained social rule of one person speaking at a time, it is virtually impossible for someone to consciously follow two persons speaking at the same time" (p. 283).

There are at least four different possibilities of how to arrange Dual Inductions with different effects as described by the Lanktons (1986):

1. If two persons talk about the same content alternately, they will fixate the attention of the listeners, with some attention being left free. This will produce less confusion.
2. If the same content is offered by two persons speaking simultaneously, they will overload the conscious mind with no attention left.
3. Different contents offered alternately produce dissociation.
4. Different contents delivered simultaneously create a deepening of trance phenomena by synthesis of both (p. 181).

As to the nonverbal communication of the two hypnotists, Gilligan (1987) proposes that, "at a most general level, these communications should complement each other. Of the many ways this can be done, the simplest is straightforward synchronization—that is, both hypnotists use the same rhythm, tempo, inflection patterns, pauses, and so on . . . The effect is like two guitarists playing the same melody but singing different lyrics. The matching of nonverbal styles tends to absorb unconscious processes, while the differences in verbalizations tends to overload the conscious mind" (p. 284). It was a special adventure for me to transcribe double inductions. This challenge took me many hours of listening again and again. I agree totally with Stephen Gilligan (1987), when he "found listening to a double induction tape one of the most powerful self-hypnosis methods" (p. 286). Finally I noticed a learning process. Somehow I learned to listen in a new way and improved more and more in my ability to separate the two voices. Many mistakes still remained in the transcripts, but this fact was commented on by Kay Thompson in a very encouraging way: "It is the first time I have ever seen anyone make an attempt to separate the words from a double induction . . . it was interesting."

13

Hans Riebensahm: Forget Pain

COMMENTS

This induction is available on audio tape in German and has been used successfully in clinical and private settings to reduce pain. With its open, choice-giving attitude it demonstrates convincingly how this proceeding contrasts with classical hypnosis where the therapist worked on the client's pain with direct suggestions alone, the client staying passive. In "New Hypnosis" (Araoz, 1988) it is the client who does the main work, the therapist offering the frame and the tools. Inherent here is the advantage of clients learning to help themselves control their pain and retaining independency (emotional, financial and temporal). The tools given to the client are comparisons and images for relaxing and forgetting and also images and processes for dissociating and obtaining distance, perspective.

The tools of the therapist that perhaps remain undiscovered by the client but still support the client's activity are indirect and interspersed suggestions, distraction, absorption in interesting details and posthypnotic suggestions.

INDUCTION

PAIN RELIEF AND RELAXATION THROUGH INDIRECT SUGGESTION

Whatever you are going to do in the following minutes, dear listener, whatever you may like to think about while I am speaking to you, what you feel and sense, I am starting off with the supposition that up to this moment and probably over a longer or shorter period you have felt certain pains, persistent or changing pains in certain parts of your body or pains that you cannot localize exactly. And I am acting on the assumption that you are listening to this cassette in the hope that your pains may become weaker and recede, perhaps even entirely disappear.

I shall now talk about some things to you and you may be surprised when you notice that, although these things seem to have nothing to do with these facts, your pain becomes weaker and weaker. That's something to make you curious. Just sit or lie down comfortably. You can also, if you prefer, move around the room or occupy yourself with some sort of thing like knitting or weaving or work while you listen to my voice.

And if you have a "walkman" you can even walk about or go for a ride or a drive out of doors. According to whatever you are doing, you can shut your eyes or leave them open, just as you like. You can change your position, move and settle down later or already become quiet and peaceful now.

Whatever you are doing and feeling now at this moment, you will notice after some time how your rhythm of breathing has changed: when you have observed your breathing for a while, you will realize sooner or later that you are breathing increasingly deeper and regularly.

At the beginning you may not perceive the changes in your body, because these take some time and proceed very slowly, sometimes as slowly as the movement of the minute hand of a clock or watch here. You certainly are familiar with the sound of the slow, regular ticking of one of these old clocks whose pendulum swings only once every second, once every second, like the heartbeat of a human being at rest. I don't know whether your heart is already beating with this calm, regular rhythm. The slowing of the heartbeat takes time, too, like all the processes that take place in your body, until the muscles relax, until more warm blood enters arms and legs, all this takes time. Or till the body feels lighter or heavier, that doesn't go so fast. For one person it's quicker than for the other. People are very different in this respect: everyone reacts in his own personal way. You will notice how you react.

Most people experience this as pleasant when the body relaxes more and more and with every breath out, every exhalation relaxes a tiny bit deeper. You feel increasingly very pleasantly removed, more and more distant, so that strange noises and pains recede more and more, ever more, into the background. With every breath you sink a little bit deeper within and forget whatever was unimportant or painful. You can perhaps forget it in the same way as after awakening in the morning, unpleasant dreams fade one after the other and gradually vanish by degrees, until they are finally only a very vague memory. I don't know how you forget, in what way, perhaps in the way that you perhaps even have still an exact picture, a detailed image of a certain particular early experience in your conscious mind, but have forgotten the accompanying feeling at the same time . . .

You need not do now something particular. You can let your thoughts come and go just as you like, and you need not even listen consciously to me now. Perhaps you are surprised. While your muscles are becoming more and more relaxed, while the air flows into the lungs and then flows out again so nice and evenly, while certain thoughts are passing through your mind, your unconscious can hear everything I am saying, and decides and chooses what of that is of importance to you personally, without your conscious mind needing to know anything about it whatever. And while I continue talking to you, perhaps you are already able to enjoy your present state. I would like to tell you something about different ways of how people—like you and me—*can fly. Yes, how to fly. That's something that really makes you curious. Right from ancient times, the times of yore, still (yours till) the present day then and now and in the future, too, often people like you perhaps, dreamt of being able to fly, soaring light as a bird. There in your imagination you may take off and fly to soar away (sore, away!)

*This interpolation serves various purposes; one is preparing for the difficulty of translating multiple meanings of the German "Sie" adequately.

then up higher to enjoy the sight of the houses becoming smaller, the fantastically delightful view of the roads and woods, the rivers, valleys and lakes and seas. So whatever you yourself have certainly experienced that in a dream and lived through something similar there in a dream perhaps . . . "Up above the clouds," sings Reinhard Mey, "the freedom must well be boundless," unlimited freedom from panic, worries and fears. Perhaps you know this song, like "Somewhere over the rainbow, skies are blue," . . . (or: "I would like to fly up above the sky and gaze in its wondrous blue. I'm sure I would know how my wings would grow. . . .") and you perhaps begin to realize this can be true for you. For when seen from high up over and above, everything seems small and insignificant, perhaps void of meaning, or maybe minute like model toys . . . and I don't know whether the pain has already been altering in the way you imagine . . . You know how . . . perhaps the ancient story of Dädalus and Ikarus, father and son, who managed to make wings . . . of feathers and wax . . . to be well . . . being able to escape from imprisonment. Ikarus wanted to fly too high, became too-high flown, hit the ceiling and crashed. Dädalus knew how to keep a balanced flight, to be able to stay in equilibrium between sun and sea . . . how to manage to finally land home as a free person—like you and I—.

People were indeed able to ascend up into the air for the first time . . . in the eighteenth century. They were French, the Mongolfier brothers, both free and easy, who in 1783 were to go up with a simple hot air balloon, then already flying over 10 kms. Furthermore, you know we can imagine pain is able to fly off . . . soar away (sore, away!) . . . a little further. Moreover (sic) you may be interested to find out how and why a hot-air balloon can fly at all.

For at first the balloon is nothing more than a gigantic sack (sag) . . .†

Well done, delicately being made of extremely thin, well airtight (air light) material. By the way, the balloon of the Mongolfier brothers . . . both fliers, up and into the bargain also paper manufacturers . . . this is a fine bargain . . . for the balloon was of paper, a material of which they had really plenty. Nowadays, when a hot-air balloon ascent is to start up, there is at first a gigantic empty skin-like cover laid carefully to lie lengthwise like . . . gently resting . . . comfortably on the grass. The material, the stuff now feels like one of these specially light wind jackets, or windcheaters . . . you know that . . . feeling light and easily . . . crumpled up to a conveniently handy tennis ball size . . . that you can then unfold again and use as required, whenever you need it . . .

A small group, perhaps three or two people—like you and I—go to one end of this skin-like envelope and open it with both arms as though . . . like to want to invite someone to go inside . . . This opening is as wide as a folding wing-door. During this, a third person has started up an engine-driven ventilator about the size of a bicycle tube or tire, gently and easily blowing air into the opening of the delicate but tough, strong skin. Now there comes the characteristic putt-putting, chug-chug snug sound of a small, two-stroke, well-designed diesel engine. Every sensation can change . . . Becoming slowly not yet round, with a slightly hissing sound, the balloon is in the process of filling itself slowly, almost imperceptibly, but with ever more still more and more air, while the ventilator is doing the work all alone on its own . . . While

†When appropriate "bladder" or "bubble," "bag" or "skin" could be used later.

this is going on, someone fastens a gondola of basket-work, a car, onto the balloon, fixes it well and strongly with safe, sound wiry cables to the eyes or lugs‡ on the outside of the opening of the balloon skin. The wind plays delightedly with this new toy, the still not quite perfectly full envelope, and can blow it a bit to and fro, back and forth . . . Small variations and fluctuations are always present there . . .

Now a fire is kindled. The Mongolfier brothers, or in French, the Frerès Mongol fier (free-air Mongolfier free-air)§ first set fire to wet wheat straw when it was not wet enough they had to wet (whet) it more.||

Today you take gas burners as these are easier to regulate properly and smoke less.¶ You can also turn off, switch'em off when it gets too hot, and also produce only the right quantity of hot air. The ventilator then blows the air warmed by the fire into the balloon. Gradually, very slowly the balloons are ready to get up, to stand more and more erect and steady, becoming firmer and firmer,# while it fills itself out more and more. Now why does the envelope on the floor begin to float and soar when filled with warm air more and more? Now that has something to do with the movement, the motions of the particles in the air.

These air particles, these particularly diversified and completely invisible, minute particles that give air in constant movement. The warmer the air becomes, the more active and mobile become the movements** there . . . and the greater the movement and activity there, need . . . as you yourself know full well require more space, more room, more freedom of action . . . for you yourself know full well . . . that just like in the zoological gardens the agile, nimble gazelles need a much larger . . . field of action . . . for their increased activity than do the usually slower, placid hippos. So then these molecules thus need and actually take and indeed occupy more room . . . more free space . . . Therefore hot air expands while also at the same time, as you well know, becoming lighter and lighter, specifically lighter . . .

Then, furthermore, while the air in the balloon can expand well and is now increasingly able to easily lighten up, get lighter and lighter . . . lighter indeed than the surrounding cool air, then the whole entire body of the big balloons (sic!) are so much lighter and begin to strive upwards, and endeavor to float up, pop up, like an air-filled pop bottle in water will bob up. The balloon full of warm air swims, so to say, in the cooler air of the surroundings.

Finally the balloons have completely filled up and are properly rounded out. The ventilator has been switched off, only the flame of the gas burner hisses and lets the hot air flow up into the balloon, now bellying out nice and firm, well rounded, ready for take-off. But the gondola car for the pilot is still on the ground. However, five fully grown people must hang on to this, so that it does not take off with an empty basket prematurely and fly away too early. For as you yourself well know, only when ready and well prepared, should one ever then let go . . .

---

‡Lugs = ears in some English dialects.

§"Fier" means proud in French—who have real reason to be proud of these feats. Also, to have trust, "fiez": have confidence. Also "fiel": gall bladder, could be used when appropriate.

||For patients with poor appetites or no motivation.

¶For smokers.

#Perhaps for persons with impotence and post-operative and reconvalescent patients.

**For patients suffering from lassitude or constipation.

And then you—like me—will be surprised at the speed, the rapidity with which it becomes smaller and smaller. But it's not quite as far as this yet . . .

For the pilot seems to be still getting ready and stowing away certain personal things, stuff needed later: provisions for the coming trip, a camera, a telescope, a good radio set to transmit well to keep reliably in touch with the ground . . . also a well-lined, snugly padded jacket, because it will become cool up there, and still a few other things to take . . . Every now and then he has to interrupt the work to regulate the flame, to let it get larger or smaller, exactly as much as necessary. The balloon sways in the wind, it seems almost impatiently to be pulling off at the ropes, to be tugging at the cables like a dog at the lead when its master is getting ready to go out for fresh air. But it will not fly away yet, not before quite some minutes have passed still . . . At last the pilot gives the order, the command to let loose. "Cast off now! Let go! Let's go!" . . .

Ten hands at the same time release the edge of the balloon, and at the very same moment the balloon lifts itself up and off, the gondola floats, floats at first only one foot above the ground. The pilot turns on the burner again, and hissing and puffing hot air streams up into the widely inflated orifice, the opening of the balloon. Numb with surprise, the people stay still, slightly stupefied and dazed. You'd be amazed how easy that is, and so are they, fully stunned standing like a shot . . . animal stopped in its tracks . . . by an anesthetic bullet. How simple and easily now it is . . . for the balloon, once free of the hands holding it fast, to ascend rapidly, get on well . . . with soaring smoothly upwards. Gigantic this full balloon, at the beginning almost overpowering and still, only after some time, can one first realize its whole magnitude. From some distance and then after a few minutes getting smaller, floating off away further over the adjoining houses and trees, driven by a light wind from the west, ever becoming smaller, the pilot's arm waving still is hardly perceptible . . . , for the entire basket and body of the balloon seem to melt together . . . , until the balloon becomes only a small, black disc on the horizon . . . , shrinks . . . , completely slowly . . . , more and more . . . becomes blurred and hazy . . . , finally is only a dot still that . . . loses itself, becomes lost sometime and somewhere in the pale grey sky.

Both hot air and gas balloons embody the principle: Easy flying is when lighter than air or, put in another way, to incorporate the adage: flying high is highly easy. High, easily floating lighter than air flying does provide a remarkable advantage over flying by aeroplanes. In balloons you fly with the wind almost quite silently and effortlessly, almost only using the natural energy of the wind, the sun and gravity. That surprises you perhaps. The energy of the burner of the hot air balloon is relatively small, negligible in comparison to the energy required by an engine to get a plane up into the air. And the noise of the burner is only a slight comparatively little trouble. And you have over and above this certainly once at least experienced that a mild noise, a slight sound will become sooner or later unimportant . . . , so unimportant, that . . . phase it out . . . you can then forget it . . . like for instance (instants) and longer . . . the roaring of the surf and the surging of the sea or the rustling of the leaves in the wind.

From out of the balloon in the wide space . . you can now hardly see and discern details whether on the ground or in the air. And in this situation many people have an entirely complete feeling of utter unreality . . . as though the things down there do not belong to . . . here where you are, even more in glass-clear, really pure air. But usually it's somehow hazy, so that distant things blend like mist clearing slightly . . . but becoming blurred. In hot air balloons you have for the most part in your own hand how rapidly you ascend or how slowly, perhaps staying to rest . . . at a certain point so far as much as one can speak of being able to rest . . . , furthermore how high you want to fly up and soar away, how far you want to distance yourself . . . from the earth for a certain time.

To fly with a glider is an entirely different feeling, quite different again. You sit in a tiny cockpit and you have certainly already had a numb leg that has gone to sleep once, or a hand that has gone to sleep, especially then when a flight lasts several hours. You know presumably the feeling of insensibility. of no feeling, reduced feeling, or lack of feeling, a numbness or dullness if you sit for long in a cool room. But the impression of flying is so strong that you can forget the numb parts of the body and can thoroughly enjoy flying . . . It may probably also surprise you, when I tell you that it is not at all necessary really having a balloon or glider to fly . . . to have this pleasantly light, easy feeling . . . Furthermore (further, more) you know you need and can use a pleasant feeling, comfortable feelings . . . today . . . , tonight . . . , the whole of next week . . . next month and . . .

Moreover (more, over), you can also fly fantastically well in your imagination, while you are still at the same time quietly sitting more or less relaxed in your easy chair or resting anywhere, wherever and whenever. For every one needs pleasant feelings . . . , here, there, in many places, over all, everywhere, any time, one can use a pleasant feeling, comfort.

You can take your time, when you want to start off on your own personal Flight of Imagination, your Fantasy Flight. A warm room is favorable. The flight can be scheduled for any time of the day, now and later. Some prefer a certain coolness, cool like a refreshing breeze . . . It is recommendable, in any case, though, to set the temperature right pleasant, comfortable . . . , or like cooling water, pleasantly cool and comforting. It is good when you carefully choose yourself a nice place where you want to sit when you start your Fantasy Flight, for if one has burnt one's hand, one cools the place under running cold water. And that helps, feels so nice, gets so much better.

Some people are quite delightfully amazed and so surprised when you state that you find that this way of flying can be just as good and will get better soon, for you can improve it . . . by even more adding previous experiences of this kind, sort of joining them together well with, perhaps, what you remember that others have told you about it.

You may find it fascinating when you experience things that you perhaps only knew from fairy tales before, now really becoming real for you. When you only just think of a wish and a short time, a little while afterwards already feel how the wish has become true, truly fulfilled for you. When you, for instance, think "light, completely light," some people already feel a certain feeling of lightness; perhaps you already feel a light feeling and a pleasant cool feeling comes.

I don't know whether you belong to the few people who have flown once or even more often, been taken up several times, with a balloon or a glider. Then you know these feelings from your own personal experience. The majority of people—most I know and most—you (sic!) can know them, though, even then when flying did not till now belong to the personal physical world of your own sensations and feelings, for almost everybody has some time experienced flying in a dream. Perhaps that was a long time ago. Why not then use this experience now? The experience of the unconscious, the dream flight, experience created in a dream. Flying with a balloon. It is the gigantic size, the tremendous dimensions, the enormous measurements that together with the quiet, slow mode of progression conjure up the feeling of unreality, entrancingly, delightful dreaminess. And the sensations change accordingly, simultaneously, so that you can ask yourself whether your present experience of what's happening is an answer to a real happening in the outside world or to an inner happening inside.

You know what a zeppelin looks like. Most airships are bigger than any balloon. The inside spaces of a proper zeppelin are also exactly as immense. And I don't know where you feel absolutely nothing at all . . . They can attain several thousand meters where you can reach whole expanses and many hand-holds and you use holds to store many goods so (good so) that is where you feel coolness, a pleasant coolness. The real zeppelin proper has in its outer skin a few openings, apertures where you cannot feel anything except a stream of air flowing out, so that is the only feeling present . . . , there are no other feelings there any longer . . . Only the helium gas, the "sun stuff" is contained or the hydrogen as a small bubble of gas in the enormous skin. The zeppelin floats in the air, high up above, and it is so pleasant, when everything feels completely normal, and it floats . . . so it gets rays of warm, golden light beaming onto it from the evening sun deep in the sky. And this pleasant feeling returns again . . .

The warm sunshine warms the outer walls, but leaves the helium cool. And everytime you are sitting as comfortably as now, this pleasant state comes back automatically . . . Again and again you have all the pleasant snug comfort . . . , then the warm sunbeams will pass through the gases, without warming these. The relaxation returns and works well where the radiation meets a solid body. That is a law of Nature, without that we could not exist. And the pleasant feelings come flooding back again when one sits like that, for the sun creates in a natural way the radiation climate, the radiant atmosphere necessary for life.

It warms the outer skin of the zeppelin like the outside walls of a house, and one only needs to sit down so comfortably like you and I now, and the feelings change so we do not become too cool on the shadow side of the radiation. And every time you feel yourself reminded of all these pleasant feelings . . . In relation to your output of warmth the surface is small—and remember all the comfortable snug cosiness, the joy of a birthday—when there is little room air (are) only slightly warmed. And it can be even more pleasant than now, whenever you need it and use it.

Your real genuine zeppelin keeps ambling along very leisurely on its course. Everything is in order, all right. Well, sometimes it seems almost immobile, staying quiet almost still, and you like me can feel so free and comfortable and—well, cosy—all the time, both now and later.

No dust can be thrown up, no house falls in ruins, the noise of zeppelins is less than that of all other motorized flying systems we know today. That is a pleasant relief . . . And this is also a reason why the zeppelin is so popular. In addition it leaves the air relatively clean, and the snug comfort and relaxation return again and again, when one really needs and uses them, for the diesel engines of a zeppelin have a very high degree of efficiency that you can also well use and reexperience any time effectively whenever you need it in effect, so the fuel is totally consumed during combustion with warmth . . . , coolness . . . , numbness only and no other feelings more . . .

A human being like you and me can easily be feeling well in this atmosphere, pleasantly well relaxing and full of well-being fine, now and later, both, any time when you need and use it, lightly and easily. While you breathe out, the air can carry much warmth out of the lungs, quite calmly and casually at leisure, especially in the form of moisture and much more pleasure, more pleasant than one had expected.

It's not the zeppelin itself then that has created this legendary reputation, but as well as its gigantic dimensions, its way of working, and the relaxation and snug comfort return quite automatically, today, tonight, the whole of next week, next month. Whoever buys toys that resemble zeppelins gets a faint idea, a weak impression of them. And this pleasant feeling returns again and again, when one needs it, every time when you really need it. Whoever produces them has probably seen them only in pictures or in dreams. The zeppelin has something about it that singles it out. Despite its enormous size, it appears tender, delicate, and fragile. Later the zeppelin was filled with helium, for helium is not inflammable, it cannot burn. And it is a peculiarly strange, but somehow pleasant feeling. The touching of a laundry iron, a stove top with 150° C usually causes, according to experience, burn blisters. And it does well then to cool a hot place well under cool water and to feel how it does get better . . . Helium feels at the same temperature equally hot. It is perhaps a feeling, as though one will be ready to do something, to undertake an important step, but blisters there are none, perhaps ready, prepared to feel even better. Why? Helium, that usually fills the zeppelin, has a low warmth conduction, an ability, that can perhaps be ready to recognize even more clearly and more distinctly that everything is in order, all right, with machinery in good running order, good condition.

The fingertips or also the palms of the hands take out of the uppermost layer of the material that has been touched, the warmth, and thereby cool it so that no other feeling is there. The amount of warmth extracted from the place touched is not large, and there is nothing more to feel, no other feeling more there, now and later, because out of the deeper layers the warmth flows back only very slowly and so everything is good and all well-being a part of the skin concerned will still be somewhat warmed by this. One can even cool down a place so far that a second person, who didn't know it before, can find it. Now that is not important for you, to remember what you have succeeded in today. Your unconscious can give it to you piece by piece at the proper time, always then when you really need it. And everything that you can not remember today is nevertheless still noted down and well recorded in your inside. Why not just begin now to feel more refreshed and more awake and as slowly as you like, wake up. And in case you still haven't opened your eyes, open your eyes before you come back.

14
Wilhelm Gerl: Hypnotic Dreams

COMMENTS

Here in a certain sense what may be regarded as the germ cell of this book emerges. After the seminar "Amnesia and Posthypnotic Suggestion" in Kiel in 1984, I had only a vague inkling that Wilhem Gerl had presented us with something very beautiful, something round and finished but also spontaneous, something like a lyrical journey through two languages. The abrupt change from one language to the other was known to me previously only for humorous communication with friends and from modern literature. I returned home satisfied. But now . . . then . . . his words must have started up something in my unconscious (or superconsciousness?). I assume that it was these words that led me to my (pre-)occupation with group inductions six years long: "And there are really some very unusual things, that seemingly develop completely on the side that really afford you assistance in a very interesting way to learn something of real importance, of prime importance—and in deed use it fully . . ." In any case "somewhere" I received the impulse to transcribe the group induction from the tape and then interpret it for myself. I was so curious to find out which hypnotic elements he had concealed in it. Transcribing is an intrinsic, intensive engagement with a subject matter, so much that I only then understand perfectly the text after the additional interpretative work. That is my way of learning. From this the idea gradually developed that my method could also be useful for other people and so I gradually began to "use fully" what I had learnt "of prime importance." Amnesia prescriptions and posthypnotic suggestions can certainly be very effective even in group inductions!

INDUCTION

[*Original begins in German*]

As you sit here (hear) like this, much is familiar to you
—sometimes so familiar, that you have the need
to get acquainted again with something new . . .
to get acquainted with something new that may mean
really directly and perceptibly a step forward in your learning

and that also (as with every experiment where you gain something)
quite naturally gives fun and pleasure.
For why should we, if we learn so much,
not allow ourselves to learn this
in the most pleasant way possible for you . . .

And you have learned to adopt a position
where you are at once connected with pleasant
experiences . . . that carry on there . . .
And you can find out—after a minute
or so (—) you feel that visually
if anything is there for you to solve, to loosen (—) something,
that would otherwise unnecessarily restrict you . . .
an attitude you want to change . . .
And you can feel it now—if you then with every
breath you take in (—) and with every breath you let out let go
and get into contact—with yourself as a whole entity—
and with this completely definite sensation . . .
y o u within y o u r s e l f . . . and you know (—) you know,
that it is only a question of time (—) until you can let
things outside—and why not my voice as well—pass by
at a certain distance . . .
can come and can go . . .
And if you like to, you can also use everything—
a voice (—) a sound (—) can accompany you
and become the voice of anything else—can
accompany you (—) anywhere else (—) where something reminds (—)
and connects you (—) with a memory to a
place where you can really feel full of well-being at ease—
while you sit here like this and look at it (—) so in
the room space that you can use—quite pleasantly—with every
breath in and out.
With each breath you take and let in
new, fresh things (—) tangibly—and you can let go
with every breath (—) you can let out . . .

And you can as you sit here like this, remember
(—) a possibility (—) of having contact that helps you (—)
with everything that appears (—) to observe it in that frame
that is for you as a complete person the most fitting . . .

Now, when you look at a picture, you sometimes see
a detail, examine it more closely—
and then take a step back away again—

or leave the picture at a distance,
to perceive the complete whole . . . and possibly
your glance may chance on a new detail . . . on a
patch, a region, the space, that sparks your
curiosity in this whole frame work . . .
while you look at it again more closely . . .
Sometimes we would like to see more clearly than before, sight more.
Sometimes it will be sufficient
just to darken it somewhat . . . so that it may appear
with its own, really its own
intrinsic clear brightness (—) form (—) movement . . .

And so you can, as you sit here, get into touch with things
that for you outside are sometimes
too far away (—) or too near (—) or perhaps
rather difficult to observe . . .
for you can move freely and learn to see things
from either side . . .
[*change of language in original from German into English*]

And in a trance you can find out ways (—) to move (—)
very easily (—) drifting (—) lifting (—) and
flying . . . And you can find your-self in a place (—)
in a position (—) where you can look at things (—)
at e a s e . . .
So you can allow yourself letting go . . .
finding the very balance (—) your unconscious
mind is providing you (—) because your organism
and your unconscious mind can do all the regulation,
all the balancing . . .
Allow yourself just to do so (—) and you can
experience things in this room from another room . . .
You can (—) experience and describe and perceive
things from one language in another one . . .
You can have a translator (trance later). You can
develop your very own, your very particular trance
later—and allow your-self (—) drifting to the middle
of nowhere provides you with a space and a place
you really can enjoy contacting.
[*change of language in original from English into German*]
You can allow yourself (—) to perceive things (—) in every language.

And sometimes it is good to have an anchor
on board on a boat trip (—) so that you can simply

allow your-self to drift . . . pleasurably (—) with shut eyes
and let the pictures pass by, showing themselves very pleasantly . . .
And from this resting point, from this place, let the things that need to
come so you really feel full of well-being
faced with these things . . . and with the help of this anchor
feel yourself anchored (—) attached (—) and safe.

And you can find out (—) which word in which place
for you can be attached to every sound, every image, and every
sensation . . . that shows you
that you indeed can find yourself as a whole
entity in trance and can learn further . . .

And you can from the middle of nowhere see things (—)
and leave it up to your unconscious (—) to let you drift off to somewhere
pleasant (—) perhaps let yourself be carried away being sure
that you are really well-anchored (—) safe and secure
in the boat (—) and can arrive there—
where you can find (—) what you need (—) to have
a wholly specific experience for your (you're) further learning . . .

As soon as you dream you discover (—) what
presents your unconscious has given you . . .
Things that simply come and develop (—)
in their own proper form (—) into what
they mean to you and can give you (—)
are like presents that you can have come . . .
And the best of all are those presents
where you feel yourself really very nicely
surprised . . .
And you can let yourself—quite two times two
minutes of clock-time—and all the personal time,
all the personal experience, that your unconscious
is ready to fill in—take place
—as soon as I say again "now,"
allow yourself, allow your unconscious,
to let you dream—in your own totally personal way;
and you can be quite curious about how feel images,
how sound images, how everything that appears can come together
complement and replace one another . . . You can
simply attend to what appears first (—)
and don't know what will appear at the next step
—n o w . . .
[*change of language in original from German into English*]

In a dream you can listen and you can move (—)
feel (—) see (—) have a look at (—) everything,
your unconscious mind is ready to show you . . .
And you can learn about dreaming (—) 'cause your
unconscious mind (—) really knows (—) a lot more
than you can (—) d r e a m . . .
And in two dreams you really experience (—) different
activities of your unconscious mind . . .
And the presence (presents) of your unconscious mind
figures out (—) to support you (—) with a different kind
of learning . . .
In a (our) first dream we very often (—) experience parts (—)
sometimes very freely appearing (—) things (—) that look
familiar, so you can (—) forget them (—) and feel (—)
a bit curious (—) about (—) what will develop . . .
and find (—) its (it's) organizing to new Gestalts (—) (new forms)
in the following dream . . . so (—) n o w (—) you can—
drifting into another—two minutes clock-time—dream
and let your unconscious mind do all the work—
let come together, bring together—organizing
every bit of experience . . .
So you will find something of importance (—)
that you will find—whenever you go into a
d r e a m d e e p l y . . .
And you may wonder (—) which language (—)
which way (—) you can go (—) your unconscious
mind is ready (—) to accompany and show you
the place, where you can find (—) what you can
use for your (you're) further learning . . .
So allow your unconscious mind to integrate
and, perhaps, to build a bridge in-to the outside
world (—) and the future—because you (—) continue
learning and you will face things familiar (—)
or really new things . . .
Let's take a familiar one (—) one that you can
connect with the resources (—) your unconscious
mind is providing . . . connecting with the sound (—)
feeling (—) internal image (—) of the place—
a very particular one—where you can really
enjoy utilizing this learning . . . will find a place
to further integrate (—) this learning (—) where you can
really use it in a very meaningful way (—) for you—

appropriate (—) for you (—) as a whole person . . .
So you can (—) let come (—) everything (—) your
unconscious mind is showing you . . .
And you can allow your-self (—) enjoy sitting here/hear,
feeling (—) have a look at (—) and directing your attention
to the middle of nowhere . . . feeling . . . drifting (—) back . . .
[*change of language in original from English to German*]

You can begin to let yourself drift back—float back
very pleasantly (—) the middle of nowhere (—) this peace—
(into English:) stillness of min-d . . . (back to German) I think John Lilly once
said in "The Centre of the Cyclone" that in a deep
trance you develop a feeling for the experience
in the middle of a cyclone . . . there all around you may be
all possible things whirling dynamically and moving about—
and at this center, this pole of peace, this dynamic equilibrium
of all forces—you gather yourself (—) and feel completely whole
You with your unconscious . . . y o u y o u r s e l f . . .

And allow yourself to take leave of yourself . . .
And you know that when you have a firm relationship,
a good relationship, you can then
forget temporarily and attend to other things
—knowing full well: you know where you can always
go again—and you know
it is always waiting ready for you . . .
That's like the sun: the sun is always there,
even then when we can't see it.
You can still recognize it from its effects
and perhaps feel it . . . And it is the center.
And the sun is inviolable.
All the powers that be could attack the sun with their weapons
—they would melt.
The sun is inviolable . . . the indestructible core of our universe.
And you are a part of this . . . and the whole entity is in the part.
Inside—outside . . . outside—inside . . .

And there came a man and said: I've found it,
what I was looking for, in a dream.
(change of language in original from German to English)
I've found it in a dream and now I know—it's the sun.
And it was a real experience . . . a re-experience,
(into German:) a recovering . . . (back to English) a recovering. And it's good to know.
And you know that it's good (—) when you feel it very basically

(—) that this is the truth, the real truth (—)
You are a part—and apart . . .
And you can come back (—) contacting in-side (—) outside . . .
letting your unconscious mind do all the work (—) really
all the work (—) today (—) in your dreams (—) at night (—)
tomorrow . . . You sometimes direct your conscious attention
to the task (—) you think (—) you will do (—) not knowing (—)
how you will (—) do it, while your unconscious mind is
already preparing to (—) do it . . .
[*change of language in original from English to German*]
Just like a woman who came about various things:
Like she told me she had letters to be written to the insurance company;
that was in debt to her so there was money for her to come
but yet she had not managed to come to write the letter to the manager.
A typical piece of unfinished business that she was always busied
and bothered with. And she mentions this more or
less casually; and we are in trance training
and I mention completely casually every so often the possibility
of letting the unconscious do all this work
—to go deeper (—) and then return (—)
and let every experience manage to come.
And the next time she mentions completely on the side
that funnily enough she can't find these letters any more.
But she knows she hasn't mislaid them, or put them aside.
Somehow she has the feeling that they have already been written
though she cannot remember having written them.
And she looks at me with a question in her eyes and I tell her:
"I am sure you will find that out." And then she goes home.
And a few weeks later I ask her about their thereabouts.
See says, "Yes, I've got the transfer—the money is there."

And there are really some very unusual things,
that seemingly develop completely on the side that really afford
you assistance in a very interesting way to learn something of
real importance, of prime importance—and in deed use it fully . . .
Just as you can indeed use this, as soon as you hear my
voice changed thus to know you can return
to us completely now and not now or not know how your unconscious will
help you and when the time will be that it experiences so pleasant for you.
It can remind you of this by handy signs or signals, with a certain
sequence of steps . . . perhaps you discover then
that you are doing something while something else has already developed.

It is good indeed all real things being equally valuable for you can simply
wake up and know that anytime you like to go deeper
you can with the help of this experience you have revived and developed
further . . . you can let yourself in peace
let a left-over piece be left behind—and look to see what the balance between
returning and letting yourself be carried back . . .

And we forget a few things almost before we have thought them . . .
some other things are still at a distance in our awareness
—and we can share them, let others participate—to
forget them then . . .
Some things stay in our awareness and we keep them to ourselves,
we keep them because they give us some hint, a certain sign, of something
we may more—clearly in this way (—) perhaps more sensitively (—) that
is immediately important (—) to ascertain and become aware of.
It's being now only a question of time, when you again take time for yourself
for come into contact again—and have all the help and assistance
you can get come to you, come to your-self—simply—as you are sitting here
like this . . . and discover whatever appears . . . happens . . . here.

COMMENTS

At both beginning and end are the familiar words: "As you sit here like this," an invitation to a journey into trance, return from the journey, the framework. Nothing more than pacing the simple fact that we are sitting there but nevertheless so much more: a well-loved anchor. I had not realized before that a cue for entering trance can be a cue for return. Slightly altered, with a different emphasis—that may well afford the whole a well-balanced symmetrical form. The words "carry on there" and "letting yourself be carried back" are used in the same way.

First then the tuning in with words playing about learning, about taking a new step. Next Wilhelm Gerl begins systematically to "beat out" the kinesthetic realm of experience. We are reminded of our "position," our bearing that may be an anchor for earlier trance experiences. He joins us to that again, where we are "connected." We can "carry on," "find" out, and "feel" what we can solve and "loosen" whatever could "restrict" us, "change our attitude" giving ourselves more or all latitude. Synchronizing with breathing, dropping words that are relevant to trance: "let out," "let go," "get into contact," "you within yourself." The vague formula "this completely definite sensation" leaves a projection room for everyone to fill with individual experiences.

The transition to the auditory system is skillfully accomplished employing the time to establish distance from the everyday state of consciousness. We hear the words: "voice," "sound," and then a harmony with kinesthetic experiences is produced: "connect," "place," "feel full of well-being," and even the visual aspect ripples in with the word: "look at it." Twice again the anchor phrase falls: "as you sit here like this." Addressing the breathing together with all sensory channels deepens the trance.

And at the latest now when the visual words: "appear," "observe," "frame," "picture," "see," "perceive," "glance," "look," "clearly," "sight," "darken," "brightness," the attention of all may well be so deeply enthralled that individual, personal internal experience appears and by the to and fro movement between near and far, the back and forth observation of the whole and the details; or of light and dark; something inside really starts moving, getting going, letting go. Generalized words guide and accompany us to an opportunity for individual experience that we might otherwise not have dared to grasp. The verbs that in the meantime have nearly all changed into an infinitive are understood by the unconscious as imperatives: "move freely," "learn," "see things from either side." There is the challenge: Dare to come closer! At the same time there is the assurance that we can do this in a competent way, *for* we can move freely and learn new things (pseudological). It is possible that already at this stage of the process an internal image has shown a new aspect to some participants.

The induction continues in the original at a new level with the use of English as the spoken language. A section is marked out. We can now slide down one story deeper. Kinesthetic words, partly in the imperative form: "find," "move," "easily," "drifting," "lifting," "flying," "position" are now combined with the visual aspect: "Look at things at ease." The command is concealed within this: "Look at things!" The word "ease" that comes then helps us to carry out the embedded command. In a way we are, so to say, promised that it will be easy for us to take a look at things. And "things" are so unspecified that everything anyone wants to project will fit. Prolonging the "s" of "ease" also serves as a chute, a slide into an even deeper region.

This is the region of balance, the place where the trance is deep enough for the system to get into balance. Wilhelm Gerl's speech demonstrates this and shows us how we can oppose polarities and thus achieve equilibrium: there is a "here and there," "this room" and "another room," "one language" and "another language." Trance, too, can be experienced in contrast with normal consciousness now. At the same time we can pay attention to the embedded commands which lead us further: "Allow yourself letting go!", "Do all the regulation!", "Do so!" "Experience things!", "Describe and perceive things!" Now notice a tidbit, a posthypnotic suggestion for a trance to go into later: "You can have a translator." While the conscious mind is still occupied to think at the translator putting words from one language into another, the unconscious mind may also understand: have a trance later!"

The next section prepares the hypnotic dreams. We are tuned in to being surprised, and the modalities are established: when I say "now" again, two times two minutes. Important, too, is the distinction made between objective time and personal, subjective time, for what can't one dream in the two times two minutes of "clocktime"! All three channels of perception may be used, integrated, so therefore: feel images, sound images, everything that appears.

In the dream phase—now again in the original English from Wilhelm Gerl, because this marks a stage so well—we are first activated, mobilized by his reminding us how we can perceive everything in dreaming in so many different ways. The "can" wording produces infinitives that are simultaneously commands: "Listen, move, feel, see, have a look!" But so that these do not sound too imperative to the unconscious, what is ready to be shown is left to the discretion of the unconscious itself. Then learning to dream is stimulated with a very ingenious, artful sentence:

> "And you can learn about dreaming (—) 'cause your
> unconscious mind (—) really knows (—) a lot more
> than you can (—) d r e a m . . .

There is, first the suggestion, "You can learn" and the embedded command, "Learn about dreaming!" This is intensified by the further order, "cause your unconscious mind!" and then, "Dream!" The difference between "cause" and "because" is certainly not heard consciously but this enables the commands to be concealed within an apparently logical context.

We are prepared for curiosity: *how* and *where* will what we can use for further learning appear? There is no doubt whatever *that* it will appear. We are requested to build bridges to outside and into the future, to integrate the familiar and the new, and—above all—to use everything. Here is a small selection: "Find something of importance! Go into a dream deeply! Use for your further learning! You're further learning! Face things! Take a familiar one! Connect with the resources! Enjoy utilizing this learning! Find a place! Integrate this learning! Use it! Let come everything! Allow yourself! Enjoy sitting! Hear! Have a look at!"

Finally, here a mirror sentence with the word "feeling" forming the axis of symmetry:

> "And you can allow your-self (—) enjoy sitting here (hear)
> feeling (—) have a look at (—) and directing your attention
> to the middle of nowhere . . . feeling . . . drifting (—) back . . ."

This is a mixture of concrete and vague contents, draped round the middle of nowhere, integration.

In German again as our means of transport, we begin the return voyage. The anchor "let yourself drift" is hoisted in the form of "drift back!", "float back." It is fortunate that the word "driften" in German sounds the same as the English "drift." This makes a good way to get hold of it again in German. And the return is not so rapid. It is good to be still drifting somewhat. Now the metaphors come sailing in. John Lilly's "The Centre of the Cyclone" for the deep trance, then the metaphor of the good, firm relationship that we can have with our unconscious as well. Consequently it does not matter if we forget something, for we can always return. Amnesia is left up to the individual unconscious. The metaphor of the sun, which is always there, assures us that everything lies ready stored in the unconscious.

I reflect on this polarity: the center of calm—the indestructible center of a fireball. Everything is within us. Wilhelm Gerl balances back with us again to the polarity of inside-outside.

This time with the story of the man who found what he was seeking in a dream: the sun or his own self connected with everything else, a mystic experience. Many people perhaps know this truth but only in their heads: "You are a part and apart." In the trance there is a chance of getting to know and appreciate this more deeply. For this story Wilhelm Gerl changes over to English again, occasionally translating a word, which assists both transition and integration. The signal for return can now be given in English as well, the renewed contrasting of inside-outside and the post-hypnotic suggestion for further learning in our dreams. And the conscious, too, is now addressed direct during this last phase of deepened trance—while we may rest assured that the unconscious has long begun to do all the work as is required usually for "unfinished business."

As an example of this is the story of the woman ("male" and "female" stories must also be in equilibrium) who wrote her insurance letters without remembering that she had. By means of this story, now told originally in German again, amnesia will be prescribed for us in manifold ways:

1. The suggestive contribution of the tale—by the example of being able to forget something that has already been dealt with unconsciously
2. Our attention is held—so that the preceding matter can become forgotten more easily
3. The topic is completely an everyday subject and causes a definite break with what has gone before

In the last section Wilhelm Gerl speaks with a more wakeful voice and draws our attention to the possibility of using this as a bridge of return. Just as gently and carefully as we were piloted into trance, we are accompanied while returning. He ameliorates the departure with the reassurance that we can at any time pick up and carry on with the trance experience where we left off and we can continue on to acquire further knowledge of trance conditions. Additional cues for return are: "a series of steps," "wake up," "return," "letting yourself be carried back," etc. What we have experienced in trance can be "processed" or dealt with in different ways: (1) some things are forgotten; (2) other things are conscious at a certain distance and we can share them and express them, and then forget them; (3) some things are conscious and we tell them to nobody at all.

All possibilities are covered, just as when dealing with resistance. "It is only a question of time"—this phrase occurred at the beginning, too. It rounds off the whole situation and points to the future for continuing the work, for further development. From this we should perhaps select something for the very near future: this attitude of being curious about what comes next, this refreshing alertness and openness that can be transposed very well from trance to everyday life.

15

Kay Thompson: Variation on Levitation and Sand Bucket

COMMENTS

The versions published here are not the original transcripts of the group inductions. Why not? Kay Thompson had a special reason for this. She wanted to ensure that everyone avoids the temptation of parroting her words. Use your own words, whenever leading a group into a state where every individual stays alone. Borrowed words would only hinder this process. You may know the content and be inspired by the examples of others, but please note this very important message from Kay Thompson given to us in an Ericksonian manner not only through words but in deeds: "One *must* develop one's own verbalization." (Thompson, personal written communication)

We find here another application for group inductions. They are ideal for teaching purposes. Milton Erickson led the group into trance in a similar way in his teaching seminars. Kay Thompson told me she works with groups on the whole not for therapy, but she uses these procedures as a "teaching and indirect introduction to trance, either for demonstration and seminars or for individual patients." (Thompson, personal written communication)

INDUCTION

Variation on Levitation

Introduction of casual questioning/curiosity approach:

Dr.: Have you ever played the piano?

Pt.: Yes.

If response is "*no*," ask if the patient has ever *seen* anyone play the piano, then ask if they watched the pianist's fingers. Omit the next comment, proceed from the "O.K." line.)

Dr.: Did you take lessons from a teacher who insisted that you keep your knuckles curved like this [*illustrate*]?

Pt.: Response – *(Whatever it is is satisfactory.)*

Dr.: O.K. – I would like you to pretend that your knees are a keyboard, and I am going to ask you to balance your fingers away out on the ends of your knees, as if you were playing a piano. [*demonstrate*] Now, please take a deep breath and let it out. Fine, now with the next deep breath you take, watch what happens to your hands and arms. See how they rise and fall with your breathing? Now I am going to ask you to do something that is very difficult, but try and do it anyway. Try to balance your fingers very lightly but exactly evenly on your knees. I know we aren't made sensitively enough to do that, but try it anyway. (*reinforce as patient accepts suggestion*) Probably one side will seem lighter than the other, but as soon as the hands know which one is lighter, watch what happens to that hand and arm. As you continue breathing easily, the fingers (maybe first the little finger, or the thumb) and then the hand will start to lift away from the leg . . . gently, slowly, evenly . . . that's right. Lighter and lighter, higher and higher . . . Isn't that fascinating? It's almost as though the hand had a mind of its own! And as it continues to rise, higher and higher, somewhere up there in the air is a pillow of air, and the hand will lift up until it finds that pillow of air, and can rest comfortably on it. (*reinforce as lifting continues*) Fine . . . and you can be delighted with everything you are learning, and some of the things you are learning that you already know you know. And when you know everything you need to know for now about how to do this again later, you can discover something still more interesting. You can discover that there is a very tiny, tiny hole in that pillow of air—and everyone knows what happens when a pillow of air gets a hole in it, don't we? (*then simply wait for the arm and hand to move back down, since that is a clear signal to the patient*)

(*If you want to go on to utilization of the trance, use the following transition signal.*) And when the hand touches, that will be the signal for you to relax completely and go deeper into trance.

(*If you want the individual to terminate the trance, then this comment might be used.*) And when the hand touches, that will be the signal for you to bring back with you all the nice comfortable feelings and learnings you have acquired, so you will be able to go on with this anytime in the future that you choose to do so.

And that's all there is to this particular learning experience.

Thank you for your cooperation.

INDUCTION
Sand Bucket

[Demonstrate to patient how to hold arms out in front, at shoulder level.]

Now, in order to help you learn about hypnosis, I am going to ask you to hold both arms out in front of you, Like this . . . that's fine! Now, to eliminate the other visual distractions here, and to help you use your imagination more easily, please close your eyes. All right, I would like you to imagine that I have here an empty sand pail, and I am going to ask you to let me hang this pail by the handle over one of your wrists. I also have a big pile of sand, and I am going to pour sand into the bucket with my sand shovel. As I take the first shovelful of sand and drop it in the bucket, you can hear the sound of the grains of sand as they hit bottom and bounce over to the sides. And the next shovelful has a different sound, not so loud. And as I continue to pour more and more sand into the bucket, it begins to feel heavier and heavier on your wrist. And your whole arm gets very, very tired with the strain of holding that heavy bucket up there, and gradually the arm begins to drop a little. And I can cheat, and add some wet sand, because wet sand is always heavier than dry sand, and the bucket pulls down more and more on the arm . . . that's the way. And keep trying to hold that pail up until your arm just can't support that weight any more. And when your arm drops down far enough to touch your lap (or whatever), that is a signal for you to just let that bucket dissolve, and let the arm fall loosely into your lap, take a very deep breath and let the other arm drop gently into your lap, too, and then, as you exhale, let all the tension and strain of holding that arm up in the air just drip out the ends of your fingers. And another scoop of sand, and the arm drops at its own rate of speed, and you can begin to wonder just how soon it will get tired enough to reach your lap . . . that's the way . . . (Continue until the arm almost touches.) And as it begins to touch, you can get ready to let it go. . . . Now! Let that arm fall into your lap, take a deep breath, relax the other arm, that's fine . . . Now let all the tension, all the strain in the arm drain out the ends of your fingers, so that your whole body can feel very loose, lazy and comfortable . . .

(add whatever seems appropriate, or go on to the following)

And after the sensation of heaviness, you can go on to learn other experiences . . . your whole body can be so quiet and comfortable that you may discover that there are parts of it of which you are totally unaware . . . if you really thought about it, you might discover that you were not conscious of your feet, and that now you can notice how they are feeling. This selective disattention is a very interesting thing, which can be useful in very many ways. And you can think about the ways, so that, if you ever really needed to use them, you would be able to remember how to forget in this way. Just as you can remember how to use things you have learned, you can now add this experience to your library of learning experiences. Thank you so much for your cooperation.

16

Kay Thompson and James Auld: Dual Induction

COMMENTS

After you become acquainted with the Dual Trance Induction by Kay Thompson and James Auld, you might be so much inspired by their humor, their powerful puns and word-play and their competent manner of working together that you would again like to copy it. Kay Thompson is very concerned about the possibility of people trying to use the content in this particular Dual Induction as a recipe. She says: "This has occurred in the past with other verbalizations I have given to people at workshops. I emphasize that *no one* should make any effort to use these exact verbalizations." And she goes on: "The Dual Induction as developed by Bob Pearson, Ray LaScola and myself, and as utilized by me, is one which cannot be preplanned. It must be spontaneous, and is best done when both individuals are capable of working in trance so that they can utilize trance to merge with the theme the other person is using, while at the same time developing their own separate theme. If it is preplanned it can never have the same effectiveness as when the individuals can work separately together." (Thompson, personal written communication)

DUAL INDUCTION

T.: The label is group induction, the fact that there are two of us would give most of you the indication that it is also a dual induction,

A.: which means, you have to listen to both of us, hm, alternately or simultaneously, which ever you choose—

T.: or both. (laughter)

A.: We will be down on the floor—

T.: Yes, we are not going to stay up here. We prefer being more in contact with the audience—

A.: even if that means standing on the floor—

T.: or having the floor under us.

A.: Yes, which ever is appropriate,—shall we move?

T.: I think we should. [They move down.] And since you don't have to see us, you only have to hear us, it doesn't really matter, whether the people in the back are in a position to see us. But as we are both fairly tall, that has not usually been a problem. And the real reason that we get down here is so we can pace, because it makes us feel more comfortable. I'm putting words in Jim's mouth. I'm not sure that they are his words, but at least that's my feeling about being down here.

A.: It also gives us the opportunity to pace. [laughter]

T.: And to place and play with the cord, that is down here—

A.: which is why we have extended our tales (tails = the Microphone cords) [laughter] This is usually a fun workshop. We are coming over with the same volume because I tend to talk very much more quietly than Kay during this sort of thing and I'm endeavoring to change that.

T.: What he says is: I've a big mouth. But he's right—[laughter]

A.: very indirectly. [laughter]

T.: You are right very indirectly or you are saying it very indirectly. (laughter)

A.: On that point I think we should point out that we will not put anyone into trance here today.

T.: And those of you who have heard me before, know that in the thirty-three years that I've been working with this, the only person that I have ever hypnotized is myself—

A.: because no one can put you into trance.

T.: We can help.

A.: O.K. How can no one put you into trance?

T.: That's the same thing as everybody, and nobody—

A.: or anyone

T.: and no one

A.: and maybe we'll have to find

T.: someone

A.: their own path to achieve the path.

T.: That all depends on whether they choose to go into their own trance in order to stay out of the one we are offering them the opportunity to go into [laughter]

A.: or going to the trance that we are offering the opportunity to go into, so that you can stay out of your own trance. [laughter]

T.: Or maybe you can go from that trance to this trance—

A.: or listen to both at once

T.:	A.:
or once at both	so that would be a real double induction, perhaps that can be one for your conscious
and that can certainly be a number for your unconscious	

That's right!
then you have the left one that is left on the left

That's what's left if you go to the other side.

You really have to wonder,
whether it is in the front of your mind
or the back of your mind,
because there is no way

that your conscious mind can really tune in

to the kind of flexibility that you need
in order to function on a level
that lets you level
with everything we say.
And when you think about the fact
that you are mostly matter
but that really doesn't matter.
Because that matter
is the kind of matter
that you permit
to happen
deliberately

and unconsciously.
And since around the matter
your body
really is made up
mostly of water.
And that water
is representative of nature.
And nature is really
what we are all about
having a natural capacity,
the normal skill,
to be able to go into trance

and maybe you would like to think about that, as they are
left or right,
because if you choose the right hemisphere

and that will be right.
If you choose the right, then the other one is left in that
part of you in that particular time.
Before you are making this decision about
whether that's right or whether you think,
it's left, you might like to consider

the analogy
of what happens when you build a house.
We really first need to have the right spot
for the place that you want to live.
And that will take quite a lot of searching.
Once you have found the area that
you want to live in build a house.
You have to find an appropriate place
in the area for your construction.

And having chosen the place
you can decide,
you can then consider

the design of the construction that you are going to build.

And that can involve design on paper
ideas from your head
and eventually
that begins to coalesce, to gel into
patterns, that you can put into a
concrete fashion
on paper.
And as you define that design
create the plan you are looking well
ahead to be able to really see
the final result.

in a way that meets your needs.

And it lets you know
that you do know
everything
about how to make the experience
that you are about to have
into a memory that you can use
in the best way, so that you can
know and be confident
that you may make
the memory of that experience change
into something that is wasn't
when it began,

only because you have not thought
about it as being what you really did not think it was.
And you can cope with that feeling
because you have laid the ground work.
And as you move forward in this process,

creating
a life style that you want,
that you know what you need
to be what you can be.

You owe it to yourself
to be everything that you can be
and to sort out the sort
of sorting that you need to do
in order to reorder your priorities
in a way that will permit you
to move on, to grow,
to see the other side of where
you are now and to know, that
when you go through that particular
door, you can be where you want
to be, that you looked forward to,
when you were back here
where you are now,

At this early stage it's really easy to change the path
you are setting up
the path that you do think to follow.

And once that design is finalized

and you have the construction materials
and the tradesmen organized
you will construct it in the way that
you have designed
Next step is to prepare the foundations
in an adequate manner, so that that house
will be built in the right way with the right support
so it will stay

as long as you wish.
And as the foundation is completed
the next level goes on, working on the walls,
the various parts have to be fitting together to create
just the right shapes
just the right patterns
to give that feeling of strength
the durability, to be able to support the loads that are
going to be
placed upon it in the future.

And as the walls go up in various stages
you have holes in them
which will later take windows to enable you
to see out of the windows
to allow the light to shine in,
to have spaces for doorways,
to allow access, egress,
people to come and go
so that you can
have that interaction
with your friends in the way that you want
in the future.

because where you are
is only one step on the way to
where you are going,
and learning to tap into your
unconscious potential
lets you merge with the universality
of those around you
and to feel at one
with all of mankind.
To let your similarities

and their differences merge
into a marriage that lets
the mirage of wavy lines
that separates you, blend,
mellow and move into a
magnificent melody
that lets you know that you can
do everything that is appropriate
for you to do.
As you build on what you learn

here and now, adding to the kinds

of things you have already learned,
that this learning listening
can be a really intriguing experience
of memory, knowing that you can tap
into that brain, that is almost like
a sponge. A sponge that has holes
like little rooms, that are very very hard
and dry when they start, but
finally you begin to soak up
that knowledge, that experience,
the information

that you can feel that sponge expand
and grow as it soaks up the information,
that means,

that you can use that resource,
that you can picture yourself knowing

As the house continues with the
ceilings and the walls
and the roof supports rising
the roof sheeting placed on them
to keep off the elements
to keep out the damaging storms
to protect those inside the house
to provide an umbrella of protection
that you choose to stand under
instead of facing the environment unprotected.
And as the walls are completed
and you have further protection
from the elements,
from those awkward forces, that you
want to avoid, to keep out of you,
you can still have windows and walls,
which allow that necessary communication.

And later you have shades on those
windows and curtains that you use to close out
the outside world when you need to
for those times of personal
privacy. Or you can have a filter
within yourself from the outside world
which allows you to interact with a
comfortable feeling with the problems
of the environment around you.
And time goes on in the house as all
these necessary trappings of domesticity
various cupboards to store things
the benches to work on,
the sofas, the chairs, the beds
and all the fittings that go with completing a house to the
way that we like to live. You can
become more and more comfortable
living in that environment you have created yourself,
more and more secure, you have that
safety and protection of being within the

which cells to squeeze

in order to get the information
that you want, and to know
that you can trust them
and rely on your unconscious mind
to have enough information
to allow it to be spontaneous,
to be comfortable,

to be complete.
And to know that that kind of completion
is always only beginning,

because the things that you do
that complete anything, indicate
that every ending is a new beginning.

[more slowly]
And as you begin again
you can wonder
whether that ending is the kind

of beginning that you and your unconscious
can feel content.

And does it really matter?

because the foundation for those
appearances is so strong

as you move along

and as you bring back those memories

learning and growing

house you have made. And even when the house is
finished in its initial stages, it
doesn't mean that it is unchangeable
for as new ideas occur, you can
remodel that structure
in appropriate ways, maybe by
changing walls within

maybe adding a whole new room.

And in exceptional circumstances
you may involve putting on a whole new wing
to extend the space that you need.
And these changes can occur in
most surprising times, sometimes without warning,
sometimes they grow slowly.

You can consider whether
this time it's necessary to do any
of these things
whether the extending you have done
to date is enough for your present needs.
And maybe that
it will just involve a different kind of paint

to change the appearances of the things
that you know so well,

and well able to support the changes that you maintain to
make

or even as you move back

that you have accumulated during the time
of building and finishing

exploring, changing

accessing, using

and developing

because that's the fun

in really understanding
what it's all about

that it doesn't matter
whether you understand

as long as you don't stand under

any misunderstandings

because you have the information
to create the changes that you want

You have everything you need

in the time that you need to create those changes.

[long pause]

You have all the time you need.

in the time that you have to cement those learnings
in a very concrete structure which can reinforce the way
that you understand the learnings that you already have.

And time distortion is such a marvellous thing

when one or two minutes can really be stretched out

and feel like ever so long

and provide so much comfort.

[pause]

I think we should leave.

Perhaps we can talk to those who are with us.

That's true, and these who aren't here with us
can certainly listen to what we are saying

here
they can hear with that ear that isn't yet tuned into
their own trance

That's true
that third ear.

Did you say a further ear?

You are sounding Australian, further ear.

You are right.

No, that might be wrong.

T.: [*change in manner and tone*] Now, that the double induction has become so popular, it's hard to realize, that there was a time that it wasn't used. And since I go back a long time, it was in the early 1970's, an ASCH workshop in Banff in British Columbia. And it was one of these faculty-sit-around-and-talk-afterwards when Ray LaScola said that he could not hallucinate. And my reaction to that was that anybody who can bleed in alternate inches can learn to hallucinate. So Bob Pearson and Ray and I were talking about this, and we just kind of talked about it, and as Bob and I talked it became apparent that Ray was going into trance. And as we kind of started talking about the same thing at different times and then about the same thing together, and then because it seemed to be working, we began making an effort to talk about different things simultaneously. And that was what we began to term the dual induction. We played with that for quite a while. We did it at some of the workshops. Jay Haley watched a tape of that and said that this was the first new thing that he had seen in hypnosis in 15 years, which as I say is really hard to look at now, because it seems such a natural useful kind of phenomenon. We do not plan what we are going to do, there is no rehearsal, it's purely spontaneous on our part. When I walked in here this morning I had no idea, where we would go with it, but we knew that you would have the capacity to utilize what we said in a way that was going to work best for you.

A.: And you must recognize that in a group situation such as this we are looking at very generalized aims, for ego boosting for growth, things that are safe within a group situation, and on an individual basis or in a small group you can tell metaphors very much more precisely to what the individuals require,

T.: that the generic group induction has to be precisely that, very generic.

A.: And those of you who are still enjoying trance can continue going on in that present state that you have achieved for yourselves and just listen to us without being disturbed unnecessarily

T.: and probably hearing us better than some of those people who are not enjoying their own trance. Have you any "questions, comments, nasty remarks" about the dual induction, the group induction, us?—One of the questions that is usually answered during the course of this is that it really doesn't matter if the two people synchronize. I have worked with a gentleman up in Vermont who spoke so rapidly that I really couldn't even begin to keep up with him. And the individual we were working with didn't bother to let that interfere.

DISCUSSION

Participant: I would wonder how much more effective this technique would be if you could do it in stereo . . .

A.: The original technique that I saw in Australia for a double induction was for the message to be tailored to the ear to which it was, so one ear tended to be emotional, the other ear tended to be linear, but in practice it's quite irrelevant, in fact it might be distracting having that sort of delivery,

T.: being restricted to it. It might well be overwhelming in stereo, it might be more effective, but again that's a matter I think that has to be based on the situation.

A.: I recommend that if you enjoy this tape and listen to it several times and really see what's going on, because you can only attend to one message at a time, no matter how much you think you are listening to both.

T.: Here I might disagree on that.

P.: I have not experienced a double induction before and that was most uncomfortable. I wondered whether I was resisting. At one point I almost screamed . . . I always tried to be clear. There was confusion and it was like: get me out! And I really worked not to scream and then decided: Well, can I get out of here, but I couldn't. And since I don't know a lot about double induction, maybe you can help me understand what in God's name happened. Was I resisting? I never became relaxed, which I think of as trance.

T.: Well, I never think of relaxation as trance, and maybe that's where part of it came from, because we gave no intimation for relaxation. And I suspect that there are a great many people who would feel quite uncomfortable with this, if it hadn't been explained and they were not in a position to have some kind of reaction or interaction with it, that it would be a natural thing to resist for a while. And one of the comments that we made was going into your own trance in order to resist the one that we were offering you the option to go into.

A.: Another problem I think, if it is the first experience you had of a double induction, is not knowing where we were going.

T.: Usually when we do this, we do two of these, and it might be interesting for you, knowing that, to see what your responses the second time are.

A.: And you don't have to go into trance. You can just choose to listen to one message or the other, or you can switch.

T.: There are a couple of people here, they didn't hear either of our messages. (We are doing it again. It is fun.)

P.: It seemed to me as you both began taking off on your individual metaphors you would ebb and flow together and separate again. I was curious if you hear what the other person is saying and begin integrating that into your own metaphor . . .

A.: If we weren't both in our own trances before we started this we would join the audience. So what tends to happen in my personal experience: this is the fourth time that I'm working with Kay. The first time I nearly lost it, the second time I was concentrating so much on what was going on here, I had a lot of difficulty, the third time I could actually watch the audience from time to time. This time I'm happy to say that I was able to just watch everyone from time to time and still carry on with what I was doing and pick up the occasional word from Kay, as she does from me.

T.: I think that's pretty typical. Usually when I ask someone to work with me with it, the thing that I have to stress is: "please keep talking!", because they tend to just go into trance and wander down and down and down and then shut up, and I'm left up here holding the mike. That is a natural development which you overcome when you get more familiar. If, when I began, I tried to listen to the other person, forget it, I was out the window, but as we go on, we don't deliberately try to merge. But there is a kind of an unconscious patterning that happens.

A.: If you intend following this up in your own areas be prepared for that, that you will take several attempts before things start to become more comfortable for you, and you do need to have that personal trance experience to be able to follow what's going on in the audience and partly what your partner is doing and still maintain the line of metaphor that you have.

T.: In a group such as this, we are playing, we are giving you the opportunity to experience something for yourself, but also to recognize that it is a neutral situation, that it can be fun. Most of the time when I used it the first few years it was intended for people who had had difficulties going into trance and who needed a very profound experience. And for a while we were kind of talking about it, as though that was the only time to use it, and then that became rather ridiculous, and so it developed into more useful use. Now, when anybody is sitting around in a group somebody starts this and somebody else picks it up and it's just a lot of fun. And I think the nice thing about it is that it helps you to get more comfortable with the natural "bright-eyed and bushy-tailed" type of trance that I am such an advocate of people using.

A.: It also makes you very aware of the multiple meanings of words.

* * * * * *

A.: The unconscious can process things in amazing ways. If you listen to one, you are getting the other message unconsciously with both messages having the same end result. It doesn't really matter which one you listen to or if you listen simultaneously.

P.: I've never before experienced a group induction let alone a double induction, and I found it's terrific. The thing I'm most amazed to hear is that it wasn't structured by you before, because the way I experienced it was this beautiful intricately blended, almost like a musical. I have a record that Ray Charles and Betty Carter sing: "Baby, it's cold outside."

A.: You are hallucinating that?

P.: Well, they blend beautifully separately and together, and one comes in and the other stops. That's how I experienced this.

T.: The few times that I have worked with somebody where we have tried to structure it, it has bombed. I just don't really feel that I could do it. Maybe somebody else can.

* * * * * *

P.: I have experienced a dual induction before and I have done dual inductions, and everything that Kay has said about the spontaneity is absolutely true and just occurred in my experiences as a therapist with another therapist one time and it just flowed. If you go with your own trance and your unconscious and you pick up on what the other person

---

Editor's Note: Asterisks denote ongoing discussion among participants not directly relevant here.

is doing and you weave that within the—and I like his word—the symphony, I just want to say that it was wonderful and I congratulate you both in your merging, thank you.

P.: What I wanted to do was not make myself go into trance, but just kind of see what would happen if I just listen to you. I didn't want to close my eyes, because then I would do it myself. I wanted to see if you guys would do it somehow and I wouldn't have control over it. And what happened was, I closed my eyes and didn't know why and then all of a sudden I heard you saying about windows and curtains and shades being drawn. Then I thought: O.K. So there was something being said that I was not consciously aware of and that was a really exciting thing for me to experience. I really appreciate this.

A.: Thank you for pointing that out to me.

P.: This is a tremendously enjoyable musical experience for me. And this is probably the first time I have ever asked a presenter a question while I'm still in trance. One of the things that struck me was Virginia Satir yesterday talked about kind of state of chaos, a state of confusion that was necessary for therapeutic change—and this seems to lend itself really quite well to that.

A.: You are in a state of chaos?

P.: Comfortable chaos. I probably chose the metaphor of music, because it's such a comfortable thing for me, music, and so, by holding on to that part of what's familiar to me, it was more of an adventure.

A.: You are getting therapy from the linear approach.

T.: Into every life some confusion should come, also some enlightenment—à la Milton Erickson. That's one of his favorite quotes.

P.: In March I attended a workshop by three gentlemen . . . and what they did . . . would be called a trio-induction. After I thought about what was happening it was clear to me, who was doing hypnotic pattern, who was speaking metaphorically, who was being more direct. Was your intention, James, to speak metaphorically or give the hypnotic pattern?

A.: Both were incorporated. The metaphor was very loose, a growth in development, one which suited professionals and within that there were suggestions of the shades being drawn, a concrete foundation being laid down for strength . . .

P.: I would like very much to use the double induction with my private clients . . . So the thought came to my mind of the possibility of my taping my own voice . . .

T.: . . . much of the time I don't have anybody in my dental office to work with. And that is effective as long as you do a generic non-time specific on the other tape. But one of the things that we talked about was putting music on that the individual would choose, so that you could weave in and out of their listening to the music and that that is an equally effective permission for the unconscious to do its own thinking and feeling and organizing by distracting the conscious mind with the music. And that's really all the attempt should be, to permit that to happen. What do you have to lose if you try it?

P.: Have you tried this with a group of predominantly left brained people, engineers, scientists, etc., and what were the results?

T.: No, I haven't . . .

A.: But I suspect it would still work. You are processing language, just the same.

P.: I would like to direct my comment rather to the audience than to Kay and the gentleman who worked with her. We are here a group of therapists, and some of us know about hypnosis more than others. I'm amazed at people trying to understand with the left side what is being really spoken to the right side. And I just wanted to comment that, perhaps the need to understand, as such, what is going on is really not necessary, that these things should slowly evolve by themselves and take root.

P.: I really want to thank you. That was a very rapid and gentle and enjoyable experience for me. One of the interesting things that happened to me a couple of years ago when I first found out about double and triple inductions. It was when I was going through a very stressful period in my life, when I found myself awakening again and again at night and ruminating about negative happenings. And so I got a tape of Carol Lankton, Steve Feinberg and Tom Contin and they were doing a triple induction. And I would wake up and I would turn the tape recorder back to rewind and lay there and within moments I was to be back at sleep again. But a side benefit that was really intriguing to me was that I ordinarily am not particularly paying attention to the words that people use so much as the tonality, and I don't care so much about auditory things. Classical music has never been enjoyable to me, because there isn't the melody that I'm looking for. And after several weeks of doing that triple induction at night I went to a concert, and it blew my mind that I could hear all kinds of things at once . . . I knew that this was directly related to trying to hear everything at once in the induction . . .

A.: Sounds like you have learned to listen.

* * * * * *

T.: . . . if I have my choice I work in a one on one or two with one situation. So I don't do group inductions that much except in a teaching situation . . .

A.: I have the same problem that Kay has, relative isolation from other practitioners, and I practice this once a year.

P.: Do you think it works, if you have a group of intellectuals or skeptics, say like college-students?

A.: I think it would be very effective, because they are diverting themselves in trying to work out what's happening.

T.: I have never found it to be ineffective.

* * * * * *

T.: I think the obvious thing that you hear from all these comments is that this has to be a very individual thing and that we act as a core from which you radiate and you do whatever it is that you need and want to do. And with that understanding I would expect that the people who were aggravated by us (which is not an unusual response: frequently when we start the double induction and when I chime in with somebody, who is already working, I know that the person who is going into the trance is going to aim all their hostility at me), are going to find out that if they really want to, they don't have to let me intrude. They can let me help, and so it's a really good learning experience. So having heard all the comments of all the other people maybe you have a better understanding of what you expect from this and what you might want to get from it. And with that kind of preparation we do it again. [This second induction had to be excluded from this book owing to space restrictions.]

V
RESOURCES

Our resources are the very springs of change, the true well of our possibilities to innovate, modify, transform and develop; our stock of apples and potatoes in the cellar; our store of cans and preserves we can draw from and fall back upon in winter or in times of need. Resources are our past successes, our frequently "forgotten" achievements, our stored, often unconscious knowledge of how we or others have solved previous problems, our whole fund of experience.

In contrast to the problem-oriented emphasis of Freudian procedure, Milton Erickson worked with very resource-oriented methods. Searching for and using resources that have been found to play a central role in Ericksonian hypnotherapy. "The best way we have of retrieving resources is indirect suggestion and metaphor" (Lankton & Lankton, 1986, p. 153). We can subsume this under the category of "Indirection" and understand "metaphor" as "a story with dramatic devices that captures attention and provides an altered framework through which the client(s) can entertain novel experience" (Lankton & Lankton, 1986, p. 154). "Indirection" and "Utilization" are the two categories, under which—according to the Lanktons—almost all of the Ericksonian techniques may be subsumed.

The four inductions within this section show very different ways of gaining access to these stocks, this hidden treasure: Paul Carter does it by attending to the process of breathing; Sidney Rosen by an invitation to an inward journey; Burkhard Peter by using confusion in an attempt to awaken memories; Paul Carter and Stephen Gilligan via age regression.

17

Paul Carter: Breathing

COMMENTS

In "Breathing," an induction taking only a few minutes, the author "utilizes" the most basic living process available in every situation. He proves that when working with breathing even within a very short time you can be extremely effective in calming the system. This is why many forms of meditation work with breathing, our link between voluntary and involuntary expressions of life. Another piece of wisdom or experience that Paul Carter works with is: Breathing in a deep trance or in deep meditation can be much more satisfying than inhaling tobacco. And, one of the main reasons people smoke is to relax with that deep breath. Once you have experienced this anchor of breathing consciously, you may bring back this feeling and then you forget the smoke.

INDUCTION

Just close your eyes for a moment and focus on your breathing for one minute of clocktime. [Pause] Take a moment to just come back here and focus your energy with your eyes still closed, focus your attention externally. Perhaps you have been listening to some of the sounds in the room changing. [Pause]

And let yourself be within yourself. And just feel your breath coming in and going out, one of the simplest forms of meditation there is. And know that you can do that wherever you are, at any moment in time. And breath is very beautiful, because it demonstrates the wholeness and continuity of life. It comes in and goes out, comes in, goes out. It is a continuous integration of opposites, and you can't breathe in without breathing out. That basic knowledge is right inside your breath, the knowing how opposites need each other and are of equal value. And feeling your breath can harmonize you, help you to enjoy again that basic process of rhythm in life, a sense of in–out, up–down, holding on–letting go.

And I'll offer you smokers another way to smoke. As you continue breathing just imagine on the next breath that you breathe in breathing in a blue cloud, a kind of clear blue cloud.

And breathe it in with your inhale and hold it inside you for one or two seconds and feel it touching all the cells and inner parts that a good satisfying smoke usually does. When you breathe out, notice, how the color has changed. And just take a few breaths like that, breathing in the blueness and holding it for a few seconds inside you, and then breathing out, noticing what color comes out. Over time the out-color will change, but you can just let it come out however it does.

And then let yourself orient again to your chair and to your sense of sitting in this room. And you might still be aware of breathing in this way, even as you open your eyes and orient back here. O.K.

18

Sidney Rosen: A Guided Fantasy

INDUCTION

So I would like to tell you all how excited I am at the opportunity to be with you and to guide you in this trance that we will enjoy together today. It's very rare that I get a full hour just to allow myself to enjoy a trance. And I don't know what this experience is going to be like for me. I'm sure you don't know what it's going to be like for you either. The only thing that I'm certain is that it will be interesting, maybe some surprises. As Erickson always said: every child likes a surprise. I'm sure that you all have different—well, what they call minor agendas—things that you would like to explore: things that you would like to see, if you could—experience, that you have not experienced before in other trances or without trance. And I'm also sure that most of you at least will experience much more than you hope for. To give you a chance to orient yourself: we know, where we are now, don't we? We are in Phoenix, Arizona, in the Flagstaff room at the Civic Center. The time is two minutes after eleven. We started very promptly. I'm used to working by the hour, I don't know whether most of you are or not. I'm going to make this into a . . . well . . . perhaps we'll make it into about a 50-minute hour, so we'll have ten minutes just to reorient ourselves at the end, afterwards. And we'll reorient ourselves at that time to be back here in Phoenix in the Flagstaff room at the Civic Center at exactly 11:50 A.M. Phoenix time.

The first thing I would like to tell you about my way of working with trance is that in a hypnotic trance you don't have to do anything. You don't have to move, you don't have to talk, you don't have to listen consciously to my words. I understand that when a person comes into this room or any other room, he or she brings with him or her a conscious mind and an unconscious mind. Now the conscious mind is interested, is observing, is curious, perhaps it's doubting, questioning, wondering, examining: those are the jobs of the conscious mind. Now your unconscious mind can be thought of as a vast reservoir of learnings, as

Erickson described it, and
everything that you have ever experienced,
everything that you have ever done,

everything that you have ever heard,
everything that you have ever learned,
everything that you have ever tasted

or smelled or hoped for is stored somewhere, and most of it is stored in the part of the mind that we think of as the unconscious mind. And in your trance you can get in touch with some of those unconscious learnings, you can find some that will be very useful for you, that will help you to move in directions that are really constructive for you, will help you to explore areas that are either undeveloped, or just ready to become developed. And you can use those unconscious learnings for purposes that you may be barely aware of and for other purposes that you only become aware of after you have used them. So we are sitting here in Phoenix, in the Flagstaff room, our eyes are open, mostly: some are closed. If your eyes are open, you begin to notice changes in the way the air looks. Somewhat warped perhaps, things get smaller and larger, you hear Dr. Rosen's voice coming sometimes from very close, at other times from very far away. You feel sensations in your body. Some of them are unpleasant sensations—feelings of tension, feelings of anxiety, feelings of tightness, and others are very pleasant—a tingling feeling here and there, energy flowing from the top of your head to the bottom of your feet. If you want to have a Kundalini-type experience, you could have that. Or a Kabbalistic-type experience, where you focus on Kefer, the spot just above your head. I want you to do that: you could visualize the bright light just above your head. And from that bright light source of energy is a flowing, sweet wave, flowing down over your face, down over your shoulders, your chest and your back, your abdomen—and to the pelvic area: down your sides, legs, drawing out any of that tension, any of that anxiety, any of those pains that were there before, like a warmth, only it's moving, like immersing yourself in a healing lotion, isn't it? And it feels so good, does it not? And you can become now, if you like, a bodyless mind. And the bodyless mind can travel anywhere in time or in space. You can go back and find that young person that you were, beginning to learn so many things, learning to read and to write. And just to tell the difference between the letter "a" and the letter "o," is a difficult task. And how do you put together a straight line and a little circle to make a "b" or a "d" or a "q" or a "p?" And are there two bumps on the "n" and three on the "m" or are there two bumps an the "m" and three on the "n"? And do you dot the "t" and cross the "i" or do you dot the "i" and cross the "t"? And what makes it even more difficult: is that there are small letters and capital letters, there are written letters and there are printed letters. And you learned to form all of those letters. You learned to write them . . . automatically. When you grow up, you will not have to think about each letter any more. You write things automatically. And there are still things to write even when you are all grown up. And you could enjoy writing them in your own way, your own style, more and more automatically as you learn to trust your own unconscious mind, because that little child grows older, minute by minute, hour by hour, day by day, week by week, month by month, year by year, until one day he or she knows who she is, who he is.

Now in my way of living I sometimes like to climb a mountain and I always wonder, what's on the other side? I know that on my side of the mountain there are buildings, there are paved streets, there are fields, there are lights, there are trees and rocks and a lot of people. But on the other side of the mountain there could be a desert . . . dark and foreboding. And I always *know* that, no matter how foreboding that desert is, I'll find something there of value, of interest for me. Sometimes I may be afraid of what I'll see on the other side. I always *know*, that I can climb to the top and take a quick peek over to the other side. And if I don't like what I see, I can always return to my side of the mountain. [pause]

Putting it another way—you can walk down the street and reach a corner. You may decide that you want to turn that corner. But you are not certain whether you want to continue in the new direction that you have chosen. And you can always take a quick look around the corner and see whether or not you like what is there. If you don't like it, you can always continue in the direction in which you were going.

And to balance the city life I find it's very helpful for me to go to the country and enjoy nature. If you would like to join me on a walk through the woods you can do that. Or while I'm walking through the woods you might want to walk along the beach. Find your own place, your own special favorite environment. When I'm walking through my woods, I sometimes feel as if I'm entering into a cathedral, the branches of the pine trees covering the entrance of the path into the woods, into the cathedral. You can smell the pine aroma, a very fresh clean aroma, isn't it? In the south of France they feel that it's very good for your lungs, when you walk into the woods, you can feel the carpet of pine needles on the ground, very soft, spongy and springy and supportive. As I go deeper and deeper into the woods, step by step—one at a time, I know that I can stop at whatever spot I wish. I can always leave the woods when I want. I'm drawn by my curiosity to go in still deeper and see some colorful mushrooms over there, blue mushrooms? They really are blue. And red ones, yellow with red spots on them. There are tall mushrooms and there are some that are just spread out along the wood of a dead tree. And the leaves are still present on the trees, and you can hear them rustling with the wind, if you listen carefully.

I remember, when I was very small, I would have climbed on one of those trees. It seemed so high up. I knew that even if I fell down, the ground is very soft. You can climb as high as you want. No bird flies too high as long as it flies with its own wings. And as we continue still deeper into the woods, we may run into an orchard, it's a magic orchard actually, as there are trees that have golden apples, silver plums, rubies, sapphires, diamonds. So we know that we are in a magic world now, a world of childhood. And in this magic world we can get any help that we need. We can call upon a healing fairy, if we need healing. And there she is! We can call upon a wise old woman to tell us what we should do; what shall we do about that decision that we have to make. That's right! She has an answer. Or we can just decide to play and to enjoy being here in special ways as time stops. And we have all the time that we need in the time that is available—to accomplish what you really want to accomplish. We can become clear about what it is that we really want to accomplish, push away all that confusing bush, all those weeds. You can see very clearly now where the true growth lies. It doesn't always lie, sometimes it tells the truth, reaching up to all the sky, embracing the clouds. And we can go out as far out as we want beyond the clouds to the planets. Or we can stay securely here, protected, warm, enjoying a cool breath on our forehead. And we take a large breath and breathe out, and in and out, and out and back, all in the rhythms of the days and the nights, the sun and the moon, and really enjoy this exploring and resting, contracting and expanding with every breath.

You can always return to your friend or guide—in the woods or on the seashore or wherever you want.

And who would like to take another trip with me? If you have rested from this one, please nod your head when you are ready to start. This trip will be especially useful for those of you who are interested in stopping smoking. Those of you who want to continue the trip you are already on, just do so; you don't have to go with us now. Follow your own path, your own agenda and enjoy your trip. Maybe you'll tell us about it sometime in the future, when we come together again.

I'm going now to remind you of an experience that you had many, many times in your childhood. You are sleeping in your own bed and you are having a dream. And in your dream you get out of bed and you go into a closet over there. In the back of the closet is a door. When you look for that door, tomorrow morning, when you wake up, you will not find it there. But it's there now. And the door opens very easily, and you walk through the door, and you are on the top of a very old interesting stairway, maybe a marble stairway, because the stone is very, very smooth, and you can even feel the polished marble of the bannister under one of your hands. You go downstairs, step by step, really enjoying the feeling of support from that firm stone. You may want to kick off your shoes, when you are part way down, so that you can feel the smoothness and the coolness of the marble underneath your feet. It does feel good, doesn't it? You go deeper and deeper with every step that you take. Just like that. Now at the bottom of the stairs you walk out onto a beach. The sand is very silky—smooth, fine sand, you can feel that under your feet now, can't you? [Pause] You step out onto the beach. As you walk along the beach, you see the ocean over to the side, and the surf is coming in and going out, coming in and out—in and out—in and out with your breathing. And as you look out over that vast expanse of ocean in front of you, you may be aware of the fact, that the salt concentration in that water is exactly the same as in your own bloodstream. You can appreciate the fact, as you enjoy the beauty and the immensity of the power of this ocean, that you are a part of this world of beauty, of nature. Your body is a part of this natural world—the world of nature. And you are beautiful, and your body is also beautiful. [Pause] You walk along the beach, step by step; you reach a large stone standing in the middle of the beach. It's very rough in some places, and in other places it's very polished, like the marble on that staircase, polished by thousands and thousands and thousands of years of water. And really it's interesting, isn't it?—to feel the difference between the rough parts and the smooth parts. We can think of what Milton Erickson said about roughage, that sickness and pain and troubles are the roughage of life. And if anybody has ever eaten Army food—that spam, that processed food—he realizes how important roughage is in one's diet.

You can get a firm hold on some of the smooth parts too, and that feels so good, doesn't it? And you look into a hole in the rock there, a deep deep hole, very very tiny, not big enough to put your hand into. At the bottom of the hole is a very precious jewel. You may wonder, how you can get that jewel for yourself, if you really want it. It is very valuable. It would give you a lot of the things that you really want in this life. You don't have to get it right now. And think about it, as you walk farther along the beach. And you can always return to this rock also, as you can return to any of the places that you have visited on this trip today. You easily can go back to any one of them at any time, just by closing your eyes, as they are closed now and picturing that particular place. You have been there, and once you have been here, you can always come back—at your own time and in your own way, to either where you experienced something that you started to experience here today or to have a new experience. So you walk along the beach, come to a garden. The garden has the most beautiful flowers that you have ever seen. Some of them are very large and very colorful—like jungle flowers, but there is a very very fine, very delicate petal, that is floating over there on the surface of the pond—so delicate and so fine. The only thing you can compare it with would be the very delicate membranes in your own body. It's as delicate as the alveoli in your lungs, the place where oxygen moves through as it goes from the air into your bloodstream. You realize that the tissues and the membranes in your own body are even more delicate than that delicate flower petal. And those flowers are really beautiful, aren't they? Very favorite colors and scents. And you realize, that they are beautiful, because they get plenty of nourishment, get clean air, and they are protected from the winds, when they become too rough, and yet they are invigorated and strengthened by some wind, by some changes in climate. And wouldn't we do everything to protect a beautiful flower, if we could help it? Wouldn't we? We would do everything to help such beautiful living creatures. [Pause] So as we are enjoying colors, the aromas, sensations, the breathing freely of this clean air, you walk back along the beach, return to our staircase. You walk up step by step, begin feeling the friendliness and the support of those steps.

Climbing step by step back to that room, where you were lying and dreaming, dreaming that we took that whole walk through the doorway at the back of the closet, down the stairs, along the beach, into the garden and back again. At the same time, you, as an adult can go back and find that young child, the child who may be really suffering, who may be having a good time, but more likely having some real problems, feeling all alone, even in dreams, feeling a lot of pain, feeling that no one understands the child. You can tell the child tht you do understand it, you ay want to hug the child, tell the child that things will work out, if you want, you can take the child by the hand and lead the child into its future. It's your present, and she will know, he will know, that he will never be alone again. The child can begin to awaken from a dream, and you as an adult can begin to awaken from your trance in your own time and in your own way. Bring back with you whatever is of value for you and leave the rest behind to develop, to be revisited, reexamined at some later time. And don't come out of your trance too quickly! You haver plenty of time, and if you would like to experience something really interesting, I suggest doing something that is not easy, but it's not too difficult either. You could awaken from your trance just from the neck up at first and feel the difference between your head and the rest of your body. If you want to do that with your eyes open, just move your head, but not the rest of your body. I think you'll find a very interesting difference. And as you wake up, you feel wider and wider awake. You can feel as if you had a really good rest: You return from a long, restful, healing, refreshing vacation. And that feeling can remain with you for the rest of this conference. And you will enjoy the rest of this conference. I'm sure I will, because I always enjoy learning new things. And I've enjoyed this trip we have taken together with you today.

It's almost 11:50, and we are here in the Flagstaff room, the Civic Center, Phoenix, Arizona, December 5th, 1986. Hi!

If there is anybody who has any trouble getting back, please come up and talk with me. And I hope, you get back to wherever you want to be. But I think, from what I can see, that most of you are quite happy with where you are right now, . . . aren't you?

No? Yes? Not sure yet? You will have to give yourself a chance to get oriented. See what you are left with and what you want to take with you. O.K. [Pause] It will take you a few minutes to fully go back to your usual state of consciousness, if you want to go back there. But enjoy wherever you are. You'll feel different when you start moving around than you do now, probably.

Any questions or any comments? Not everybody is ready to move. Some people are moving, that's fine. You leave it to whenever you are ready to. If anybody wants to make any comments, any questions, that might be of interest to the rest, you can do that. If you want to talk to me individually, come up and talk to me. O.K.

[Comments from the audience]

COMMENTS

Sidney Rosen's guided trance is an inward journey, starting in the Flagstaff room of the Civic Center in Phoenix, Arizona, the actual location, and ending there 50 minutes later. It shows how the conditions of time and space can be utilized as a frame for trance work. Having paced the situation and assisted dissociation of the conscious and the unconscious, he leads us inwards by helping us to focus on visual, auditory and kinesthetic perceptions. I guess this sequence is deliberate, with Sidney Rosen bringing in his spiritual knowledge and helping us to become a bodiless mind very quickly. After taking us back to an early learning state, he invites us to join him mountain climbing and then wondering, "what's on the other side" of the mountain or reaching a corner and being told "turn that corner." To deepen the trance, he invites us to accompany him "deeper and deeper into the woods." This induction is a clear example of how the symbolism of nature can be utilized for the process, in which we finally find ourselves in the magic world of childhood, in a magic orchard, where we can get every form of help. With the orchard theme is seeded the final goal, the lovely garden, where we shall be at the deepest point of this trance. At this stage there is a confusing interruption, the possibility of coming back, with Sidney Rosen using the technique of a fractionated trance in the form of an invitation to come out of trance and find security by checking if everything is all right in order to go much deeper afterwards. This also serves as a check for the therapist, because he can now obtain a clear response from the audience and find out if the people are still in contact with him.

The new journey down into an even deeper trance picks up the theme of childhood and starts descending into the dreamworld, step by step down a marble stairway, another familiar, traditional symbol. Finally we face the ocean of the unconscious on our walk along the beach, see the jewel in the hole in the rock, a symbol for a point we can't even reach, and find the lovely garden.

I remember from my experience that I became creative at this point, sucked the jewel out of the rock with my mouth and felt very contented because of this idea.

An especially moving and healing experience within this trance is Sidney Rosen's careful leading back to the present, the return part so often ignored, almost neglected or sadly shortened during trance inductions. Why miss these opportunities! At the very end Sidney Rosen invites people to talk to him individually also. This, too, is something I have often missed in many other group inductions with strange people. I really appreciate Sidney Rosen's offer, I think everybody who does a group induction with people one doesn't know should express this invitation, if possible.

19

Burkhard Peter: Forget the Forgetting in Order to Remember

COMMENTS

One month after the seminar in which this group induction was given, I met the same group again. One person came to me wondering what Burkhard Peter had said. He wanted to know the exact words because he had felt it had been effective for him. There was a vague idea, something about having to remember what he had forgotten. During the induction as well as in the following weeks, he had regained access to a forgotten body position, a very straight position in which he had felt powerful and free. He realized that this position had fallen into forgetfulness when he had begun to build up his practice, working very hard with many debts. Now he could feel that this was something before he had become bowed down and bent of which he could make use again.

I imagine that this induction was effective not because of clever technique alone—notice, for example, the "chain" phrases, the train of suggestions—but because Burkhard Peter did what he had promised: comply with the requirements of the setting and utilize our expectations.

INDUCTION

We have time still, plenty of time to have a good time. So leave yourselves time! Feel how you are sitting there and well, I would suggest change nothing in particular, nothing specially be changed. If you have your eyes held open, then leave them both a piece quite open still . . . so long . . . quite a piece still . . . till they're both close to (they're both closed, too, two) falling shut. If you have your hands resting on your thighs or they are crossed or resting on the armrests, then leave them both still there, letting them do nothing else, still allowing them not to feel anything in particular, still giving them leave not to think of something special. Take plenty of time still for yourself so . . . you see what is here and there is that to hear what you are hearing, well, and still be simply feeling what you are feeling. I mean truly perceive the quietness descending more and more still.

Stop doing anything at all still. You may let both your eyes rest on one point and then spot what happens, when you leave them to rest on one spot. When I, too, let my eyes rest on one single spot, I still spot that pointing to how my perception has changed. Maybe it may be for one or the other much simpler to let both eyes rest on not only *one* spot; but maybe needs spots—two spots or three spots—in order to change from one spot to another and then back again to one spot and then still again to the other. Like it is with feelings similarly. One can feel the body. One feels this (spot), one feels that (spot). One can let the perception, one's observation, rest on *one* feeling. Still feeling only *one*. Maybe for one or the other *one* feeling is not enough still, and maybe goes swinging back and forth to and from here and there between this feeling and that feeling still, here and there from this to that . . . till this point, that spot in time where it becomes quiet and becomes still and where all movements cease, standing still on the spot, where all becomes slower, still slower, where all becomes still quieter, always (all ways) more still.

And then, only then may you begin to go deeper and deeper and deeper still into yourself, to a spot inside, maybe go deeper and deeper into trance. Only then when all's still, all have become still, till you have stopped the swinging and your perception has got stuck on one spot, and has been caught up on one particular point. You begin to spot the point of how this inner perception begins to change, so it may well be that the perception of the body changes. Though the body can still become light or heavy, so it may change within limits still. You may feel or not feel anymore: where are the hands? Where are the feet? And spot down, now, pinpoint well: what did I already forget to feel, forget to hear? And maybe you may like to begin to remember, to remember still just now, just this very moment. What did you remember, did you feel just now? Do you remember . . . what . . . have you seen just now, this very instant? So now you may begin to remember just now, begin to remember a spot, a point of time in your life. Time can flow, so fast, so slow. Can you remember on the spot now the point from just before? Can you forget to forget to get to remember? Can you begin to remember how you forget? How do you begin to forget and how do you finish with that? How do you begin to remember and how do you finish with that and forget? Is it feeling or thinking? Or do you forget to remember? Or do you forget in order to remember?

I think everyone has an individual own way to remember and to forget, to feel. Everyone has his completely own way as a child to forget and as a grown up to remember. Like we have as a child learned to forget, so we can begin as a grown up to remember the manner and mode of being a child, being like a child, to think like a child, to feel like a child, to remember and forget like a child. You may remember year for year to forget the years from today onwards to forget in that you forget minute for minute, hour by hour, year by year; from today you may begin to remember year by year, to remember that childhood being as . . . little boy, little girl—to think, to do. Remember a certain, particular situation still, a very special situation. It may be sad or good, happy and merry. Little children can change with a standing jump: just now they were still crying, had wept, had quarrelled, and now they are playing together again.

Little children can very quickly forget from just now to afterwards, later on. It is not at all necessary to forget. One need simply only follow what is happening. If I am now still sad and then straight away after glad, then I need not forget my sadness of just before in order to be cheerful and in good spirits straight after. Children can do that. Children can be different from one moment to the next, and they are still the same, though. It is still the same boy, still the same girl. One moment this, one moment that.

Children can leave time for themselves, take time to learn wonderfully well and truly to learn slowly and carefully. Children begin to learn and do not know or realize that they are learning. Children begin to learn to crawl on all fours. And they think nothing at all while doing so. And they do not know that they are doing it, but they enjoy doing it. Can you imagine a very small child that stands up on both legs for the first time, its face beaming with pride?

Every person has a personal history or herstory. And it is fundamentally exclusive, indivisible, all one alone. And everyone can still remember this, the own individual history, step by step and piece by piece. And it's fun still to remember if one believes one has forgotten. It's fun to discover that one can now stop forgetting and let return drop by drop, let piece by piece the knowledge come back. So that you know, like this . . . Leave yourself time still, time again to learn and again to experience that one and that other one to observe, no more to forget . . . [long pause] I need not say that every person will still in that person's own time and at that person's own individual rate return and then, when it is right, completely come back here.

20

Paul Carter and Stephen Gilligan: Age Regression

INDUCTION

G.: You sat in a classroom long ago, and sitting in a classroom long ago you listened sometimes in certain ways. You communicated in special ways to those people around you. Do you know this game: post-man? (whispering something in neighbor's ear and saying "Pass it on")

C.: The subject for this afternoon will be all of us, and we are going to do some work Stephen has been getting to with regression. In traditional hypnosis you give direct suggestions to help someone regress in trance. It may be suggested that he should go deeper, deeper and deeper, and then as I count from one to ten you will get younger and younger. But a regressed state is actually very easy to set up naturalistically, without any formal induction, without even a formal trance really. You can begin to introduce or develop a regressed like state just by using some of the very powerful associations to childhood by games, songs, different kind of ways of using your body and any other number of things I have written up there. Either you bring them in and actually do them like you sing a song from childhood or you bring in one of the teachers that you had when you were five years old, or you bring your mother and father in. And did you notice that, by the way, even still you might be forty years old, fifty years old, still when you get together with your mother and father, it's almost like you were six again. They are some of the same parents. You can also simply talk about it, where we are so far: In a hypnotic induction it can suffice many time to simply describe or talk about some little songs or some other childhood experiences to set up a regressed state. (Laughing) Moans? Where did we go? (with the game: post-man) Right over there? That's it. What did he say to you?

M.: He's bringing me into a trance.

C.: Now, what did he say exactly? Can you remember the words?

M.: He said: you can go deeper—deeper—deeper into a trance.

C.: Was there more?

M.: No.

C.: Not yet?

G.: So much for these brilliant intellectual developments that occur in hypnosis workshops. [Laughter]

C.: So in any case you can use almost anything as a powerful association for childhood to begin to set up a sense of an earlier time, the environment of an earlier time. The value of doing that is to begin to bring out again childlike qualities, not necessarily specific memories, where that's one focus in therapy: to develop very specific memories. What I'm going to suggest that we focus on this afternoon—certainly specific memories will come out—the focus here is more on developing a quality of being a child again, which can be developed through some specific memories and through some activities of childhood bring out that quality of childhood, meaning the softness, the flexibility, the ability to learn, that tremendous ability that we have very developed as a child and start to limit more and more as we grow up, of being able to learn, fantastically complex tasks like speaking a language at a rapid rate compared to later on in life, where that rate seemed to slow down a little bit. That can be available to you again through regressing and developing the childhood kinds of qualities.

G.: So we would like to ask you at the outset to think and identify, what associations, what ways of being, what games, what songs, what sorts of values do you remember as being associated to your childhood, uniquely associated. What did you learn, think, do, experience as a child that you tend not to experience so much as an adult?

C.: So for example sitting in a classroom and the teacher asks a question, and nobody wants to answer, right? [laughter] So you sit there and cannot look straight ahead, hope that she or he wouldn't notice you.

G.: Maybe you have had experiences sometimes of being called upon in the classroom, and you hadn't done your homework properly. And you know that the teacher is going to ask about that homework. And you are able to wonder: Is he going to call on me? And what ways did you use as a child to try to distract the teacher from calling on you, that always seemed to work the opposite way? Somehow the teacher just knew when to call on you.

C.: [Pointing] The young man over here? Ja? [laughter]

G.: [To man] Can you elaborate a little bit?

T.: One way I used was to pretend not being there, which only worked when he didn't look in his book. When he looked in his book and then said: go on, it's your turn, you are lost. Because he did that anyway.

C.: So you made yourself invisible? Hm? But then he called your name from the book.

T.: Yes. So this only worked when he looked into the class.

C.: How many of you had that ability as a child to make yourself invisible? Become one of the invisible people? Have you seen that movie? Do you have that movie in Europe yet: "The Enchanted Forest"? Or is it: "The Animal Forest"? It was made in South America. About a family who goes down to South America. And the child is taken by the Indians there, by the invisible people? I guess, you didn't see it. I'm starting to feel I'm the only one who has seen that movie.

G.: Change the subject! [Laughter]

C.: You see, we tried those things, and sometimes people just don't relate to what you are talking about. And whenever you begin a hypnotic induction you often times start by throwing out an idea like Stephen talked about not doing the homework. Some of you didn't respond, or others of you started responding stronger, which gives you an idea of how to proceed.

If you are working in a group, for example, you put an idea and you see who responds strongly to that idea. And if you want to focus on that person's development, then you may focus on that idea a little bit more. And then you might want a shift to another topic for a while to see, who else may respond to a different idea. It's the same thing, if you are working with a family, presenting some different ideas. In any case we will do some things in here, where we present a whole variety of ideas, some of which will probably be meaningless to you individually, some of which you will probably find rather meaningful. You can certainly notice what you respond with and feel free to focus on these things that are useful to you.

What we would like to do is a group induction to give you an opportunity to just experience some changes inside yourself. Before the beginning of this we are going to ask you to take out something to write on, a piece of paper or something. Get one from someone near you along with a pen or a pencil.

G.: Your learning task, one that you mastered long ago, is to let yourself master it again in the present.

C.: Now most of us as adults believe they are supposed to know everything already. Or at least know most everything, for example, how to write. And because of that it becomes much more difficult to learn. For example, to learn a new language, it's much more difficult, if you think you've always mostly taken care of your language learning, you're done already at once. And so it's often much more difficult to go through some of the frustrations and changes that go on, when you are learning something new. Many people don't, whether it's learning a new therapy skill, learning a new sport skill, learning a new language skill. Often times we stop. But as a child generally you don't think you are supposed to know everything. That's a good thing to remember. I would like to ask you to be willing to take some time to not know again. To be a little bit like a child again and to just feel what it is like to explore. And part of what helps the child do that is not being concerned about where you are going. See, now as an adult you know, you are supposed to be very successful. So that if you are not that way when you begin you think, there is something wrong with me. But as a child you don't know so much what it means necessarily to be that successful, you just enjoy playing with new skills where you are.

C.:	G.:
	So even as Paul is talking about that topic that really is oriented to the adult life

so you can begin to allow yourself to make that change
in a very
simple way

and wonder what it would be like to be able to hear the voices
Listen to the voices now much more as a child.

So for that purpose what we'll ask you to do is:
put your pen or your pencil
in the *other* hand, not
the hand you normally
write with, but in the *other* hand.

I remember, for example,

ten years ago, there was a young boy,
that lived with us. Little Eric was six years old,
in the first grade,
Little Eric was learning in the first grade
a variety of different things.

And what we are going to ask you to do
not right now, but in a moment,
is to write your name.
And when I'm going to ask you to take a minute
of clocktime to do this
normally you can write your name
in a couple of seconds, so you all know you can do that.
This is a different task.
What I'm going to ask you to do
is really slow down.
Take a few seconds,
actually 5 or 10 seconds for every letter in your name.
Make it very very slow.
Let yourself watch each line
develop
very very slow.

He was learning to write "Eric."
His name was "Eric" with a "c."
He was learning to pronounce

words and letters.
He was learning to tell a big A
from a little a,
big B
from a little b,

Big C
from little c
a p from a q

a t from a u
from a to c.
And he learned all the tasks and different things.
And Eric's school had an open
house for all the different parents to visit.

So go ahead, start and take
a good full minute at least

clocktime, about ten seconds
for each letter. Write your name,
your first name.
Moans

We would go to the school and see how the young children do it.

Barbara, Wolfgang, Moreen.
One letter at time.

And if you already have finished
more than two letters,
then slow down.
Cut your speed to the half,
real slow.

And when you have finished

your name
if you need more time
take it!
If you don't need more time,
then just below your name begin
to write your address, the number,
street, where you lived as a child,
when you were going to school.
If you can't remember it, then
just write any one you can remember
even where you live now.
Write very slow!
Even a little bit slower than you wrote your name

to make the letters of that and to form those numbers.

And as you do that

Open house for first grade children.

And Eric had Frank, his father.
Paul and I were
like uncles to him, as we
were living in the same house.
So the three of us went to that classroom
together and visited the first grade classroom in order to
examine, to explore, to discover. Little Eric was learning.
Now, what do you learn in grade one? And the seats we walked
in were very small. And the teacher said: Please sit in the
first grade seat. And we sat down, Frank in one chair, Paul in
another chair, Stephen in the third chair. And we felt
ourselves really develop
a sense of remembering what it was like to learn as a small
child.
And Mrs. Bigger
was a teacher.
And grade one teachers often times have
strange sounding names, the teachers.
What's the teacher wearing?

What did the teacher call you?
And what you wore and where you sit.

And how long can you sit comfortably.
And who sat in front of you?

And what kind of desk was it now?

And what kind of pencil is it?

you might begin to remember some of the feelings you had

learning to write those numbers
learning the one

and learning to write those letters.

Then go ahead and finish this address slowly!

And when you have done
you can put down your pen and pencils,
let your hands rest on your lap and close your eyes and
let your mind go!
And when you learn those letters
you have to learn the big A
and also the little a, and you
have to learn the printed A
and the cursive A.
And you try to learn the difference
between A and day and pay, and is the
circle on a p the same as the circle
on a day?
The hump on the m the same as the
hump of the n? And learning to write
them not only down, but learning
to write them in between the lines
And first it's so hard to get
them to stay in between the lines.
And when you finished writing
put your pens and pencils down
and sit back comfortably in your chair

and let yourself go!

We didn't only learn writing as a child.
We didn't only learn counting in
a trance. As a child you learn
many many things

And what kind

of feeling to learn to write and write right numbers.
Learning the 1, the 2, the 3, and learning more and more
unconsciously. Write right, write!
And Mrs. Bigger showed the different pictures, cat,
dog,
the different animals.

And every child had a different animal.
Every child developed a special relationship.
If there is a rabbit
or if there is another kind of animal.

You are going to develop as a child
a variety of emotional relationships.
You are going to develop as a child
a variety of different associations.
You are going to develop as a child
a variety of different understandings.
How to spell your name,
different understandings.

How to address that teacher?
And you learn
in terms of values.

Some cats are your companions, and some cats you don't want to
pet. You learn to differentiate and you can learn to find those
relationships that allow you to be secure.
And in a trance you can go very deeply
in your own security.
And as a child you learn, for example,
to ride a bike.

You learn to sing songs.

You learn a game.

Maybe you learn the alphabet song:
A,B,C,D,E,F,G,
H,I,J,K,L,M,N,O,P,
Q,R,S,T,U,V,W,X,Y,Z,
Now I know my ABC's,

Tell me what you think of me.
And there are so many different
ways of learning your own language,
your own songs.

I remember Henning teaching me the rhyme:

Schlapp, schlapp, schlapp,
die Milch ist gut.

Guten Morgen, liebes Kätzchen
Ist hier noch ein freies Plätzchen?
Schlapp, schlapp, schlapp,
die Milch ist gut.
Schlapp, schlapp, schlapp,
wie wohl das tut!
Now you were very proud to learn a song.

So go and take some time to remember
a certain song that you learned . . .
as a little girl, as a little boy.
Maybe she used to sing you:
Guten Abend, gute Nacht
mit Rosen bedacht
mit Nelken geschmückt
schlüpf unter die Deck.
Morgen früh, wenn Gott will

wirst du wieder geweckt,
Morgen früh, wenn Gott will,
wirst du wieder geweckt.

Many children learn how to swim.

You learn to ride in a car and look out
and see: *the different scenery is changing*
The images are changing
the feeling of movement
is changing. And
feeling the security in a trance . . .
feeling the security in a trance
through and through.
And even move back in time further . . .
And for a nickname,
and knowing which nickname meant which relationship,
a certain name for you, how your parents were calling you,
when you knew you were in trouble.
A certain name, parents will call you,
when you knew you were well liked.

And different names and different values
and different associations.

And different roles in the classroom.
Some of which you learned how to stand out
as the one with the good song,
as the one with the jokes
as the one with that special pat,
as the one with that special ability,
as one with a certain value,
belonging to a certain family,
belonging to a certain culture,
belonging to a certain set of understandings.
And in trance you can review those understandings.
You can shift through those understandings
with the feeling of security,
with the respect for all the learnings.

And as a young baby

you understand feeling
and you hear a voice
and you don't need to hear the words,
you can just understand the feeling,
when you hear an angry voice,
you feel that anger.
You don't need to know what that voice is saying
you just know the anger.

And when you hear a loving voice.
you know that feeling
and you don't need to know
what she's saying, what he's saying

You just know that feeling of love in the voice.
And as a baby
you can hear the feeling
and you can understand
the experience full and completely.
As a child you learn to explore
with your mouth.
As a baby everything goes to
your mouth.
You see a rock
and you want to know how it feels
in your mouth.
You see your father's shoe
You want to know how it feels
in your mouth. You see a spoon,
you want to feel it in your mouth
and taste that spoon.
And it's nice to put your fingers into your mouth,
your thumb.
And it's a good feeling as a baby
to have a thumb
or a couple of different fingers
in your mouth and enjoy the taste

with an appreciation of the developmental ability
to *learn new values*
appropriate for the present self,
new values . . .
and that's very difficult to hear sometimes
name changes . . .
you hear sadness.

You can hear voices through walls

and you learn about relationships.

And in trance you can be able,
with the security

of the Deeper Self,

to review those experiences

with a sense of knowing the values
for the present self. As a child I had a windbreaker jacket.
I really enjoyed that windbreaker jacket.
And then one day
there was a loss . . .

a loss of that windbreaker jacket
There was a sense of attachment
to something very special . . .
the jacket wasn't there. I thought . . .
Look over and find it
But the loss couldn't be denied.

I didn't know what to do . . .
what to say . . .
Go to a different state

and feel the security of that thumb

in your mouth.

And you enjoy a simple movement as a baby

And how many of you may remember
the gentle rocking
back and forth
back and forth, back and forth

And you can feel that rocking now,
that gentle movement
back and forth
a loving movement
a loving pose in your body,

And you might feel very secure,
when someone rocks you back and forth,

back and forth
it's so nice to feel that good
sensation again inside your depth.

And there are so many memories
within you
so many experiences of the self

and at this time

we would like to ask you to allow an image

to allow an image
of a small child to develop

And you may recognize this child
or you may not
you don't need to

go to a different place

go to a different state of security

a state in which you can be all alone

with your own sense of safety
You may not know
how you get there,

may not know where you are,
may not know how the solution will develop,

how the reorganization will develop
how those new learnings
are developing,
how you learn to move your hands differently.
One little hand
one little finger. This little piggy went to the market
this little piggy goes to the store
and where does this little piggy go?

And you have a sense of your hand changing inside . . .

of the different values of self . . .

reorganizing . . .

in accord with your present needs . . .
so much to review and reframe . . .
different grades . . .

different subjects . . .
geography . . .
history . . .

mathematics . . .

Just allow yourself to see

or to sense, to feel
a young child near you

Maybe one year old
maybe two years
maybe five

some young child

Allow yourself to begin to develop
a sense of that young child.
Is it a boy or a girl?
How old is that child?
What's he or she look like?
What is he or she wearing?

How big is that child?

15cm, 20cm, 25cm?
50cm? A full meter? How big is that child?

And as you begin to get acquainted
with this child
notice that that child is beginning
to move closer to you

And just observe that child
observe how he or she moves
get a sense of him
the expression of his face

and let her, let him
come closer to you
and let that child take your hand

take you by the hand
and feel that small child's hand
in your hand

Feel the softness

language . . .

reading . . .
learning to read . . .

maybe four years old . . .

the reading, the learning . . .

the patterning . . .

You can feel it!
You can feel it!
You can feel it!
And that sense
of knowing where it is: the center
Here you are: . . . the center

Here you are: . . . the center
The child is getting bigger.

Here you allow yourself to appreciate

varieties of ways that you can become

experientially intimate.

And you can really enjoy
developing further
that which is there . . .
that where is there . . .
yourself over there . . .
yourself over there . . .

moving closer now . . .
it is coming closer now, little bit more . . .
moving . . .

a child moving

and you can feel very secure
being with yourself.
How you don't need to hear me
You don't need to hear Stephen
and you can let yourself
simply be in your own world
alone with the child
And you can be very secure
alone with the child

and feel the softness of that hand
the littleness of that hand
and let yourself enjoy
the experience with a tear
with a sense of feeling
with an awe of that little hand

And in a moment
when next we say the word "now"

to take a couple of minutes of clocktime

to let that child take you on a journey

And that child can take you by the hand
and lead you
and that child's hand in your hand
leading you, guiding you somewhere in particular.
And you can let your unconscious help
you going along
go along

And you can let go, and you don't
need to hold on to.
You simply enjoy a journey

And observe your feeling
your vision
what you hear and see and feel

a child feeling
a child sensing . . .

Hear the other sounds . . .
and that beautiful sense of the music
of integration, of intimacy
. . . the sense of being alone together now.
Where two selves become
one with the other . . .
with the other . . .
for the other . . .
You can experience various emotions

right in the inside
You know, when it's time

and know that you are here
and there.

You can be able

All the time in the world for your unconscious

to let that child share with you something the child knows

and you have forgotten about.

And you really can enjoy
letting that child show you

in a fresh fashion
a very very fresh fashion
in a new fashion, a very very precious . . .

very very valuable

learning . . .

as that child takes you on a journey
and the journey beginning

in time

second time, foreign time, here back,
the journey
with that child

Now . . .
And you can let go my voice and go all the way
And sometimes the child will show you a very special place.

And you can stay there for a
while and just observe
feel and sense
at that place.
And sometimes
the child will show you something

something that you need

To pay attention to in order to
heal
your own self-image

in order to heal your own self-awareness
in order to heal your own self home
in order to make whole

your own being again

our being that is soft and hard

big and small

You can feel free to get a sense
of anything you might need
at this moment

nourish the self
many years of clock time

through the years

1975
68, 67
where will it be?

who knows?
Nowwwww!

In a very very tender fashion

in a very very gentle way

in the middle of nowhere.
An opportunity to review
here and there
simultaneously

And to know of the reformulation

the value
to respect then
to respect now
the needs of the child
the needs of the adult

the needs of then, the needs of now

two hands
two shoulders
one neck . . .

two hips, two ears, one spine . . .
two eyes
two hands
one self

perhaps a hand
a gentle touch

perhaps some time
to be with yourself and feel
and see and listen

perhaps the chance to say something
that you need to say

say it
and begin the process
of making yourself whole again

speaking a word

expressing a feeling

redeem the time
asking

a man

moving your body.

And when you are ready, feel free to take a moment
to simply appreciate
and find a place for this child in you

find a place in your own being
for this child
and you may be aware of the need
to spend more time with the child

you may be aware of the need to cry
the need to laugh
you may be aware of the need to move

And for that reason
find a place
to keep this child near you.

two understandings
then and now
one unified vision . . .

the middle third
the middle third.
A Trance Parent self

to guide the child

to guide the child

a sense of letting go

hearing

redeem the time

and the unread vision

of the bigger dream
Why should we celebrate the dead men more
than the dying?

a sense of growing
. . . the sense of knowing
a simultaneous self
a life of learning

a simple self

finding new relationships
And you really can't
predict how
that movie
that past with the heart
that path with a heart
that past with a heart
that path with a heart

And in your unconscious you can
find that place
a place which is appropriate
and comfortable for you

in your heart?
in your mind?
in your need?

in the back of your head?

Find some place to keep that child
so that you know you can return

and dream again, play again with the child

And yet for now allow yourself

to let go

to absorb the journey and it's memory in you

the memory of the soft feeling.
And bring back with you
what you want to continue
to think about and leave
with the child what you prefer
to leave with the child for now.

And when you first begin to walk
it is quite a thrill
just to be able to take one step
and then another
and still stand up

First it was easier to run than to walk

Take steps from your path

Take steps

little baby steps

little baby feet

little baby's
shoes
little baby's nose
little baby's toys

little baby's love

the love of the little baby

for the self

the little baby's eyes
to tell you
Grow . . .
know . . .
Yes . . .
Grow . . .

And your unconscious can organize the best variety of
different ways to learn to be able to develop mental
strategies that fit . . .
organizations that reflect
inward and outward
the depth of

your own being.
You have that voice

and baby is there too.

It was sort of like falling forward and letting your legs
follow along as fast as they could. But after not so long
you mastered walking and it became so natural that you didn't
even think twice about it. You were already learning to skip,
to jump, to hop, to walk on one leg, to walk backwards.
When you have mastered one skill you move on to another. And each new one again as you learn to experience
it more and more completely in yourself. And when you get stuck,
it's nice to return to some of the earliest skills, so that you
can remember, what it's like to learn. And sometimes you'll be
very stuck, because you are working on a task too complex for
you at this time. And so it's good to let go a bit for a while.

And be able to return

Return to something of a more simple form, something more basic
like the movement of taking a sweater off, like breathing . . .
like the experience of opening and closing your eyes . . .
like the feeling of the first time you lifted your hand and
found your face.

Have the experience to be able to let yourself know there is a
lot more where that came from. So take a few moments and give
yourself some messages of self-appreciation

And remember whether your tears are crying
or your tears are laughing.

and thank yourself

The tears are water
and they are the same

tears.

And both are water of your heart

or water that is nourishing for both
your eyes and your inner being

So when you are ready, feel free to
allow yourself to come out
and reorient
to the room again
and appreciate your ability to do what you have done.
To let go as much as you did let go,
to hold on as much as you did hold on,
and know that both are important to your growing power.
To appreciate your ability to remember
what you did remember
and not remember what you didn't remember.
And appreciate your ability to begin to develop
the feelings and sensations in a trance state
and to let them go again also.
And then, when you are ready let yourself awaken.

And you don't need to come all the way out of the
trance, when you reorient back to the room.
I remember, when Erickson regressed with me,

for that degree of movement

in that style

in that way that suited the needs of the entire self.
And going to a light trance, come out: gently
You may go into a deep trance, come out: gently
going to a medium then, deeper trance,
light trance, come out: gently . . .
Go into medium and deep and light and deep and light
and a deeper trance, come out: gently . . .

and give yourself that sense
of knowing both sides now.

That's it!

Reorient back to the community of big people in your own rate
and pace!

took me on a trip in the Grand Canyon back,
ate breakfast with me
went to the swimming pool
and then asked me to come all the way back to
1978, 77 or whenever it was,
come all the way back

at a very very gradual grade

I opened my eyes

let that breath

and smiled at him

and very very gentl

and he said: You haven't come all the way back,
have you?

Let that breath

I said: no

be able to shift!

and he said: You really don't need to, do you?
Because you really can learn

time to come out

and better in a trance.
I was there to learn

And need go back here.
Come out very very gradually at time

Now for the completion of a trance
it's often times useful to take
as much time as you need.
Hello!

feeling your hands
feeling you hear
now as you are here now!
Hello!

COMMENTS

This Dual Induction by Paul Carter and Stephen Gilligan gives a theoretical and practical course on how to do a group induction at the beginning, especially focusing on the aspect of getting a response from the group, "utilizing" what is in the situation. Meanwhile, when the official group induction begins, the group has already oriented to trance and a task can be given. This writing task is especially good for eliciting regression.

When the authors find their particular rhythm, I always think of their way of doing a double induction as creating spoken songs. Here they play together like children, their voices first alternating, then slowly tuning in together in harmony. As with all of these powerful confusion techniques, they create a frame for letting go, because we cannot follow consciously any longer. Paul Carter and Stephen Gilligan have found a perfect balance with each other, and although it has a somewhat shocking aspect with both voices speaking at the same time, this induction allows extreme relaxation and regression, once we let go. After letting us regress before school, Paul Carter sings us songs in German, language "little children like," while Stephen Gilligan utilizes the time to give us subtly imperceptible therapeutic suggestions. What a wonderful form of therapy, caring for us competently like parents with touching songs, constructive words, and full awareness of our process of growing and developing! Notice how they create a balance, for example, when Stephen Gilligan talks about a loss, Paul Carter juxtaposes humor and spreads the idea of how a little baby wants to put its father's shoe into its mouth.

There is the simple idea of returning in time to the state of a baby and letting us grow and gain more, again, letting us develop a picture of the young self and meet it for integration with the present self. It is really a touching atmosphere where this giving hands can happen and new self appreciation can grow. Notice also the gentle way they lead us back to our grown-up state and the present. Connecting us with our resources can be done in a loving, respectful way.

VI
THERAPY

Hypnotic therapy in an Ericksonian manner means helping the clients to make their very own unique and individually necessary changes. Jeff Zeig states that Ericksonian therapy departs from not only traditional psychotherapies, but also the classical methods of hypnosis. "In the Ericksonian model of hypnotherapy, clinicians do not program; they structure communication to have maximum effect so the patient can change many aspects of life, not merely the presenting symptom" (Zeig, 1987).

Whatever technique is used for this purpose, even those seemingly manipulative ones such as confusion techniques, it must be seen against the background of deep respect for everybody's intrinsic healing resources. This allows therapy to be done in groups, even in groups casually meeting at congresses where the members do not know each other; here understanding group inductions as providing an opportunity to progress with one's own development and to fill in developmental gaps privately within this healing atmosphere, as demonstrated by Ernest Rossi. Both Manfred Prior and Sandra Sylvester take "Healing" as their theme; Jeffrey Zeig selects healing "Ego-building." Ernst Petzold and Wolfgang Herzog show their healing induction as used with a real family in a therapeutic setting. The last two above-mentioned contributions have commentaries and/or introductions written by the authors. My most beloved "Rainbow Meditation" by Sandra Sylvester had to be excluded at the last minute, because of space limitations.

21

Manfred Prior: Teddy

COMMENTS

I witnessed the birth of Manfred Prior's "Teddy" induction from quite nearby. In a way I was able to watch how in a Teddy repair workshop Teddy was "carefully and circumspectly taken in hand by the master" to make members mobile and renew skin and fur. The caution with which he offers exactly what is necessary to gain trust, convinces us that we may give up our wounds in the workshop of the unconscious to our inner master for repair.

INDUCTION

Probably some of you have had a strenuous day behind you and your thoughts are still not quite free from the strains of everyday life. That is a good start for a small dream journey, on which you may be easily able to experience trance as being specially agreeable and healing.

To get ready you can prepare yourself for going into trance—safely and quietly whereby some of you may make yourself so (sic!) comfortable and be sure that it's sometimes a good thing to ease into an even more comfortable position, while others of you have already let your eyes rest on something and know that there is nothing else to do, just listen to my voice, follow any thoughts that occur and just be ready to let anything just develop by itself from what has already begun—

Begun in that you let yourself sit here, get atoned to this
room, and listen to my words,
gradually letting relaxation happen, giving thoughts leave to
come and go and then letting them go piece by piece (peace by
peace) is also something pleasant that has possibly already
begun;

Translator's Note: In this induction—as elsewhere—there are several "mistakes" in grammar and syntax. These ambiguities are used to deepen trance (i.e., through soft confusion) and to elicit more associations.

and while your conscious mind is still awake listening to me,
may be on some other levels some slide or glide already may
began, (sic) started happening, a slide a glide into a completely
personal, very specific individual form of progressively
self-developing, self-deepening relaxation.

And your conscious mind may remember that you may be awake when you go on a dream journey, while unconsciously your breathing has begun giving piece by piece and quite (peace by peace and quiet) more rest-room and your body all quite by itself finds more comfortable positions, or you can with the conscious mind think (sink) and reflect on beginning relaxation and trance afterwards and meanwhile some parts of your body can now already understand more of this very special form of wakeful relaxation that occurs in therapeutic trance and some of you take right down to the sensations into the very fingertips your own relaxation process into your own hand like adults, who know how children like you know how to like putting little hands into a reassuringly big hand or like adults, who know how babies like you know how and like taking hold like grasping and like keeping hold tight and like begin held—tight safely and pleasantly.

And grownups also like to hold on to whatever pleasant relaxation or remembering has already begun to develop and they also like letting go whatever tenseness they are still thereby held by for it can be very pleasant, this partly holding and letting go, holding the party (sic!) like letting and leaving hold, the small childlike party relaxation, holding and leaving hold, the wholly loosely leaving go of holding so and like be letting yourself drawn and addressed by the letting go, from holding up and holding on loosely to the leaving hold, from finding a hold in the tighthold of leaving letting go into the quiet, safe sliding and gliding to the age-old new experience and remembering, the memory and experience of retirement, withdrawal, going inside to the little warm room inside, this snug little cradling bed, that you all have, the warm bed with the cover, the pillow, the toys, the dolls, perhaps the Teddy that you hug snug in your arms all cuddled up and the favorite dollies and teddy bears—yes, you enjoy this very much feeling so very safe and secure here.

For some have been weakened by difficult times, have wounds only superficially healed and hidden pains, the hair or—rather—fur has become bare in many places, some parts have been neglected, some limbs or may be remember a member may have become limp and numb, some parts stiff and cramped, and some almost completely immobile—and behind their dulled gaze, there where their hair or fur has thinned, their skin grazed, some dream in secret, age-old healing dreams.

And teddy bears and dolls can dream, wide awake in children's arms and don't always know whether to wake and dream or sleep in a waking dream and always slide and glide down deeper and deeper into your own (yawn) personal dream world where in changing darkness lights forms and colors live, pictures, memories or symbols appear more, perhaps dance and spring speak or sing about childlike lovely thing so that afterwards the healing dreams can like thinking (sinking) lead-sinkers by co-incidence (incidents) sink into the kingdom of forgetting again. But before then it may so happen that the dreams shall progress more vividly, lively dreams perhaps about a sheltering home, perhaps about moving things, or dream a dream in which the dreams of yore (your) dream about wonderful, miraculous healing, and so maybe dreaming of coming with the wounds, complaints and troubles into a workshop, a proper well-fitting Teddy workshop, where it's clearly usable (you 'se able) to mend and repair (re-pair) and find all you need for repairing and making up.

And the Teddy is like all teddy bears; who like absorbing the congenial atmosphere of the room, like sniffing around for a while, taking time to look around comfortably and take careful note of all the marvelous details, until after some time a friendly master craftsman enters the workshop, a nice quiet old man and—after him—his helpers. And as anyone can soon see and feel and sense, these are people to whom you can feel a lot of confidence, really trust, for they really know how to understand without a lot of words troubles, cares, wishes and longings and say simply and confidently "let's see how to manage that!"

And so they instil others with confidence and trust, with an invitation to open up—and trust this happening completely of its own accord after some time. And here too the Teddy is like all teddy bears who let trust in them be, examined by that peaceful, sober gaze and wish for healing. But the master says to the Teddy to his great surprise: "Somebody like you, a real genuine old raggedy stuffed Teddy was discovered recently in England by a collector who had given his whole fortune of many thousand pounds to own someone like you. A specially lovable collector's item like you should stay as it is as far as possible. Let's restore only what's most important, so people can recognize your true worth. And we will manage that easily."

And while Teddy's still rather amused and 'mazed by this new perspective, this new aspect, he is carefully and circumspectly taken in hand by the master and the Teddy feels this big comforting hand that feels like saying: "Let's see how to manage this, let's see how we can make the best out of it."

And at first for sure it is the hands that gradually feel how the master craftsman and his assistants already begin to repair what's most important: First of all they straighten out something on the outside, carefully care for one hurt, then another, then they splint something that is broken and soon you don't know anymore exactly what's being worked on until this very moment: sometimes it seems as though the assistants (assistance) mainly help simply to understand what is on hand and suddenly you realize in the meantime you have somehow experienced progress within or you notice that inner parts are to be re-arranged properly, and in the meantime feel how the external wounds are healing, because they are working on so many things simultaneously with such speed that it is amazing to see how to manage that, how to take time for thorough work to limber up limbs, make members mobile, strengthen and expand internal things and in between even carefully renew and partially replace the old brittle straw stuffing. And during this whole procedure Teddy is being safely held and the master and his helpers make sure that they only repair, refresh and renew, mend and strengthen what is really desirable and where this farsighted master craftsman deems it seems to be really sensible and important.

And finally, after inconceivably long reeling moments of
eternity—

eyes are shining certainly with more self-confidence and
conviction
(as if they want to see how to manage it),
skin, fur and hair feel good and fresh and fair,
numb limbs awake again and members now gain
more and more of their former strength and fitness,
legs stand more sound firm with feet upon the ground.

And finally with the assistants a magnificent mirror is
fetched
so to say "just look into the mirror anyway
and see how your body has become lively and flexible
how it is standing there, head high, straight erect, with hair
how face and skin are fresh and taut (taught) again

with eyes looking forward . . ." and the confident attitude . . . of the old master and his helpers express the attitude: "Let's see how to manage that! Let's see how to make the best of it." And from this upright position and with this confident, steadfast gaze you see eyes looking forward to the things that lie ahead, to free and cheerful times and tasks to come, to one or the other both delicate and difficult matter. And they look at these matters very closely; they observe all the important details that matter. And in some situations they see very well plastically and with good prospects so when some things pass through the mind, it is the very first time that inside comes with confidence: "Let's see how to manage that!" It's the first time you really think: "Let's see how to make the best of it."

And it is really the first time you can also see after a time
that you really do make the best of it!
And while looking and realizing this notice hearing the
master or ownself (sic!) say with this same confidence:
"Let's see how to manage that. . . .
Let's see how to make the best of it . . ."
so that it soon becomes natural and customary to think and to
say:
"Let's see how to manage that to solve this here. . . .
Let's see how to manage that I feel better allround . . .
Let's see how to make the best of it here. . . ."

And, in the meantime, the master has tilted the mirror onto its side slightly facing upwards and is moving it gently to and fro—till the mirror becomes transparent till you can look right through far into the future and with this confident gaze see where and how to get the best out of it—bright prospects—and what you can achieve.

And sometimes you step into these pictures of the future as into an open space or onto a stage and feel how this future feels.

And if something is still not quite right, you can observe another picture changes right until it's really good and then becomes completely light and shining bright. So that you feel really attracted towards it in a way that letssteps (sic!) in the direction be easy and becoming comfortably effortless.

And after you have absorbed everything so the sight of this perspective is familiar, the master moves the mirror a little towards the inside and now it shows all the little steps needed for you have made progress. And so you can take all the time you need to observe and note every single detail so exactly that you can be guided by them later. And teddies like people like looking at good films time and time again and discover something new every time.

But shortly before viewing everything to the very end, they just hear the master craftsman saying farewell: "This mirror is from now on forever your very own mirror. You will always have it at your own disposal for your own use. And you will be able to see yourself in it whenever and however you need it. Let's see when you notice this steadfast, confident gaze looking forward to the future has already become an established automatic habit. Let's see how you make the best of it.

Do come again soon; the door to my workshop is always open to you. See you soon! Goodbye!"

And while the master and his assistants are gradually receding and moving away and drifting off like visions in a dream, Teddy is succeeding and gradually becoming quite clearly conscious of the fact that teddies often forget to remember after dreamy waking dreams and sometimes can become so forgetful and sometimes self-forgetting while humans may be becoming conscious that during awakening it is possible to retain the relaxation and let go of what passed (past). And so here they become more and more aware that holding on tight to the letting go that began here in that with the ability of sitting here and listening to my words it may be possible to feel that after phases of stillness it's always natural to move about a bit, just as in the morning we want to rest for a while, to stay a moment longer with what is already vanishing and what we often vainly tried to hold on to (too). And often on awakening we have that sure feeling that we have dreamt well and are well-rested, restored, full of well being; no alarm clock is ringing, we stir gently, move easily and enjoy for a little longer the transition from the dream to the wakening state till our limbs, indeed all our members, begin to stretch and sometimes see open eyes and return refreshed to the starting point, the outset of our dream journey. Hello . . .

COMMENTS

This is one of the inductions where the language is most carefully considered and polished. Linguistic trance-inducing specialties include rhyming words, the multiple meaning of words as well as the soft confusion of puns and other forms of word-play. The use of homophones, e.g., piece and peace, has been named the Kay—Thompson-Technique by Jeff Zeig. There is also hard confusion in the trance-deepening phase and, symmetrically, in the future pacing part, where sentences do not end properly or parts belong to different sentences. An example: "all the little steps needed for you have made progress." The three words "needed for you" overlap both parts of the sentence with the middle word "for" like a pivot. You can relate: "All the little steps needed for you" . . . or: "All the little steps needed, for you have made progress."

Manfred Prior loves playing with those verbal techniques provoking time distortion and age regression, but the content of the induction with this powerful image of a Teddy being repaired is equally well calculated to be in equilibrium with the firework of techniques. The healing suggestion in the embedded command in various contexts: "See how to manage that, . . . see how to make the best of it" gives confidence that we will manage whatever is necessary.

22

Jeffrey Zeig: Ego Building Through Imagery

COMMENTS

This induction has already become a classic for me. I referred to it repeatedly when planning this book. With regard to the choice of inductions to be included, too, it served as a guide and a textbook for identifying and carrying out a group induction. When Jeff Zeig in his caring way looked at the progress of this book and advised me that the inductions could not stand on their own without comment, because the reader might not understand what is happening, I could reply: "If any, this one can. I'm not going to comment on the wisdom of your main intervention. Into every induction some secret should come—also some clarity."

INDUCTION

In doing group-hypnosis, a therapist cannot really build responsiveness with individuals, and so it's a different form of hypnosis. Because, as I discussed this morning, one of the important things about hypnosis is accessing individual responsiveness. When you work with group-hypnosis, it's more difficult to develop that kind of responsiveness to minimal cues. And yet you can still experience some other things about hypnosis, as for example the focused attention, some of the sensations of dissociation and also some of the internal imagery that can be part of hypnosis. And remember, that part of the process of using hypnosis is to reach people, so that they can leave experiencing themselves as "more" than when they started.

In order to more fully begin, let me ask you to sit in a hypnosis position. That involves putting down your books and papers and adjusting yourselves so that you can be comfortable in your chair. Then, I recommend that you put your feet flat on the floor with your arms against your sides so that your thumbs are not touching in any way.

Now, why ask people to sit in this position? One of the reasons is that you want people to be open, you want them to be open to the experience of learning about their personal abilities in trance. Also, you want to establish a cue, so that this posture can be used in the future. It can be very nice to have a cue in posture that can be used in the future, so that when you find yourself sitting in this position, you can begin to remember some of the hypnosis feelings and some of the hypnosis imagery that will become a part of this experience.

And, you can be interested in having the experience; at the same time you can be interested in learning about the experience. So, the first thing that I would like you to do is to just look up to the top of your head as high as you can, then take a deep breath, close your eyes . . . slowly, exhale, relax your face, and then begin the process of going inside to find certain sensations.

And, those of you who have experience in hypnosis can recognize very quickly some of the developing comfort. And, those of you who are just learning, can just sit back comfortably, listening to the real meaning that some of the suggestions can have for you. Understand that any time that you want to, you can make any of those small adjustments that maximize your capacity to be yourself more . . . absorbed in the experience.

And, you can hear the tone of my voice, and you can actively listen to the tone, and you can recognize full well some of the developing changes. One of the changes you can notice is that after awhile it may seem to you as though your feet were farther away from your head. It may seem to you as if your left shoulder were farther away from your right shoulder. There may be a sensation that your head is balanced in just the right place. And, there can be other changes.

You can look behind your eyes and notice that there is a vast unending expanse of blackness. It can be a little troublesome that there is this vast, empty space. And, you may want to put something in this space. And, it can be a pleasant surprise to notice that your inner mind can begin to supply some depth and some texture. And, as you pay attention to the depth, you might begin to realize that certain colors can become apparent—can become really apparent to you. And, as you pay attention to the colors, it might interest you to notice that there is brightness. And, even though you couldn't really explain it, there can be a familiarity to the colors, that previously you hadn't realized was there. And, in paying attention to the colors you can open your eyes . . . to the fact, that there can be movement to the colors. And in noticing the movement you can realize that there are shapes and patterns, and how nice it is to sit back and let yourself focus on the developing changes because as you do that, just listening, there are other changes. You can notice the changes in your breathing rhythm and the fluttery feeling around your eyelids; the alteration in your pulse rate and your breathing rate; and, you might also notice, that somehow you synchronized your breathing rate, so that your breathing rate is very similar to the breathing rate of other people, perhaps people next to you. And, all along you can realize that you are becoming a bit more absorbed in the experience, so that after a while it can feel to you as though you become a bodiless mind, just drifting in space, drifting in time.

And, many pleasant memories can return, memories that can begin to come alive. Realizing, that as you remember certain experiences, you can . . . begin to reexperience certain memories. And, the colors . . . you might notice, that one of the colors has a rough edge to it, and that other colors have gained unexpected depth.

And, it can be interesting to you to transport yourself inside in one of those colors and realign the color, so that the edge that was there before is now straight and firm. And, while you do that, in a moment I'll count from one to ten, so that you can use that count to transport yourself to a room of your own, a place just for you, where you can sit yourself down in an easy chair and feel yourself at home in the easy chair. Nice to feel yourself at home in the easy chair. Recognizing that as I count, you can use this opportunity to count yourself silently along with me.

Beginning the count now: One, just slowly and easily, Two, just slowly and progressively. Feeling yourself, three (free). Four, more alive. Five, to the capacity of your inner mind. Six, to help you learn. Seven, something about your personal capacity to. Eight, be more yourself. Nine, fully absorbed in the experience. Ten, all the way into that room of your own, where you can sit yourself down in the easy chair and be yourself at home in the easy chair.

And look around and explore the room: Notice the darkness, the colors, the patterns, the shapes, the movement in the room, realizing that in a moment something special can happen: When you look toward the door of the room, you can see another "you" standing there, straight and tall. A "you" that represents (and re-presents) the best "you" inside. I think, that when you see that other "you", you can pay special attention to the posture. I think, you can notice that the point in the middle of the breastbone aligns, with the point in the middle of the lips, with the point in the middle of the forehead. It can be pleasant to notice the attitude of that other you, the sureness. So that even though you haven't been in this place before, that other "you" seems secure and at ease, even though the first steps may seem tentative.

So look towards the door; see that other you; notice the posture; take time to really remember. Because, there is something else that you can do, a little bit difficult at first, but I'm sure you will be able to. I would like you to go over to that other you and slip yourself inside that possibly transparent [trance-parent] you, but there also might seem something very solid.

So take the time now, transport yourself inside and get some of the feeling of what it's like to be in that position where the point in the middle of your breastbone, aligns with the point in the middle of your lips, with the point in the middle of your forehead. And, you might want to take some time to memorize those feelings carefully, so that they can become a part of the functioning of your personal reactions.

And, explore the room from inside that other you, the first steps may seem tentative, but there is a certainty about the movement, nice to feel that certainty. Because after a while I'll ask you to reorient yourself, and in the process of reorienting you might want to take some time to really remember in a line that capacity of your inner mind to cue you in to your own ability to be even . . . more absorbed in the experience. Realizing that from time to time (and time and time again) you can find yourself in this position where the point in the middle of your breastbone aligns, with the point in the middle of your lips, aligns with the point in the middle of your forehead. And, then you can realize, that that part is inside, making itself known. But, at other times you might want to consciously align those three points, so that you can consciously get some of those feelings. Understanding that now and then (and again and again) in familiar ways you can take that feeling of having a point in the middle of your breastbone aligned, with the point in the middle of your lips, with the point in the middle of your forehead, here and there, now and then.

So in a moment, to reorient you can take one or two or three easy breaths and stretch yourself and then reorient completely, refreshed and wide awake and alert all over. Just take one or two or three easy breaths, and easily reorient yourself easily.

COMMENTARY

Now let us have a look what happened in that induction of hypnosis. I can give you some stages that I went through in my mind. The first thing that I did, was to orient you to the idea of trance. Before we even started the hypnosis, I did some talking with you to ease you into the trance experience. In my preinduction talk I wanted you to get into the mentality that trance is imminent. So the first thing to do was to orient you to the idea of trance.

The second thing was to give you a task to carry out, a conscious task to get you into a set of responding. So, I asked you to put aside your notes and sit in a posture that I suggested. At first I was interested in getting conscious responsiveness. And, in an individual session especially, as I got that conscious responsiveness, I would learn something about the individual personality. Does the person respond very quickly? Do they carry out the suggestion just as I asked? How did they insert their individuality into the situation? So I'm watching for information. Working with an individual that information would guide my induction. The diagnosis continues throughout the trance. It doesn't just stop at the beginning. You continue to diagnose as you work.

The third step in my sequence was to elicit absorption in an internal experience: I gave you a number of choices. You could be absorbed in internal sensations that I suggested like the sensation that your left shoulder is farther away from your right shoulder, or that your head is farther away from your feet. Also, there were the visual images that I suggested of colors. Let's think about those physical images. They were suggested carefully. What does it mean, when your left shoulder is farther away from your right shoulder? It means that your shoulders are broader. Now in English the metaphor of broad shoulders is used to have a certain meaning. Is it the same in Italian? Yes. So you use your images. Carefully. You have a direction that you want a person to start thinking and so you use certain images.

And the same underlying meaning is true of "your head is farther away from your feet." If you experience yourself taller and broader, you're experiencing yourself as being a bigger person which was one of the goals of the induction, namely, ego building. So seeded carefully at the beginning of the induction was the end result. The purpose of the induction was that people would feel themselves to be greater, as a unique person. If I know that that's the projected endpoint, I can seed it very early. Seeding is a very important technique. In the social psychology literature they talk about the concept of priming behavior. Priming is a very effective technique of influence. So you move towards your goal by seeding it and moving in small steps.

I'll repeat the stages of the induction: Orient to trance. Give the people a task to follow. The third step is to absorb them in a memory of any kind of internal experience to the point at which the experience becomes automatic: The sensations just happen; the visual images just happen. At the same time, you're seeding into the future.

When I talked about being a bodiless mind, this meant to establish a neutral state, a transition state between the induction and the utilization. It's like when you are in a car, you can't go from reverse to first gear. Although you don't recognize it, you always go first into neutral.

Throughout the process besides using seeding, I am also using some confusion. Just a mild confusion by shifting images rapidly, by pausing on words, so that people don't fully feel on balance. The fourth step is to establish dissociation. The fifth step was to ratify. Actually this time I ratified first and then I did the dissociation. So the steps are not always done necessarily in linear order.

Now, what do I mean by ratification? Ratification is a technique of pointing out changes. For example I said, "Your breathing rate is changed; your pulse rate is changed; your blood pressure is changed." What's the implication of those statements? There are two implications: One is, you are responding, and another implication is, that things are different now. But I didn't say, "You are responding" or "Things are different now." I just pointed out the changes. Erickson maintained that the simplest induction technique is to get people absorbed in a memory, and then point out the changes that happened as they absorb themselves in the memory.

The next step, the sixth step, is to elicit resources of the patient. Often, the resources are hypnotic phenomena like age regression or time distortion.

The next step is to develop that resource. That's harder to do in a group induction, because each person will have a different resource. But when you are working with an individual, you look for the hypnotic resource. The next part is to initiate the main therapeutic intervention, remembering that all along you want to continue to elicit active responses from the patient. Throughout the entire process you are seeding, using confusion and getting responses. How many of you opened your eyes during the trance? [Show of hands] Why did so many people open their eyes? Because I said so? But did I really say so? It was an ambiguous statement. I talked about opening your eyes to an idea. But I hesitated just enough to make it a minimal cue—an injunction—because during the trance I also wanted you to learn about your responsiveness. I didn't have to tell you to close your eyes. You do that, because you wanted to.

In conjunction with the therapy step (and in this case the therapy was based on a visual image, the image of seeing yourself in the room), I would do a few things. First you develop the resource; then you apply the main intervention; then you check out the therapy to see if it works. Maybe you ask the person to have the image now and to indicate that they are really getting it. The next step is to give them process instructions—instructions as to how they can use the resource in the future. The last step is the step of termination. In termination you give a person choices. "Take one or two or three deep breaths and reorient completely rested and refreshed."

23

Ernest Rossi: Private Therapeutic Work in Public

COMMENTS

Ernest Rossi's work is really something between a group induction and an individual therapy session, or an example of how you can use a group induction to select a demonstration subject for individual therapy. The theme of his congress contribution was: "Learning the Indirect Forms of Hypnotic Suggestion." And so it is meaningful, too, to call his procedure an indirect group healing process, because the demonstration subject serves as a crystallization medium, helping the others in the audience with their own processes. This can easily be seen in the last section, where Ernest Rossi talks about the mutual healing process between therapist and client. Of course, this also works for a whole group. With his profound honesty and his courageous openness, Ernest Rossi allows a deep relationship to his client to develop and this spreads to all the people in the audience (learning from a model).

INDUCTION

I would like to give a demonstration of giving the power to the unconscious rather than to my ego or the conscious mind of anyone in the audience. Some of you will want to be observers, some of you may wish to explore the possibility of participation. I will demonstrate a very simple procedure that can work with an audience of this size as well as with one person in your office.

Those of you who would like to explore the possibility of allowing your unconscious to have a therapeutic experience this afternoon by serving as a demonstration subject should put your pencils down and put your hand out about like so. And know that we are going to make requests of your unconscious rather than your conscious mind. I would like to have you begin by simply tuning into yourself, and I would like to ask your unconscious some questions that can be answered by movements of that hand. Already I can see some of you whose hand is moving up a little bit all by itself.

Now, if your unconscious has an important therapeutic need for coming to this conference this afternoon, that hand will lift just a little bit all by itself to say "yes" to you. And if it's possible for you to achieve a therapeutic result privately within yourself, that hand will lift a little bit more. Otherwise the hand will get heavier and want to fall.

That is our art this afternoon to do some private therapeutic work in public. So simply allowing your hand to continue floating higher and higher as your unconscious begins to review the sources of that problem. And perhaps your unconscious will allow your conscious mind to recognize what's happening within, or perhaps it will say nothing this afternoon. So what you receive consciously at this point really does not matter. Only that hand lifting up saying "yes" is the important issue.

As the hand continues going up, you can begin to turn into your breathing. For those of you going into trance, your breathing will seem to become easier, softer, and that hand can continue lifting. For many of you there will be a delicious feeling of comfort, as the parasympathetic system becomes more dominant, as the hypothalamus normalizes its function, reducing stress, potentiating the immune system all by itself. So simply allowing to continue with comfort, and for some of you your eyes have closed already, and that automatically increases the alpha of your brain, simply allowing that you continue with comfort. And continuing with comfort . . .

And as the demonstration continues, the unconscious within some of you will allow you to stand comfortably almost as if you are naturally awake. And if you find yourself getting ready to stand, that could be an indication, that it will be safe for you to come forward and serve as a demonstration subject in front of the group. Others will feel no such preparatory movements to stand, meaning that your unconscious prefers to allow you to stay there in your seat, continuing your inner therapeutic work entirely on your own, taking up a few hints from words that I say and utilizing them in your own creative way.

Those of you, who feel those preparatory movements to stand, I would like to have you stand at this time. Very, very fine! And those of you, who are standing, I'm going to request in a moment or two, that your eyes open automatically and you pretend, that you are normally awake and find yourself comfortably walking forward to the stage. That's right!

Others who have not stood up, can continue observing as well as walking privately with them . . . Simply continuing with comfort . . . And I can tell to the audience on many levels . . . I can say, for example . . . that when Erickson did his deepest and most profound experimental work, he used to allow his subjects to continue going into trance for at least 20 minutes, before doing experimental hypnotic work. He felt that 20 minutes at least were needed to affect the profound physio-psychological changes for deep somnambulistic trance phenomena. This does not mean that every therapist needs to take this length of time, many therapeutic effects can be achieved much more rapidly. But for the deep experimental work Erickson would take at least 20 minutes and sometimes hours to allow the trance to deepen. So simply allowing that comfort to deepen, allowing the unconscious to review what needs to be done.

And there can be memories; there can be dreams; there can be emotions; there can be a review of early memories . . . And just what those memories are, the unconscious does not always let us know, so that a valid hypnotic work is always a surprise for the ego. The ego is always enriched. How different this is from allowing the ego to limit what the work shall be!

So that the indirect forms of suggestion, I feel, could be better termed to be "the language of human facilitations." In hypnotherapeutic work we seek to enrich consciousness by helping it break its arbitrary limitations, what Erickson called "learn limitations."

We all have important developmental gaps, Erickson maintained, and the eight last years of his life, when I worked with him, I saw him work with many, many professional psychiatrists and psychologists, sometimes for an hour and a half, sometimes an afternoon, sometimes for a week, and always the orientation was the same: What are the developmental gaps in this highly educated person? What are the things that need to be learned?

For example, my last afternoon with Dr. Erickson, just a few weeks before he died, were videotaped by Dr. Moore, as Dr. Erickson attempted to help me with a developmental problem, the problem was that I lacked confidence in working with touch in hypnosis. I lacked confidence in taking the verbal initiative. I learned during that last session the profound effect of some early childhood training. For example, when my father would say to me, when I was a little boy, "Who said you could talk?" At the dinner table my father liked to be quiet. If I dared to say something, he would give me a terribly withering look as only an Italian man can do, and sometimes mother said, "Did I say you could talk?" [tape changes]

I know, when the lids of the eyes are ready to close, that is very characteristic of someone going into trance. I know, that it's very hard and difficult for him to keep his eyes open. Patients try to open them occasionally but then close them with a sigh of relief. Will it be O.K. to guide your hand upward?

-Yes.-

And that hand and arm can have a life of its own, where it can express in its own movements in ways that your conscious mind may or may not understand to solve an essence of a problem that you are resolving here today. That's right! And simply allowing that hand to have a life of its own. And so we see a spontaneous movement beginning to happen. That's right! And as that hand is moving all by itself, will your unconscious also allow your head to nod? Very fine! So that when your unconscious wants to say "yes," it can nod your head all by itself?—And will that really be all right? Very fine!

And as the unconscious continues working on that problem, what will happen to your hand, as my hand approaches it? Will there be a numbness or will there be a sense of attraction? Or will there be a heightened sensitivity? A weight? A lightness? That's right! You see, I'm allowing the unconscious to make the decisions. I'm allowing the unconscious to choose its own ideal sensory response in a way that will in some symbolic manner be related to the resolution of the inner problem. That's right! And now, will it be O.K. for the unconscious to allow you to not only nod your head automatically, but also to speak automatically? Will that be O.K.? And is it possible for you to speak at this time? And can you tell me, what that hand has been experiencing? And tell me, what sensation happened, as I approached closer and closer with my hand?

S.: I feel that hand grows warm.

Rossi: And I'm going to ask your unconscious to continue with that pleasurable warmth, that pleasurable floating, as your conscious wonders, in what way this is symbolic of the problem that is resolving itself. Very fine! I would like you to continue with that . . . you can review in memories of struggles as a child. That's right! That's right! As an adolescent, as a young man in his 20's, up to the present time. And I would like to have you say to this young boy, that young man, who may or may not look like you, I would like to have you say to him the words that he needs to hear. That's right! Simply hear them quietly, privately within your own mind. And I would like to have you see him beginning to grow up now, day by day, month by month, year by year, hearing what he needs to hear. That's right! And is that adolescent hearing the words he needs to hear?

S.: Yes.

Rossi: And simply continue for another few moments. That's right! And as he continues for a few more moments, there is an almost visible, hardly perceptible deep sigh of relief; I can see the minimal cues of relaxation, comfort, the tears, that are almost ready to come, as he has access to the source of his problem and does the therapy for himself privately within. And that really is happening, is it not? And you could see the emotional involvement does not permit him even to speak. He falls back with a simple head nod. Most of his creative energy is going inside doing the therapeutic work.

That reminds me a little bit of a dream. Also during dreams outer action is inhibited, so that inner work can be focused upon. You all heard the old folk saying: Empty barrels make the most noise. When profound inner work is being done, when a client is obviously involved doing rich inner work, we allow this work to proceed with as little interference as possible. That's right. It's continuing. I don't know how many of you can see it, but now a minimal fold is appearing on his face, a minimal facial cue of distress coming in, very different from a couple of moments ago, when he was close to tears and gratitude for doing some inner work. So now I see a new movement is taking place, and perhaps this is the moment for me to make a new therapeutic intervention. That's right! And is it important for me to know anything? And is that going well?

S.: My feeling is that I am still lacking what I lacked in my childhood. [S. reports a dream lost in recording]

Rossi: Can you say what that's like? That's beautifully expressed: a soft hand introducing you into the world. Can you tell me more what that means?

S.: My father was not there. I feel that everybody can see my developmental gaps.

Rossi: Can you appreciate the honesty of this profound emotional truth?

S.: Yes.

So here we have a true portrait of this person's developmental status. The true need for father support, the true need for relief to find himself avoiding a mother's overdemanding attitude. And we see the beginning of the self-therapy that's taking place. There is no neurotic problem here, there is a simple, honest, clear recognition of just where he is emotionally. And he is already making therapeutic efforts to reveal himself to the world, this true picture of himself, and that is the function, the creative function of the dream to help consciousness recognize a true inner situation. The fact that the symbolism is so clear in a dream is another indication of the essential clarity and strength of this young man. His very presence here in front of this group we see now is part of the therapeutic process. That he is carrying on in himself for sometime as recently as a couple of days ago.

Now you want to know, what indirect suggestion is? Consider all the things I said from my induction to this audience, consider my theoretical remarks on the nature of hypnosis. Apparently I was giving an intellectual presentation. I was talking about giving primacy to the unconscious and allowing the unconscious needs to have prominence here today. Consider exactly how his responses, his words, his experience here today are following my theoretical remarks. In the guise of giving a theoretical discussion, I was actually giving a series of indirect suggestions for someone's unconscious in the audience to respond in just this way. To serve as a demonstration subject certainly was primarily to have a healing experience, so that we are serving the needs of his unconscious and the total development of this personality. So this, for me, is the essence of therapeutic hypnosis.

And is that still going well? So you see, he has started to give himself therapeutic suggestions. You heard of the technique prescribing the symptom? He is doing that for himself. And are you familiar with the concept of prescribing the symptom? Were you aware that you were using this technique on yourself?

S.: Yes.

Rossi: So he was not responding on an intellectual level, but on a more spontaneous imagistic, truly imaginary emotional level, only on reflection can he see the intellectual. Is this correct? It simply came to you. And you can see with the spontaneous smile when he told us about wearing the pants with holes, that this truly has a therapeutic meaning for him. It is satisfying, it is fun, it is humorous. These are all indications, that a piece of therapeutic work has satisfactorily been completed. Now tomorrow he may or he may not wear pants with holes. Whether he does or not, the therapy continues nonetheless.

It reminds me of a similar quandary I had within myself about whether or not I should really wear my hypothalamus shirt this morning. Even when I went to the lecture this morning, I was not sure what to do this morning. I preferred to let my unconscious give me the appropriate feeling at the appropriate time. Apparently it was done well: the audience laughed. It may have seen contrived. Nonetheless, I made a point. I increased my personal skills in front of an audience to do such an outlandish thing.

What am I doing now? Have I forgotten the client and go on into my narcissistic ruminations as I talk about my hypothalamus shirt? Or am I still giving him indirect suggestions, letting him know that I personally gain strength by actually carrying out the fantasy? But trusting my own unconscious enough to leave it to the last moment.

Am I still giving him indirect suggestions? So as another therapist talks about himself . . . he is really giving indirect suggestions. This is something, that most people don't understand about Erickson even today, when they criticize him. And what's happening now? The smile indicates—what does the smile indicate?

So to be able to say "it gains strength" for you to be in front of the audience. I see many profound significances in our work together this afternoon, because although I had a father, he was too autocratic. I, too, miss the supporting father. Perhaps that's why I worked so well and hard with Erickson. He was a supportive and nurturing father. And even today, five years after his death, as I continue to edit his papers, seminars and workshops, is this really selfish dedication or my continuing to give myself support. So my professional work is nurturing and supporting me, healing the developmental gaps of the lack of a supporting father, just as this is the case with this young man.

Am I still giving indirect suggestions? I am actually functioning on two levels. I am really talking the truth about myself and in speaking the truth, I am healing myself, and yet, on another level, it's also healing for this young man. So I am using indirect suggestion, implication, two levels of communication at least. If I do that, do I feel manipulative? I do not feel I'm manipulating his mind, even though I'm making available healing. All my stories can be taken as metaphors, but they all have profound truth in my personal experience. I do not presume to make up metaphors. I only talk the truth of my real life experience, because I know, my patient's unconscious can read the truth and separate out the falseness. I know that many failures in hypnotherapy come from the egotistical presumption of the hypnotherapists, who feel they can operate and manipulate a patient's mind and not be engaged in a truly mutual healing experience.

And I notice this little movement of his head. Can you say what this was? So these are ways of releasing the tension. So now we see a spontaneous movement into another form of bodily healing, releasing muscle tension. Once again I did not direct this therapeutic process. I simply picked up a minimal cue, a spontaneous piece of behavior. And once again I facilitated by talking about it, by supporting it. That is, every client has within himself the healing power. If we can simply be simple, humble but careful observers, we can provide the most inside force, support and facilitation for the healing process. So I am an observer and a facilitator. If you call this being a hypnotherapist or just a nice guy, I leave it up to you, too. And how is it going now?

S.: I want to say hello. Thank you very much!

—Thank you very much!

24

Ernst Petzold and Wolfgang Herzog: The Black Eye

COMMENTS

Some family therapists know that hypnosis happens in every family naturally. Ericksonians also know that "family members create a dual, triple or quadruple induction on the therapist" (Lankton & Lankton, 1986, p.26). So it is quite natural to utilize this fact and work with a "therapeutic counterinduction" (Rittermann). That is what Ernst Petzold and Wolfgang Herzog did with an "Anorexia-family" in their family-confronting therapy.

One condition for the therapeutic setting is the presence and participation of the entire family during the sessions. These were held at 4-6 weekly intervals in conjunction with a co-therapist and one-way screen work. The identified patient (I.P.) was already in such a really alarming state that hospitalization was being considered. Ernst Petzold closes his commentary, which is presented in shortened form in the introduction to the "Black Eye" induction, with the words: "The following should be read only by those who themselves have worked with anorexia-nervosa families, and who know the desperate, magnificent endeavours of S. Minuchin (in "Family Lunch") or the Mailand Group with M. Selvini (see, for example, "Paradox and Antiparadox") and are familiar with the 'absurd' therapy of a Carl Whitaker or the provocative therapy of Frank Farrelly, with whom Pet. had worked together fairly intensely during the previous weeks."

INDUCTION

[Transcript of (part of) a Family Session as part of an anorexia treatment.]

The Punt family had applied to us (i.e., the Psychosomatic Out-Patient Department of the Heidelberg University Medical Clinic) half a year previously and named the problem as being the anorexia of Vera, a 16-year-old, who despite previous therapeutic attempts weighed only 36 kilograms (172 cm tall). We agreed upon an out-patient family therapy of 11 sessions, in which all family members participate. These are:

Father, 45 years old, commercial clerk, slim, taciturn, slow-speaking;

Mother, 43 years old, housewife, plump, talkative, "pretties herself up" carefully for the sessions;
Mona, 20 years old, and
Anna, 19 years old, both are preparing to take the German School Leaving Exam that qualifies for university entrance;
Vera, 16 years old, who still attends school, is the I.P., and sits in the session with lowered head and with lips pressed tightly together;
Toby, 10 years old, a later child, a nice "Clever Dick," and the family's "sunshine."

The first few sessions were used for the joining phase. The parents were pressing for our expert opinion and advice as to how Vera could now gain weight, whereas our answer was that even babies already know how much food they require, that Vera can therefore decide this on her own, though on the other hand the family council can however at any time *unanimously* decide on hospitalization, if Vera cannot manage alone.

Through the use of family sculptures, working with the family history as well as that of the families of origin, the perceptual and experiential space within the family's relational network gradually widened out. As a working hypothesis, it could be stated that in both families of origin, stable figures for the father role had been missing. Whereas the mother had never known her father, who was killed during the war, and was brought up at the maternal grandfather's, the father's parents had become divorced when he himself was 10 years old. Now Toby, the youngest, was at this critical age.

The situation at the beginning of the sixth session was strained to the utmost: external signs were Vera's further loss of weight to 32 kg and the clearly visible black eye of the father. In the first part of the session Pe. mentioned the absence of Mona, whereby the family had jeopardized the whole setting. A further confrontation with reality was in relation to the finances. The family was then asked what they would like to discuss during this session. The "healthy" members wanted to talk about Vera, the "ill one." Vera herself made the decisive statement, "I want to have courage for life again." Toby, the youngest, had realized that the parents' cohesion is crucial, and suggested symbolically in play that the father and mother move closer together.

The mother's share of the talking showed sufficiently the maternal dominance in this anorexia family. She demonstrated a classical symptom induction, as her words conjure up the very state that ostensibly is complained of with such verbosity. She wanted to know what she had done wrong, falsely, with regard to Vera and answered her own questions herself. By humorous terminology and transformation ("Verasation," "fathering," "my falsification") Pe. tried to dam and redirect the torrent of words and resolutely resolve the family clinch around the I.P. Converting the mother's "What was false, what have I done wrong" to "my falsification" with a twinkle in the eye, allowed her to drop the paralyzing burden of guilt. The question of guilt was also the main theme when Pe. brought the father's black eye into the arena. "It was nobody's fault," was the father's spontaneous answer—his next sentence, though, referred it to the mother, who had caused the black eye "without meaning to." The inability to solve conflicts attributed to anorexia families is explicable, as in this example, also by the fact that the real reasons for the clash may, right from the beginning, not even become conscious.

The family was undecided about the question of Vera's hospitalization. The therapist was expected to solve the dilemma and make a decision. Pe. showed that he did not intend to enter this trap and this successfully resulted in the father hesitatingly siding with Vera, who did not want to go to hospital. This achieved an important immediate objective: Vera, who had had great difficulty finding out her father's standpoint, because usually the mother got in the way and stood between them, had now obtained open support. The discussion in the pause, which took place with the colleagues behind the one-way screen, brought out the discrepancy between the sensible statements of the individual family members and the lack of unanimity about the next step still. The feelings of the therapists mirrored the family conflict.

H. to Pe. "You do everything alone!"

Pe. to H. "You don't help me!"

The team decided that the family really did require the playful elements in the situation (Vera spoke of "joyful living" or "love of life"); on the other hand, there must be a clear decision reached about how matters should progress. The therapists agreed to assume roles in a way that would loosen the control and checking within the family. They decided namely on disrupting the previous pattern of roles. The younger (H.) wanted—with the aid of circular questioning—to obtain an impression of the family situation at home. The elder (Pe.) wanted to yield to his playful impulses and, through this, depart from the behavior pattern of a therapist as expected by the family. The therapists also wanted to take a part of the "craziness" over to their side and, as a consequence, the family would gain more space and freedom to become clear about themselves.

Participants:
M.:—Mother, Mrs. Punt
F.:—Father, Mr. Punt
A.:—Anna
V.:—Vera (Index Patient)
To.:—Toby
Pe.:—Ernst Petzold, Therapist
H.:—Wolfgang Herzog, Therapist
B.:—Günter Bergmann, therapist behind the one-way screen

[The door opens, B. appears]

B.: Well, if you people here can't agree now to speak properly, then we back there can't understand a word! We can't manage like this at all!
H.: All right, Günter, go now . . .
Pe.: Now they're starting to make a fuss as well. This is pure hell!

[simultaneously]

A.: . . . just a small room and . . .	Pe.: (to M.) O.K. then, we'll come back to that later.
H.: What would still interest me	But this is important. One must stop

would be how Vera sees the mothering of the father, recently.

A.: (fiddles about with her shoe)
V.: I would say: I find it much better like this. I think it's good, that he's so . . . talk more with him . . . (incomprehensible)
H.: Father?
V.: Yes.

H.: And what does the mothering of the father look like at the moment?
V.: Well, she is more friendly.
H.: Mother is more friendly to F.?
V.: No, M. . . .
H.: You must really concentrate! The question is: What does the mothering of the father look like?

V.: Yes, I'd misunderstood that, too.

H.: If you observe what the mothering of the father is like, how is mother towards father at the moment?

V.: More attentive . . .

simply, finish the falsification.
M.: First of all, one must know: Where is the falsification?
Pe.: Yes, well it's a sham quite obviously when others say plainly and clearly: "I don't want that any more." That's a sign. Isn't it? Then you could just say, "O.K. I don't want to any longer."
M.: Yes, yes, Mona has already said that. But I—I can stand Mona's absence well now. I . . . (incomprehensible) let go . . . Mona is away and I can let go well.
Pe.: Good, congratulations. And where is the problem? You learn from mistakes.
M.: That's true, one learns from mistakes Only through experience. That's probably (points to Ve.) the case with her, too.
Pe.: She learns through experience.
M.: She learns through experience.
Pe.: Right, right, you learn through experience, from experiences with your husband, from experiences with your daughter Mona, with your daughter Anna, from experience with Vera, from experience with Toby. You learn. Important!
M.: Yes. Only with advice and instructions, you can't change things though.
Pe.: There you are. No problem then.
M.: Well, I don't quite know exactly what you mean.
Pe.: I wanted to talk with you over the topic, what I said, "I want to talk with you about falsification." Falsification must stop. Recently I was in Lübeck. In the Church of Mary there twenty years ago—I don't know whether you have read about it—when it was being restored and renovated, they discovered really fabulous, really super, just . . . ravingly fantastic frescoes. What was it? An artist—Marsha?—I don't know exactly. What had happened was that a highly

(incomprehensible) . . .

H.: Where do you notice that?
V.: Well, first of all when talking, and for example, yesterday I noticed,—normally mother would have disagreed, and there she just agreed. For F. had told M. then what she had done wrong, told her her mistakes . . .
—now it's gone, I don't remember any more . . .
H.: It is sometimes hard, thoughts disappear sometimes. But when you concentrate . . .
V.: Ah, yes I know: that she had before just not seen to one's going to bed earlier.
H.: That means that F. would like M. to set clearer limits for Toby, so that he goes to bed . . . (incomprehensible) . . . that he sets clear limits.
V.: (wants to speak)

talented young man had simply painted frescoes up on it. And all admired the fantastic super frescoes from the Middle Ages. Wasn't true. Was the newest modern art. Falsification. Faker. Forgery. Then people stopped, finish, full stop. Now the Church of Mary is like it really was. In other words; one must stop falsifying then when one realizes it's a mistake. Vera, for example doesn't know that it's a mistake—if one wants to live—if one doesn't eat. For one must eat, then one needs something to eat. That's very clear, indeed. No one can live without eating, that's clear enough, isn't it? When V. says: "I want some more," give her something to eat. Don't say anything at all. And when they are hungry, then, then let them—F. can do that, can't he? You really don't need to do everything on your own.

H.: You'll get a chance afterwards, O.K.? And when you see everything now the other way round: What does the fathering of the mother look like? . . . (All are silent. Anna looks at the clock.)
H.: It's so quiet here, here one can't even have a quiet thought . . .
Pe.: Now there's one point that interests me. Is it Anna's turn now or Vera's?
H.: Vera's.
Pe.: Why not Toby's?
H.: That's a good possibility . . .
Pe: Here, why not—you have just (to T.) got a piece of bread from me: What does the fathering of the mother look like?

H.: You must concentrate clearly, if you are clearly concentrated you can answer the question, too. You, (to A.) too, can answer that!

T.: Uh, what? . . .

Pe.: How does the fathering of the mother look like? You don't need to bother in the least if both speak here, do you?

H.: It goes in turn, that's important.

T.: Yes, all right. But I don't get it.
Pe.: What, you don't get what a fathering

H.: You can begin . . .
H.: You can report to us very clearly what you have noticed.
H.: That's important to us . . .

H.: Can't anybody help him with that?
A.: I would say that at the moment—the contact between us is better, also that from my father to my mother.
H.: That is indeed a very important point.
A.: Yes, that there's no more such loud talk, not so much quarreling any more, but otherwise . . . otherwise often loud answers came, given in a strict tone . . .

H.: And . . . we do that sometimes, too. We are indeed also strict sometimes, and here it is sometimes loud, too. That mustn't necessarily be bad. The question is: How do you know what M. likes? From what do you see that? How can you tell that your mother likes that? How do you feel that?

looks like?
Pe.: You're a crafty one, you smart aleck! What does the fathering of Toby look like?
T.: Yes . . .
T.: I don't get it.
Pe.: Don't get it?
T.: Naw . . .
Pe.: Then I'll tell you. Come over here. That's the mother. You take her now. Put her in your place. Take her!
T.: (takes M. by the hand, takes her to his seat and puts her there, next to F.)
Pe.: And now, look whether F. does that properly, whether that is a proper fathering of the mother. Do that. How does F. do a proper fathering, how does he do that with you? Do it as if it were you where Mummy's sitting now.
T.: Huh?
Pe.: I'll help you, you needn't be at all afraid. How does it look now: the woman who is sitting there now, is called Toby Punt. And you can have this Toby Punt fathered now. What does father do when he fathers you?
T.: Strokes me . . .
Pe.: Good, then, take his hand and do it.
T.: (places F.'s arm around M.)
Pe.: Is that right?
T.: Yes.
Pe.: That's the fathering of the mother, come, let's look at it from here. Is that a good fathering? Or can one do it better, hm? Now some mothering of F.
T.: oh . . . , oh . . .
M.: (to T.) The opposite way round.
Pe.: That was a falsification again. Both begin with p: Prompting and Ph–alsification.
M.: Yes, "both begin with P."
T.: (put M.'s arm around F.)

Vera can also answer.
V.: . . . (incomp.) . . .
H.: M. likes it then when F. puts his arm around her . . .
A.: Yes.
V.: Yes, I suppose so.
H.: That is a good observation, isn't it? Perhaps you have others . . .

M.: Very good.
Pe.: And now do some mothering—is that right? O.K.?
T.: Yes—she should stroke him.
Pe.: Then show her how.
T.: (guides M.'s hand in stroking movements over father's head, now M. strokes F.'s head)
Pe.: Atta boy! You did that fine!
T.: (pulls M. out of his chair.)
Pe.: Oho, out—that's my place!
M.: (sits down on her chair)
T.: (sits down on his chair)

A.: Yes . . . be friendly to each other . . .
H.: From what do you notice that mother likes that?
A.: (incomp.) . . .
H.: Ah, I see. (to Pe.) Umm—we should change places . . .
Pe.: We must change places. (Both change over) Oh—I haven't anything left to eat. I'll fetch myself something to eat. Is anyone else here hungry? Nobody more hungry?
H.: P'raps we could do something a bit bigger some time, p'raps a proper meal. But what? What could we cook?
Pe.: Cordon bleu -
H.: Cordon bleu is good. Hors-d'oeuvre - (appetizer)?
Pe.: Real turtle soup.
H.: No, we can't do that to the poor animals. I'm against that. But a really delicious Parma ham . . .
Pe.: Parma ham . . .
H.: But more hors-d'oeuvre variety!
Pe.: Yes, melons.
H.: Melons, exactly.
Pe.: Golden honey melons.
H.: As Günter always does them . . . But soup's not bad either—but what soup?
Pe.: Turtle . . .
V.: No turtle—tomato is better . . .
Pe.: Shark . . . sharkfin . . . something special—mad—fantastic . . . bizarre . . . that you can sip daintily or lap it up, sucking noisily
H.: Well, I think shark . . . (incomprehensible) . . . shark is good.
Pe.: All right, then: Parma ham with melons, sharkfins . . . hm?
H.: We'll make of course various main courses—cordon bleu is already very good. (V. looks around, somewhat confused, uncertain)
Pe.: Croquettes with it . . .

H.: Exactly! We'll do that then, one after the other, so they can leave themselves time and eat that one after the other. So not everything gobble—gobble—gobble all mixed up . . .
Pe.: Something good to drink as well . . .
M.: They're wallowing in food before our eyes . . .
H.: Mousse au Chocolat—that must follow.
Pe.: Or what about a fantastic Indonesian rice meal?
H.: Well, I don't know. There we must agree to the right sequence . . .
Pe.: Ah . . .
H.: What we first . . .
Pe.: But now I'm just considering . . . I'd like really something delicious. Something really quite delicious, epicurean. If Mona were here, she could advise us. She knows that.
H.: Another possibility of course still would be to do it like this: on the first Sunday we could do our first plan and on the second, the rice meal. Or the other way round . . . We could ask Mona which sequence . . .
Pe.: Right, so it could be: on one Sunday, make a French meal with several courses where all can take part, all who want to take part, all who want to have joy in living. Therefore all who want to have joy of life—(half singing) do it like the Frenchmenjoy (sic!)—(claps his lips appreciatively) . . . not only with food . . . But—we were really talking about food. Yes, from the French one can learn a thing or two or more about living—Well, "savre-vivre" (sic!) . . . does anyone here speak French?
T.: Nooo.
F.: (points across to Vera)
Pe.: Vera?
Ve.: But I've only just begun . . .
Pe.: Begun—"savre" is savre? I don't know any French . . . You must tell me if that's right.
A.: I don't know that word.
Pe.: "Vivre?"
A.: To live, life.
Pe.: Right. "Savre?" Well, I think it means "learning life" or "knowing how to live."
H.: Savoir!
A.: Oh yes, to know, knowledge.
Pe.: To know—savoir! Right, thank you!
H.: There we are back again at our beautiful banquet, or fantastic feast.
Pe.: The banquet comes then to . . . (incomprehensible) . . .
T.: We could eat a sucking pig.
Pe.: Sucking pig . . . roast porkling . . . that's an idea, a suggestion for a third Sunday.
H.: The third Sunday.
Pe.: The third Sunday: already on order.
H.: But I'm absolutely positive that Günter must be there—he likes eating, doesn't he? (B. pops his head round the door)
B.: I'll tell you something: It's real torture there behind the screen when you can't make up your minds together about what you want to eat. Behind there, you get really rageingly

ravenous, raving hunger! That's the result of that: *we* get hungry! *We* can't come in! Indeed, you two are in this here together . . . (disappears again)

Pe.: He didn't hear, get that, that he can share Toby's sucking pig—he didn't hear this. Oh well, let's continue. What comes the following Sunday?

H.: I like Chinese . . .

Pe.: Chinese—Peking duck?

H.: Have you (to all present) ever made that? When you have the duck—that's for the first—the thing of foremost importance: then one must first make a little cut behind, sort of slash in the skin, and then with an air pump blow the air under the skin. That rises up and so becomes really crackly, crisp and crusty! Well, it's mad, but it really works! You think perhaps: Hm—that won't work. You think, it won't work—but just a little slash, snip, and then the air pump.

Pe.: Know-how! Not only French, but Indonesian, and Chinese now as well. Know-how! Therefore: Air pump in, so it beautifully bellies out and is scrumptiously crunchy, crisp and crackly. And then one must brush it over, or not?

H.: Exactly. With a sort of marinade of sherry, and a soya sauce must go in, too, and honey. And that becomes really brown and crackling. A stuffing of course . . .

Pe.: Chestnuts . . .

M.: Toby's mouth is already watering—drooling. (laughs.)

Pe.: Raisins or sultanas . . .

H.: And of course there's still the food, the meal where you don't need the air pump. Therefore the good traditional German . . . I don't know . . . do you like béchamel potatoes?

Pe.: Mm, I'm just crazy on them, I could just live on them happily. Do you like them?

H.: Béchamel potatoes—we cooked them once in peaceful Greece for people who had treated us before with fish that they had just caught from the sea. And they wanted to give us great enjoyment. And we cooked béchamel potatoes. And then suddenly a friend of the family had to visit his ill father in hospital. That means . . .

Pe.: You know, I think they're getting really envious. They're already jealous . . . and we'll stop now. Four meals . . . Shall we go to them, or shall we come to you?

M.: Well, I don't know what you mean now? For a meal, or what?

Pe.: Well, we don't want to make you any more jealous. We've just exchanged plans about what we're going to eat on the four Sundays coming. That's clear enough, indeed.

M.: (laughs) Then tell your wives that—let's see if they cook that for you . . .

H.: Well, I must pop in to Günter.

Pe.: And ask whether he still . . . whether he still

H.: Hm . . . (nods)

Pe.: Whether he still wants anything. Right. Then we'll go now. Mr. Herzog will go to Günter—and have you anything else for us you would like to talk over with us? Toby's taken over the responsibility, O.K.?

(Both go out.)

(Cut)

COMMENTS

Double inductions lend themselves as a natural method particularly for family therapy. Here we have, in the first part, a dual induction with a naive cotherapist (using) family members as "unknowing cohypnotists" (Lankton & Lankton, 1986, p.181). As Ernst Petzold has the mother concentrate totally on him, a chance for the index-patient Vera to talk, opens up. After this, the authors develop a spontaneous therapeutic dual-induction to counter the "destructive utilization of trance capacities" (Ritterman, 1983, p.37). They help by provoking a healing chaos in this rigid family and talking seductively about food, joy of life, the *joie de vivre* of the French: sexual and social components enter here. This sixth session was the critical session and brought the turning point for this closed family system. There were five more sessions. Two years after the therapy had ended, Vera had gained 18 pounds and her sister had lost 18 pounds, true equilibrium! The right balance!

25

Sandra Sylvester: Self-Healing

COMMENTS

Sandra Sylvester clarifies the insight that it is so very necessary for us to care for ourselves. Which professionals regularly do their own meditation or trance work for their own personal benefit? Sometimes we expect this from our patients who are visibly in a state of need. But only when we are able to care for ourselves prophylactically and hold the way to our resources free from weeds, are we able to help others to find their way to their own resources. I believe it would be of benefit to all of us professionals if we could use Sandra Sylvester's healing image for our everyday meditation to purify and prepare ourselves for our work.

INDUCTION

It has been my experience, that those of us in the helping professions: medicine, mental health, counseling, spend our days serving other people. Our patients come to us with whatever it is that they cannot handle in their own lives and bring it to us. We listen to them, try to be as fully present to them as we can, and then help them access the resources within themselves to handle their presenting problem. But, just as the shoemakers children have holes in their shoes, we in the helping professions often do not take the time to nurture ourselves, to allow ourselves to get the same kind of care that we are so willing to give to others. Therefore, the theme for this particular induction is personal healing, personal nurturing.

Please sit in a position which is poised and balanced and comfortable for you. . . . You can do anything you want with your eyes. Leave them open or closed, whatever is comfortable for you. . . . In a moment, I will ask you to take five deep slow breaths and exhale each one completely. When you get to the fifth breath, take a deep full breath and hold it. At the same time you are holding your breath, roll your eyes back in your head as far as you can, continue holding your breath for a moment or two and then let your breath out, slowly and completely. At the same time you can relax your eyes.

Begin now, taking a deep breath, letting it out fully and completely. . . . Take a second breath, letting it out fully and completely so that the third time you breathe in, you are inhaling fresh new air and taking all the time you need to let it out fully and completely. . . . Take a fourth breath . . . let it out fully and completely. Now take a fifth breath and hold it. At the same time roll your eyes back in your head as far as you can. Slowly let go of your breath and relax your eyes. Continue breathing normally and easily, so that each time you exhale, you can let the tension drain out of your body. Let the tension leave your body through your fingers and toes, spill on to the carpet, seep through the carpet into the earth where the tension can seep into the molten core of the earth and be transformed into pure light. Feel that each time you exhale, you are a little more comfortable, a little more relaxed than you were a moment ago. Throughout this induction, if you feel tension creeping back into your body, come back to your breathing, reminding yourself to let go of tension each time you exhale.

Next, feel the coolness of the air when you inhale, and feel the warmth of the air as you exhale. . . . Imagine, the warm air of your exhalation going to any muscles in your body which are tight. Imagine the warm air warming those tight muscles. And those tight muscles becoming soft . . . and warm . . . and heavy. Continue to breathe in cool air and breathe out warm air through any part of your body which continues to hold on to tension, allowing yourself to give that part of your body a little bit of extra care by warming that part of your body with warm air, feeling that part of your body becoming soft and loose and heavy.

Know, that at this moment there is nothing special for you to do. Know that, for these few moments taken out of your busy day there are no demands being placed upon you, . . . no expectations, . . . That for these few moments, there is no one to please, . . . no one to satisfy. . . . These moments are moments where you can be in solitude, . . . moments in contact with your inner self, . . . where you can begin to allow your sense of comfort to become quite profound, going to the core of your being.

Today I would like to suggest a theme for your consideration, a theme which has been used for millennia as an image of healing, . . . the image of warm oil. Warm oil, as you know, has always been used as a balm of the sick, warm oil has been used to soothe wounds, warm oil is used to massage sore muscles and relieve fatigue. It is an instrument of healing.

I would like you to visualize a large pitcher of warm oil. Notice the color of the oil. Feel the warmth of the oil by dipping your finger in the oil and rubbing your finger and thumb together. Notice that the oil is smooth and slippery. It lubricates the surfaces of your finger and thumb so that they slide over each other smoothly and easily.

Also notice that next to the pitcher of warm oil is the persona of someone whom you can trust. You may not know who the person is, all you know is that you feel comfortable in the presence of this persona and that you can trust them. That person begins to slowly lift the pitcher of warm oil, and carefully and gently begins to pour the warm oil on your head. . . .

Then something surprising happens. . . . Instead of the oil pouring off of your head, your head opens and this warm oil begins, very slowly to cascade down the bone structure of your body. As you feel the warmth of this oil moving down the bones of your forehead, feel it fill the orbits of your eyes, . . . notice how the lubricating quality of this oil allows your eyes to move smoothly and easily. It is as if your eyeballs are floating in a bath of warm oil.

This warm oil continues flowing down the bones of your cheeks and into the hinge joint of your jaw, lubricating this joint so that movement is comfortable and easy. As this warm oil soothes any aches, any tension, this oil moves down your jaws and lubricates your jawbone so that each of your teeth seats comfortably in your jaw. Your teeth feel better. This warm oil continues to cascade down each of the cervical vertebrae of your spine, falling over each vertebra, filling it, flowing down to the next one, filling it up, flowing over and down to the next one. Any muscles attached to the cervical spine are attached in a comfortable, smooth, gentle, easy way. Any knots of muscular tension melt away with this warm oil. You can begin, very carefully and gently, to let go of any tension as you feel this warm oil cascading down each of the bones of your spine, separating at the end of your cervical spine and beginning to move down each of your shoulders, filling the ball and socket joint of your shoulder. You can feel your shoulder seating better. Any movement you imagine doing with your arms is smooth, comfortable and easy, even pleasurable. This warm oil continues to flow down the bones of your arms toward the joint in your elbow, fills that joint, so that your elbow moves with smoothness and grace. It continues to flow down your arms, flooding all the many bones in your wrists and hands and fingers. And just as you allow tension to pass through your fingertips, so too your fingertips can open, and this warm oil can flow out of your fingertips to the floor and in to the earth where the tension is transformed.

Continuing now, to feel this warm oil filling and overflowing down each of the bones in your thoracic spine, flowing around each of your ribs. Notice, that as you breathe, your ribs move so smoothly, they separate so easily as your lungs fill with air. Notice that the muscles attached to those ribs move with a smoothness and an ease, that you haven't known for a long long time. It becomes effortless to breathe, to move air. And again, as you do this, if you notice any part of your body, which continues to hang on to tension, spend a little more time there until you feel the tension melt away.

This warm oil continues to cascade down each of the bones of your lumbar vertebrae allowing all of the muscles attached to these bones to become soft and loose. When the warm oil reaches your pelvis it floods each of the ball and socket joints of your hips, allowing your hips to be seated in just the right way for freedom and ease of motion. Then this oil continues to flow down your legs, into the hinge joint of your knees, flood this joint and float your kneecaps in a pool of warm oil. Then allow this warm oil to flow down your legs, into the many bones of your ankles and finally flow along the bones of your feet and toes. Then your toes open and allow that warm oil to flow out onto the floor and into the earth.

This physical healing can extend to an emotional and a spiritual healing as well. So allow yourself to let go of any thoughts or any painful feelings. Allow yourself mental comfort and spiritual comfort. Give yourself the same nurturing, the same care, that you so willingly give to your patients. Now you can begin to feel that care being given to you.

Allow this process to go on for as long as you wish, knowing that even though just three minutes of actual clock-time goes by, it will seem as if it's all the time you need. In this time you can be aware of aspects in your life that need to be finished, that need healing. Just let closure come now in the privacy of your own mind. [pause]

And now, begin the process of allowing that warm oil to finish its flowing through your body, to flow completely out of your body. Allow the openings in your head, your fingers and your toes to close. Continue to feel the presence of this nurturing persona, whom you trust. Then, as you begin to leave this experience and as you begin to reorient yourself to this room, allow yourself to take with you whatever has been valuable, so that your day can be enriched, and the contacts you have with other people today can be enriched.

Then begin to reorient yourself to this room and to the sound of my voice, to the presence of others.

VII
INTEGRATION

Ericksonian therapy, as it looks for resources, however, does more than just focus on positive forces. It works with all parts of the personality towards it becoming a healthy whole, taking into consideration the sun *and* the shadow (see Kelzer, 1988). Drawing on the wisdom that negativeness, if suppressed, will slip into the system anyway through the back door and possibly provoke severe diseases (accidents, suicide, cancer, or psychosis), hypnotherapy greets the shadow at the front door and works with it for integration. This is a contrast to other approaches such as "positive thinking" (Murphy, 1962), where negativeness is just avoided and excluded. In a group it is more difficult to confront unwanted, undesirable, as yet unaccepted forces and so this has to be planned carefully.

The induction by Charles Stern, here with a wealth of the author's own comments, is concerned with the integration of opposites such as "truth" versus "craziness," "teacher and pupil," "group and individual," or "conscious and unconscious." Paul Carter has us integrate "completeness" and "separateness," two human realities that are mutually incompatible and exclusive on the conscious level. I myself strive towards the "impossible" integration of the opposite states "waking" and "dreaming" within the still relatively unknown lucid dream state. Jeffrey Zeig aims at reconciling the beginning and the end state, the seed and the fruit, whereas David Cheek links conscious directives in self hypnosis with automatic body reactions (ideomotor responses).

26

Charles Stern: The Map Is the Territory

COMMENTS

If you were to just casually read the text of Charles R. Stern's induction, it sounds like a lecture. The comment indicates, however, that here there is a really carefully constructed, metaphorical group induction. This is a good example of how group inductions can be used naturally in a setting where people expect a lecture. Good lectures—like good sermons—are always somehow group inductions for they demand focused attention: and after listening again to some lectures by Kay Thompson or Jeff Zeig, I am sure they would agree with this statement.

The goal of this induction is the integration of opposites, which was seeded right from the beginning. The stories and pictures from nature give the induction the power to reach its goal.

INDUCTION

There is a story about a Zen master who was being interviewed. The interviewer asked him if his teachings were humorous or serious. The master said: "Well, sometimes I take humor seriously and sometimes I take seriousness humorously." And the interviewer called him crazy. The master just looked at him and said with a smile: "That's true, I'm crazy. But don't disregard my teaching just because I'm crazy." He said, "I'm crazy because my teaching is true."*

COMMENTARY

This story has several metaphorical aspects. The teacher-student relationship is isomorphic to the hypnotist-subject relationship. In other words, it sets the parallel contexts of the story and the here-and-now situation.

The statement of the Zen master that he is crazy is a way to disarm resistance to what is being communicated in the story and in present reality. It also adds a "twist" from which comes

*Benares & Camden (1977). *Zen Without Zen Masters*. California: and/or Press.

a bit of confusion. This moment of confusion tends to suspend the listener's critical judgment long enough for the speaker to deliver his point ("I'm crazy because my teaching is true.")

Text

Heinz von Foerster was talking about how two things like the map and the territory are really one thing, not separate, how individuals and groups are not separate. We don't know what an individual is unless there is a group. But you can't have a group without individuals. You can't have one thing without the other.

Commentary

This discussion of Heinz von Foerster is a reference to a lecture he made just a few minutes earlier which was received enthusiastically. This brings interest and a focus of attention of the audience to the present hypnotic situation. The mention that "the map is the territory" is counter to the general belief (à là Korzibski and Bateson) that "the map *is not* the territory."† This also attracts attention and causes a momentary confusional state which readies the audience to hear what is next to come.

The reference to individuals and groups is, in addition to being isomorphic to the listener's situation, a statement that things may not be what they at first seem. Also, the audience is expected to identify with either the group or the individual, but to realize that, in this context, they are essentially the same.

Text

It's like a coin. You can't have heads without tails. If you try to scrape away the heads side of the coin, the tails side will always be there. If you scrape away the head of the coin, the only way to do that successfully is to scrape away the tail side as well, because there are always two sides, but the coin is one thing. There is no separation, there is no difference, and yet there seems to be a difference.

Commentary

This reference to a coin being one thing with different, yet inseparable, sides is a paradox of sameness and difference. This concept is interesting and may sustain the audience's attention while simultaneously eliciting some confusion. Milton Erickson said that there is generally at least a little confusion in any induction of hypnosis.

Text

So we come into this world in a group of people, and yet we are individuals. We grow up in this world with other people interacting with us, and yet we are separate, and yet we are a unit

†Bateson, G. (1972). *Steps to an Ecology of Mind* New York: Ballentine.

with those people. And so, how much separation is there really between one person and another, between one way of thinking and another, between your conscious and unconscious mind?

COMMENTARY

This section brings the sameness/difference paradox into the realm of the developmental issue of separation–individuation as well as the division between conscious versus unconscious mind. It sets the audience up for the following story.

TEXT

And there are many cultures in this world, particularly primitive cultures, that understand what Heinz von Foerster was talking about. The aborigines in Australia, for example, understood that they are not separate from the earth, and the earth is not separate from them. If an aborigine is conceived near one of their sacred objects, which is always a mountain or a tree or a stream or some natural occurring event, they're considered part of that event, even though the event or its coming on this earth was 40 million years ago. So primitive cultures understand there is no real separation between one thing and another. It's just the way of talking about things. And there is a collapsing or a *cooperation* or a complementarity between what seems to be opposite. That's why there is no resistance in psychotherapy, because there are really no opposites. There is only finding a way to cooperate. There is only finding a way to show that those opposites are really connected, that they really are one.

COMMENTARY

Primitive cultures—aborigines—understand there is no *real* separation. . . .

This is the direct opposite of what one's senses tell us and yet there seems to be some truth to it: the "collapsing or a cooperation or a complementarity between what seems to be opposites." This sentence is a way to ease the tension or confusion of the previous paradox. It implies things are complementary and not separate in the sense of opposed to each other and these positions are cooperative in nature.

"Cooperation" is emphasized here and it implies that even if the listener and the hypnotist appear to hold opposite positions, they can transcend it through a cooperative effort. Thus, a seemingly logical progression from groups of people to specific groups of people (aborigines, etc.) and down to the psychotherapy relationship has occurred.

The idea that "all is one" seems to be the opposite of our individualism and our western psychological notion of separation and individuation. However, there is research in the area of subliminal communication which indicates that the experience of oneness may be the more healing concept.‡ It certainly parallels our psychosocial development in the sense that early we are rather undifferentiated and as "separated and individuated" as we may later become, it

‡Silverman, L. H., et al. (1982). *In Search of Oneness.* New York: International University Press.

is always (if it is "healthy") in a context of human interaction. Thus, this metaphorical group induction tends to foster age regression and the monologue thus far serves as an induction and as a carefully constructed mind-set (frame of reference) for what is to follow.

TEXT

There is a small tribe in India (the Todha Tribe) that has a very interesting ceremony and I think it explains why this particular culture has no wars; they are non-violent people. They are highly cooperative with one another and their disputes, when there are disputes—and that's a rare occurrence—are easily and quickly settled; there are very rare conflicts. They can settle those disputes, those occasions when they have difficulties with solving a particular conflict, they take it to a panel of elders. And the elders listen to both sides or all sides. They consider all sides and then they decide what the solution will be. And when the solution to the conflict is made, everyone accepts it. They don't just pretend to accept it and later on get upset about it or act out what they truly felt. This is because they understand that they live in a unit, a society, a clan, a village, that they are individuals, but they are not totally separate from the group.

And this society, this village, this small group of people has an interesting ritual that helps us understand why they don't have very many conflicts, how they settle these conflicts so easily. The ritual is called: the "face-uncovering ceremony." And this ceremony takes place shortly after the birth of a baby. The baby is born in the hut, where the parents live. And that baby is kept in the darkened hut for a couple of days with just the mother; just the mother getting used to the baby and the baby getting used to the mother in the dark, the baby sucking the mother's breast, the mother nurturing the child without the light intruding, a very intimate experience. And then one morning, just before the sun rises, one of the elder men goes to the hut and takes the child gently from the mother and goes to the temple, outside the temple, where all the men of the village are gathered. And the elder man holds the child in his arms, the blanket around the child, and a flap of blanket over the child's face so the child cannot see; and it's still dark. When the sun begins to rise the elder man holds the child facing the sun as it rises and uncovers the child's face. And he says to the child: "See the sun, see the men, see the temple," welcoming the child to life, to nature and to that child's village, family, clan. And then all the men of the village gently file by the child and touch the child in a welcoming, comforting way, welcoming that child, accepting that child. And the child drifts in and out of sleep, is content, is calm, very relaxed. And the elder man holding the child takes that child to the center of the village and hands the child to one of the elder women of the village. The elder woman holds the child before all the women of the village assembled there. And holding the child in her arms, she bows deeply, and all of the women bow respectfully in return. Then, one by one, the child is held by each woman and comforted and passed from one woman to the next, welcoming that child into life, the village, the natural surroundings, to the comfort of being. And by the time the child has been held and comforted by each of the women, there is a smell of rice and millet cooking for the festival to celebrate the child's birth. And the men have gathered—some of them in a circle—and one man stands in the center while the other men in the circle dance around to the slow beat of the drum. The man in the center of the circle recites poetry: poetry about the child and the child's birth, poetry about nature, acceptance, comfort and oneness, oneness with life, oneness with nature, oneness with the family and sacred traditions of the clan. And one of the priests goes and gets some sacred milk of one of the sacred cows and places a small drop on the child's tongue and soothes that child, and the child begins to *drift into* a very *deep* and very *comfortable sleep*, feeling that acceptance deeply, that comfort, that sense of calm.

COMMENTARY

The Todha Tribe story follows the above themes by posing an atmosphere of "togetherness" and cooperation from birth throughout life in an accepting and safe environment.

It establishes first that what few conflicts there are in one's life, can be resolved amicably.

The "face uncovering ceremony" assists in age regression. It involves all sensory modalities and covers all aspects of the child's life with warm acceptance. References to the child drifting off to sleep during the ceremony is a way of perpetuating and deepening the trance being experienced by the listener.

TEXT

And every child is allowed this ritual, is given this ritual, this acceptance, so that when the children in the village play together the older children take care of the younger children. The older children protect the younger children. And there is rarely any kind of dispute among them. They don't fight over their play things, they cooperate, they share, because they know that they all belong and are accepted and accepting of each other.

COMMENTARY

This reference to children who grow up in an accepting environment, who learn to be cooperative and relatively conflict free, is a way to elicit responses from various "parts" or aspects of the listeners that may lead to the reduction of conflict and to the development of congruence among various aspects of themselves.

TEXT

They feel their experience, the unity of life within them and between them and among them, deeply and comfortably. Every breath they take is experienced in a calm accepting way. It's been said that these people spend a great deal of time in a kind of trance-like state. It's placid and easy, their movement in their bodies "flows," as they would put it. They walk like the river flows—easily and comfortably. Just as in the river, any obstacles are flowed around and over. And eventually time will wear away those obstacles and the river will flow more comfortably as it moves along.

Commentary

"Flowing" in a trance-like state and "cycles of life" refer to the ability to be unhindered by life's obstacles, but that life can go on naturally in a balance. Notice, however, that these are vast generalizations into which the listener can project his or her own images of what it is like in his or her life to "flow" or be "congruent" or "calm."

Text

And there are so many cycles of life that people experience and they don't even realize it. When you breathe you don't think about breathing, but the air comes in and the air goes out. And it comes in again and goes out. And it just flows in and out like all the other cycles of nature, cycles of life, birth, death, rebirth, going and flowing, moving back and forth in life. There are good times and there are bad times. Underneath it all there is a unity of nature, of self and of connection between self and nature. Even the sad times will come and go and happy times will arise again. And we'll begin to know that in this unity the good times and the bad times are the least important. The most important is the underlying experience that everything is all right, everything is one unit of balance. And it's nice to feel that balance. It's nice to experience a congruence with life.

Commentary

Throughout the text, reference is made continuously to "opposites" (good times, bad times, etc.) which is then transcended through reinterpretation of them as complementarities connected on a different level. This repetitive theme serves as a metaphorical suggestion that conflicts (opposites: thesis-antithesis) can be transcended (resolved: synthesis) through a process of taking a meta view; to see that the tension between opposites itself indicates a connection (you cannot have a tug-of-war without two sides pulling) and that this tension can be modified until there is no tension (both teams may agree to lessen the pull on their own respective sides until they are merely both holding the rope—still connected and balanced but without struggling) or to the point whereby both relax their grip and drop the connection completely.

This, then, is teaching the listener, through metaphor, how to escape a paradox and let go of an internal (or external) struggle.

Doing this with metaphor has the advantage of not being directly resistible since the theme may not be *fully* grasped consciously and even if it is, it does not tell anyone how *they* should deal with their own paradoxes and conflicts. It merely offers a paradigm within which they may place the problem and then solve it.

Text

On the surface of the ocean there may be a storm raging, but underneath, deep down, everything is calm. Life goes on and it's all right, it's just all right. It's not good or bad necessarily, it's just really all right, even though on the surface there may be a storm or may be the hot sun, but deep beneath the surface, it's all right.

COMMENTARY

The metaphor of the ocean storm on the surface with relative calm on the bottom is a reference to conscious-unconscious dissociation and a message as well about inner peace in the face of a "storm" of problems in the outside or the conscious world.

TEXT

And you know, the analogy has been made between human beings and water flowing. And, after all, we are mostly made of water, and yet water is operating gently and comfortably in forms of beautiful clouds, and the clouds eventually rain and nurture the earth. And the earth gives that water back to the flowing rivers, and the rivers give it back to the ocean, and the ocean gives it back to the clouds. And you couldn't have a cloud without water in the ground or in the ocean. And you couldn't have water in the ground without the cloud. It's all one thing, a cycle, a cycle of life. Evaporating and raining and evaporating again, the breath of life, breathing, the earth breathing, the universe breathing, and yet, when you breathe, do you really breathe? Or does life breathe you? You really don't know, only because you and life are the same, one unit, one single thing. And it's nice to be comfortable with that idea. Some people are not quite so comfortable with it, and that's all right as well because of the flowing and the reconciliation of opposites. Some people call those things conflicts, but really they are only both sides of the same unit, the same idea, the same pattern, the comings and goings, the rising and the falling of the tides, or your chest, of your breath, the wind and the rain.

COMMENTARY

The above essentially applies to the earlier water analogy with the addition that humans are now more directly identified *as being* essentially water. In this way the metaphors of nature and objects are anthropomorphized. A hypnotherapist using metaphorical interventions, to be more effective, generally attempts to get the subject to identify with the elements of the metaphor which elicit a change in that person's frame of reference.

TEXT

Milton Erickson used to say: "My voice will go with you, wherever you go. You may hear my voice in the sounds of the wind or the rain, you may hear my voice in the sound of the heater fan or in the motor of a car or in the laughter of children that play." All those voices that are close to you, and my voice will go with you wherever you go, because you really learn, and when you learn in relation to another, that learning is a unit, and that learning goes with you. And it's nice to know that you have good learnings, useful learnings, comfortable learnings at your disposal. And anytime you want them, all you have to do is reach down inside and allow those learnings to surface from the depths of the oceans of your mind. And the tides of thinking gently roll again on the sands of understanding in the depth of being. What is it really like, you can really wonder, can you not? What is it really like to just be . . . without having to do anything in the moment. What is it like to not have to, just for the moment, react to the past, to not have any concern about the future. But just to be all right. And no matter what storms there are on the surface, underneath there's just being all right, not good or bad, not in reaction to something, not a label, no concept, but just being, breathing, the inhale and exhale automatically coming in and out, the cycle of living without trying, without having to do anything. And to know, on that level, not really just a self-acceptance (because there is no separateness to accept one part or another) but to feel the self in congruence with the past, in congruence with the future, to just be, even for a moment in time.

COMMENTARY

Erickson's statement "my voice will go with you . . ." is an additional device to link listeners interested in Erickson with what has been said. It also serves as a "future pacing" device and a posthypnotic suggestion to continue these learnings and have them triggered by ordinary environmental stimuli.

TEXT

And, as you continue, utilizing whatever experience, learnings that you want to take from my words, from your own understanding, your own perspective, you can allow yourself to learn even more deeply by not having to try to do anything. But just be for a moment, just for a moment in time. And you can continue that as long as you like today . . . here. And those of you who would like to make a comment or ask a question, that will be all right. I'll wait. If you would like to ask or make a statement, you'll probably awaken as much as you need to in order to do that, and that's all right. Some of you would prefer to continue the experience you've begun, and that's all right as well. I'll just wait and see what follows, what develops.

COMMENTARY

The final sections become increasingly more obvious and less indirect and relate what was said earlier to the listener, but by this time the majority of the group has been in a trance and is following along in an open and accepting manner. Therefore, the messages are more likely to be accepted or at least seriously considered.

27

Paul Carter: Parts Work

COMMENTS

Paul Carter in his induction gives an example of the mutual process between the therapist and the client. As he wanted to demonstrate with an individual his way of working with parts he prepared for this by initiating a similar process with a group induction. The setting is unusual. During the group induction we worked together with a partner, thus experiencing in advance what was to be demonstrated later. I remember this experience as being very vivid and exciting, although there was also deep concentration, especially as we did not know what would happen next. Paul Carter led us through a process where the different states were to be integrated on a trance level, something that is impossible on a conscious rational level.

Working with parts in trance as Paul Carter does is a very powerful therapeutic tool. Even now after I had read the induction again before writing my comment, it had the effect that I had to integrate certain opposite parts in a dream the following night.

INDUCTION

I'm interested—not right now, maybe in 10 minutes—to do a demonstration with one or perhaps several people, and since just by chance you all happen to be people, I thought I'd select one of you to do that together with. Who is interested in that? O.K. Those of you, who are interested, can I ask you to come to the front and sit up here, maybe as best you can, here, somebody may bring chairs or not on the stage now. We're going to do a little bit of work here, so you probably want to sit in a chair, or if you are comfortable as you are, I just want to have a sense of who you are. Maybe those of you, who are not working in the front row, if you could take a seat in the second row, who don't want to do a demonstration, because if you are sitting in the front row, I might think you want to do a demonstration, then you would be in a dangerous position. So, if you wouldn't mind changing. Fine.

There are several reasons, I have done this—I guess, you could call it a technique, couldn't you? One of those old stage-hypnosis techniques actually, where you ask five hundred people to come to the stage, and then slowly you find the one who is already in such a deep trance, that anything you do won't interfere with it, and then you demonstrate what an incredible hypnotist you are by selecting that person as the volunteer.

I am going to say a funny thing. I'm going to say that I don't use techniques. Now, that's a description of my perception, as we have been talking a lot about here in this congress. You can certainly perceive most of the things I do as technique. And for a long time I perceived it that way too. I really got into technique, I was fascinated with it. And then after a couple of months I guess of that I got really fed up with it. I think, it was the same reason, that I got fed up with mathematics for a while. I personally love mathematics. But my particular involvement became such a game, that I lost my sense really of what I was doing. And I find the same thing true with technique. I find it much more effective for me, personally, not to work with technique. I'll tell you what I sense I work with, and see if that makes any sense to you.

The reason I asked you to come up here is, so I can have a few minutes just to kind of look at you, and you can have a few minutes also to look at me and look at yourselves and I can look at myself. And then maybe together we can get a sense of where we are. I would like to work with somebody, who feels good about working with me in this kind of way and who I feel good about working together with, because therapy in my opinion, hypnosis also, is a very mutual process. I think that both, client and therapist, client and counselor need to be very selective about what they choose to do, who they choose to work with and so on. I want to give us both a chance to do that. And I won't call you up here unless I really truly have a good sense of working with you. And I'll expect you not to come up here unless you really have a good sense, that's the right thing for you to do at this time.

And another thing that can happen is that you can do a lot of work sitting where you sit right now. And I'm going to be working with somebody up here—and you can certainly take the opportunity to simply respond and go along with your own experience and see what that's like. What I want to do, is demonstrate a kind of integration of (whatever you want to call it) direct, confrontive, conscious oriented approaches with the indirect, unconscious, metaphorical, holistic kinds of approaches. Now I find a very funny thing in my life, a very funny thing in the people I work with, which is - I think, we actually live at this point in time (and this is my most accurate assessment that I can make of myself) in two realities simultaneously. And I would like you to get a little bit of experience with what I mean by this, before I actually work with someone up here. I think it will help you to understand, if not fully in a cognitive way, at least understand in some kind of holistic way, what it is I'm working with and how I view the world.

I think perhaps one of the most important things in learning someone's approach, I certainly felt this with Erickson, is learning the way that he or she actually perceives. So much we study what people do and act and again, if we are really into this sense of the unity of doing and perceiving, then we need to pay a lot of attention to how someone perceives too. That's something I focused on when I sat with Erickson, trying to get a sense of how he actually perceived as he was working with people. And again it was not separate from what he did. So one of the things I like to do is position myself exactly like him, I spent a lot of time doing that, moving in rhythm, in his rhythms, like him, adjusting my eyes. His pupils were rather unusual, I figured, well, they must go along with it, they were primarily dilated, though occasionally one would constrict, while the other one would remain dilated and so on, and I just played with that a little bit, and worked with trying to apprehend to perceive the world as he did. It was very interesting. It's a very interesting exercise to do, to work at that level. You find a lot of things that may not make sense from the outside, make a lot more sense, become more possible.

So, what I would like to ask you to do is face a partner, someone near you, just turn to someone next you. And if it's possible, turn your chairs to face each other, if it's not, just turn your bodies. O.K.?

So, let's begin with some silence, and take a moment to, if you need to continue, make a few adjustments for your own comfort to just let your eyes close for a moment and we will start with an inner focus. We will start there. And what I would like you to do, is just take a moment to think about what you sense, what you can remember in terms of a moment in your life, where you experienced tremendous completion, tremendous sense of, "everything is O.K." I don't know what your words will be for that, a sense of wholeness, maybe when you fell in love or listening to a certain piece of music, maybe during some trance experience, or something that you participated in some activity, maybe after running or swimming or hiking. Just let yourself orient to one particular experience, where you had a really tremendous sense of wholeness, completeness, that kind of sense inside yourself: everything is O.K., where you think, "I really don't need to do anything at this moment. I don't have to go here, I don't have to go there. It's really O.K. just to be, just exactly as I am. I'm complete." Some people talk about it, at that moment where you think, "Well, if I die now, it would be O.K. with me, I feel so complete, I feel so whole." Some people that thought immediately makes them feel so unwhole that they don't like that. So it's not necessarily that way for you. I'm asking you to simply find a moment, as best you can, where you get that sense of wholeness. And focus on it for a moment. Notice some of the details of that experience for you. If it is a specific memory, notice what it is that you were looking at or what was around you. Maybe you weren't paying attention to it, but just notice, what was around you. What you can see around you, what you can hear around you, what you can feel around you. And notice inside you, what you felt just inside yourself. And if you can't think of anything in terms of your own experience, then just think of something in the world that you think is very complete, maybe another person you like and you feel is a very complete person, very whole person, or maybe something like the sun for example, some symbol of completion for you.

Now what I'm going to ask you to do in a moment is open your eyes, not yet, but in a moment I'll ask you to do that, and allow yourself to look at the person in front of you, while continuing to feel the sense of wholeness, this sense of okayness, the sense that you don't have to do anything. And maybe realizing that inside them they are experiencing something similar. So as you look at them, you may just notice and be aware, that they too have this experience of being whole and complete.

So slowly let your eyes open, softly, continuing with this sense of wholeness. And just let yourself take about 30 seconds just to look at your partner. Open your eyes to your partner. It's a very relaxed kind of looking. Just you are opening your eyes. And maybe your focus will be continuing to sense and feel this wholeness inside you. You can even keep the memory of whatever you have been thinking about inside your head. And you may notice this is difficult, immediately you focus in a different way. If that's the case, just close your eyes and go back to reaccessing your sense of wholeness, the memory you had. You can practice this a little bit. This is something, you can actually practice, until it becomes easier for you to simply sit with somebody with your eyes open to them in the feeling, in the state, in the vision, in the awareness: I'm O.K., I'm complete. There is nothing that needs to be done here. It's O.K. to sit here for a moment, at least for this moment. And as you look at the person, you see what it's like to realize that about that person too, that that's one of their realities. I mentioned the two realities. This is one of the ones I was talking about. That that person in some way is whole and complete, doesn't need anything and actually has some experience of himself or herself in that way. It may be very limited, certainly it may be limited, and it is one of the realities we live in that we are whole and complete, that we are connected, that we are connected to everything. And in that sense too we are whole and complete. Which means the person that is sitting across from you is whole and complete too. And you can just notice what this is like. Notice, what you see, if you see anything different or what it is you do see and what you feel, what happens inside you, as you sit in this kind of way . . .

And then let yourself take a nice deep breath, let go this and close your eyes again, just feel your breath for a moment, let your breath be like a transition, a way of transporting you from one state to another for a while. And I'm going to ask you to shift now to another reality, not the reality, but what I call another reality, that second reality, and to do it by thinking of an experience in yourself, in which you felt tremendously in need. Maybe you were tremendously hungry, you had been hiking all day or something and gone without much food and you were really hungry. Or you were really thirsty, you were out in the middle of the Arizona desert, and it was so dry, and you got really really thirsty, or maybe in some way you were hurt and alone and you really needed, you feel tremendous need for some kind of an emotional support from a friend. Just let yourself think of one time or one experience of being in need. Again, if you can focus on one experience and just notice, what is around you, where you are, what can you see and notice around you, what can you hear. Are there voices of people you know, sounds or silence, what is there? And focus inside yourself too and notice, what you notice inside. Are you talking to yourself? Are you saying: I'm scared, I'm hurt, I'm thirsty, I'm hungry? And what do you feel inside? Is your heart beating fast? Is there a pain somewhere? And just notice the sensory experience, the sensing, let yourself sense, the feeling, the vision, the sounds, the emotion, the surrounding of this experience, and know, this is not all of you, this is not the only reality you live in, but it is one reality. And once again I would like to ask you, in a moment, to let your eyes open and again allow yourself not so much to look, but just to open your eyes to your partner and see your partner from this reality, in this reality, and just notice what it is like for you. And so let your eyes softly open and focus or attend to your partner for a while. And again there is nothing you have to do with this other than just notice, what this is like, what you see, what you sense in your partner and what you feel inside yourself, what you see inside yourself, what you hear. And if you lose it, if something distracts you or disturbs you with this, you find it hard or anything, close your eyes for a moment again and take a deep breath. And just let yourself orient again to your breathing and to just that sense of being in need, then letting your eyes open, when you are ready and just taking a moment to sit with a person and notice, what it's like, to sit with a person noticing this reality. Look in the eyes of your partner, and just notice that inside that person is the knowledge of this kind of reality too. It's something that as human beings we can all sympathize with, the knowledge of this state of this reality of need, of incompleteness, of the sense of incompleteness.

And when you are ready, let yourself let go of this again and let your eyes close again and take a deep breath, feel your breathing. And if you like, you might go back again to that sense, as you breathe, to that first reality you explored of wholeness, and just take a moment to connect back in, to adjust your body, to stretch your neck if you like, to feel yourself and to connect back in with that sense of wholeness. And just remember that is one of the realities we live in. And knowing your needs in no way invalidates also your reality of your sense of wholeness and completeness. That is true too. And let yourself check back in just for one last time here a moment to that sense of need and be aware of that too, and know that that is simply one of the realities at this time that we also know about and live in, in different ways. And you may not quite understand, I don't understand, how those fit together all the time, or how those integrate. That's what the unconscious is so good for. So just let yourself feel your breathing for a while and just ask your unconscious to accept these two realities, and do what it can to integrate them more and more, to continue to work with the process of integrating these realities of your life, or these states, if you prefer that word. The state of need, the state of completeness. The state of separateness, of partiality, experiencing the separateness and the state of connectedness, of unity, of wholeness. And as your breathing relaxes, your unconscious can continue to develop whatever sense for you at this time, you may of integration, and then orient back again here to this room, softly letting your eyes open. Now. Huuuhh. O.K. Now I'm going to trust you, when we finish the workshop to take a moment with your partner, whom you did this exercise with, just to talk for a moment, because I would like to move ahead now. So, will you do that? Because I know, some of you just had an experience which I think would probably be nice to complete with your partner, just with a few words. And so I would really like to ask you to do that, when we finish here today. O.K. if you need to whisper something in ears right now or something, go ahead and do that. O.K. Any *comments* from you, that you wish to make at this point? Anybody?

P.: I had trouble doing the last part of the exercise, when we were to integrate the separateness with the wholeness, because for me the wholeness included the separateness. It was both and—instead of either/or.

P.C: Right. Now that's exactly what we need trance for. What's your name?

P.: Jack

P.C.: So Jack just made a statement of his belief system about wholeness and his belief system about partiality, which is what we work with. And when I ask you to experience wholeness, generally you are going to work with it at a level of your belief, of what it is, which it sounds like you did, because that's what you just described. The integration process is very difficult to do at a conscious level, because of the nature of your beliefs about the different states. It's the same problem I have at a conscious level, wholeness means everything. So, how can you connect it with partiality?

P.: I could feel the parts separately, and then I could feel them together, simultaneously.

P.C.: Aha, so you shift into a level of feeling, and that's like shifting into a trance, it's analogous to that, shifting into a different framework. At the verbal framework with which he was working, this made no sense. He's saying to himself: "You can't do that, because—how can you integrate something, that's already integrated, and so on. That's stupid, you know. You are at least wasting your time, if not being stupid." So you shift to another level. In your case you noticed, that if you sort of *felt* something here and there, that the feelings could come together. The comment was gone. Great! With wholeness and need it may be more obvious that they fit together or something. But many times in therapy the parts seem much more clearly; "Wow, those are just opposite." I hate you and I love you. They are just absolutely opposite. And so it makes more sense to see if there is some way to integrate.

In any case, this is, what trance becomes very useful for. It becomes necessary to let go of the models, for a while and to integrate the two. That's really what you are doing. You are not really integrating wholeness and partiality, but you are changing your models, so that you develop something new now which can include more of what you are calling wholeness and more of what you are calling partiality.

Now, if you never experienced partiality in your life, if you never experienced that, and you never experienced any sense of need, any sense of limitation, never, ever, then you don't need to do this. Right? Then it's really irrelevant. This is only for the numbers of us, who experience that at some time.

28

Hildegard Klippstein: Wake Up for Lucidity

COMMENTS

This group induction was held after I had reported about research on the subject of lucid dreaming where the dreamer is aware that he or she is dreaming while he or she is dreaming and thus has freedom of decision; he remembers waking and dream life and is able to carry out a planned action (compare Garfield, 1974; LaBerge, 1985; Kelzer, 1988; Tholey & Utecht, 1987). On reading this induction again, I can sympathize with possible critics of this book and hear those who may not be informed about this subject, shout: "That is not only non-scientific, but the inclusion of such a controversial subject like fire-walking proves it is all humbug." Well, fire-walking and lucid dreaming are hobbies of mine. I have taken critics seriously who reproach Ericksonians with "uncritical disposition, mimicry, ancestor worship and dogmatism" (Peter, 1988, p.92) and have left in the other direction. In doing so I follow Erickson, whom I never met, but whose message to me was that I may use my own possibilities. I want to expand the limitations of present day scientific frame of reference. "Erickson did not respect any mystical or antiscientific bias" relates Joseph Barber (1988, p. 27). Here we are confronted with his barriers, I guess. Trance has been used for fire walking possibly for millennia, and trance also can be used to proceed further into dream development and to learn to experience such fragile integrative states as lucid dreaming. It has been successful in individual therapy (Klippstein, 1988). Whether this also works with groups is now beginning to be explored. (I have had several positive responses up to date.)

In this induction I use the colors of the rainbow in order to count the group into trance, hoping that Sandra Sylvester approves my learning from her. My idea was: why not count in colors! This might be more colorful and invites finding an integration in the new experience with the fire.

INDUCTION

Let's do some hypnotherapeutic work to wake up even more.

You sit in your chair, more or less comfortable and you can feel your feet touching the floor. While your awareness can check your position, leaning more or less comfortably against your back-rest, you can . . . allow yourself to relax, because you never learn better than when you are relaxing.

You can see the things and the people around you, the colors of their clothes (close) you may like more or less, unless you have already decided to . . . close your eyes to . . . experience more of this comfort.

With your eyes closed my voice may sound different, you can find that out, if you want to, and all the noises in this room may sound different, the silence may sound different. You can . . . find out, more, while you . . . allow yourself to listen to yourself and follow your inner sensations.

You feel your breast moving up and down with your breathing. Let's begin with breathing consciously. When you inhale, count to seven in your own rhythm, hold your breath counting to seven and exhale counting to seven again. And go on with this for a while counting to seven, while you inhale, holding your breath up to seven, counting to seven, while you exhale, at the same time you can listen to me and follow my suggestions. Those of you used to meditating may have experienced that breathing in this way is useful to purify the whole system right at the beginning.

Can you feel the coolness of the air, when you breathe in? And the warmer air, when you breathe out? Every breath is a fresh breath, when we . . . consciously follow our breathing. And it's so nice to . . . feel your face muscles relax, your jaw hanging a little slack perhaps, while the skin muscles of the forehead smoothed out, eyes shut very lightly and forehead may be becoming more and more sensitive with every fresh breath. Hearing these descriptions and at the same time counting your breaths you may . . . open up more becoming more receptive to this special feeling of transparency in your forehead, because you realize that the forehead is a very sensitive part of the body particularly for changes in temperature. You can . . . feel with your forehead that the air in this room is cooler than your body temperature, when you are ready to . . . open up for this sensitivity.

Now breathing naturally again, your conscious mind can just follow your breathing, while your body may . . . find its own most comfortable breathing rhythm, or your body can follow your breathing and your conscious mind can . . . find the most comfortable breathing rhythm for you . . . That's confusing. Why not notice the confusion technique in order to . . . allow yourself to go into a trance state quickly. Experienced hypnotherapists can't help noticing. Everything is all in order, all right with this. Hypnotherapeutic technique of confusion provoke you to . . . let go, to adjust and clear your mind in a new way in order for you . . . to be able to reach a higher level of awareness. Erickson said: "Any trance that is of sufficient level to let your unconscious mind take a look at what's going on, is sufficient . . . And you should . . . use your mind at the unconscious level, even while you are using it at the conscious level" (Rosen, 1982, p.64).

When I was a child, I liked playing a little game. With my eyes closed I liked lying in the sun, with my face towards the sun, wondering which color would develop before my eyes. Sometimes I put my hands over my eyes to close them even more and aid to add a little bit of pressure in order to intensify the brightness of the colors. And the colors used to change. With my eyes closed I was very much awake, interested so much in the changing of the colors.

I didn't know in advance which color would come next, doubling my involvement and interest. I guess by this time I had forgotten my body and I used all the energy I usually otherwise wasted on muscle tension to increase my inner awareness and comfort with every color I was able to see.

When I got older I learned by heart the seven colors of the rainbow: *red, orange, yellow, green, blue, indigo, violet.* Wandering through these wonderful seven colors step by step becoming even more involved . . . I wondered where the bright white light was.

And only later in Physics at school did I learn about the wonder of the bright white light, consisting of all these wonderful seven colors: *red, orange, yellow, green, blue, indigo, violet.*

And I don't know whether you are able to distinguish the various components of that bright white light you may or maybe not be seeing with closed eyes when you look up to the inner sun in the middle of your forehead from the very beginning or only later admire one or more than one of the wonderful seven colors of the rainbow, that may lead you, too, to a state of well-being and comfort. At the same time your attention is increased by every color you are able to see: *red, orange, yellow, green, blue, indigo, violet.*

Maybe these colors are quite vague at the beginning. Maybe some of you already see them very clearly also, within the possibility you may have the sensation right from the beginning, and there with the possibility you may develop the sensation after a while. You don't know at what moment it will develop. It's the same with lucidity in dreams: You can . . . retain your consciousness, when you go to sleep and dream as the Yogis do, and you can . . . awaken in your dreams after having slept for a while. But you don't know exactly at what moment you are going to awake in your dreams.

So you may be curious about which path you are going to follow. Let your deeper and higher self decide whether you follow each of my words leading you to a more and more relaxed state with every word, where your consciousness can work even better showing you wonderful colors . . . or whether you become ever less conscious or even more unconscious for a while hearing my words more from a distance—all in order to follow your need in (you're needing) to total relaxation first before you awake to consciousness again, perhaps being surprised by a wonderful color, while your body is still sleeping . . . just as in the morning, when you are lying in bed, your body still totally relaxed from sleep, when only your head has already woken up.

And I guess all of you know the story of *Alice's Adventures in Wonderland.* But did you also know that this is one of the most wonderful trance inductions you can find in world literature? Let me show you. Of course it's a special trance, because you can be wide awake reading a book. Perhaps you remember the beginning:

"Alice was beginning to get very tired of sitting by her sister on the bank and of having nothing to do: once or twice she had peeped into the book her sister was reading, but it had no pictures or conversations in it, 'And what is the use of a book,' thought Alice, 'without pictures or conversations?' "

Feeling sleepy and bored is the best preparatory condition to readily go into a trance. Lewis Carroll also involves Alice in a communication with herself. You (the reader), or listener will go on to look inside. And what are you going to find? A blank sheet, a tabula rasa, where everything can develop from inside. Alice's blank sheet is the boring book of her sister. Observe carefully what happens inside you, when I read the last sentence again: "Once or twice she had peeped into the book her sister was reading, but it had no pictures or conversations in it, 'And what is the use of a book,' thought Alice, 'without pictures or conversations?' " Maybe your own pictures and conversations may be already beginning to develop.

So far, so good. As far as we are by now you are experiencing via the visual and the auditive channels. You are invited to look and listen. Let's be curious about how the author brings in the feeling sensations: "So she was considering, in her mind (as well as she could, for the hot day made her feel very sleepy and stupid), whether the pleasure of making a daisy-chain would be worth the trouble of getting up and picking the daisies, when suddenly a White Rabbit with pink eyes ran close by her."

Suddenly the dream begins. It didn't take the author more than twelve lines to take you to the entrance of Wonderland. You will not be as astonished now as Alice is, when you hear the White Rabbit talk and see it taking a watch out of its waistcoat-pocket. The rabbit is in a hurry and infects Alice with its speed. "Alice started to her feet, for it flashed across her mind that she had never before seen a rabbit with either a waistcoat-pocket, or a watch to take out of it, and burning with curiosity, she ran across the field after it, and was just in time to see it pop down a large rabbit-hole under the hedge."

Are you burning with curiosity too? There is such a strong desire to follow.

Please observe yourself very carefully to note how you become involved in the story. It's always the same process. When you are well prepared, *suddenly* you are right in the middle of a story, *suddenly* you . . . change your state of consciousness, *suddenly* you fall asleep, *suddenly* you fall into a dream, *suddenly* you fall into trance. And as you are observing this with great interest, you can have the experience of falling anywhere, but at the same time stay where you are as an observer. Here you can . . . see and hear what's going on and understand the mechanism of human consciousness. So I would like you to reduce your speed of falling into the story, because Lewis Carroll's trance induction is almost irresistible: "In another moment down went Alice after it, never once considering how in the world she was to get out again. The rabbit-hole went straight on like a tunnel for some way, and then dipped suddenly down, so suddenly that Alice had not a moment to think about stopping herself before she found herself falling down what seemed to be a very deep well." The author knows a lot about human consciousness. Note how he manages Erickson's "stop and start": "Either the well was very deep, or she fell very slowly. for she had plenty of time as she went down to look about her, and to wonder what was going to happen next."

It's necessary to change the tempo of this sudden falling, otherwise it would be too frightening. The word "tunnel" can pace and lead to that narrowing and focusing of attention, yes, indeed, perhaps even to the "tunnel vision" often experienced and associated with hypnosis. "Well" and "fell" rhyme, a device for deepening trance and eliciting regression. "Well" with its connotations of comfort and health may be an assuring anchor to counteract any anxiety aroused by "falling." Get some more overall general view and distance with every word I read to you and feel at the same time your curiosity about how the story continues.

"Down, down down. Would the fall never come to an end? 'I wonder how many miles I've fallen by this time?' she said aloud. 'I must be getting somewhere near the centre of the earth.—But then I wonder what Latitude or Longitude I've got to?' (Alice had not the slightest idea what Latitude was, or Longitude either, but she thought they were nice, grand words to say.)" Nice, grand words you don't know the meaning of provide the best opportunity for projection of your own inward content.

"Down, down, down. There was nothing else to do, so Alice soon began talking again." And then, talking about her cat, Alice practices confusion by turning the sentences around: "Do cats eat bats?—Do bats eat cats?" It's also a rhyme. By now on page seven the author can be sure that he has caught the reader's attention, so the fall can come to an end and other events may occur.

What about you? Involved in the story and nevertheless having an overall general view over the story? Did you . . . find this wonderful balance in Wonderland, being on two levels of reality at the same time? Listening with red-hot ears to the fascinating story like a child and being led by your attention in an adult manner, watching what's going on. That's exactly what you can practice in one of your next dreams. When you . . . follow the story while dreaming—just in the same way as I interrupted the flow of the story—ask yourself in the bright white light of consciousness: Is this a dream? Is this a trance? Where am I? You can give yourself an answer. You may look for some events or details typical of dreams just as you can find some details of your experience right now typical of trance. You may look back over which ever way you came to this scene and verify the dream reality by noticing a sudden shift. What I always do to test the dream reality is fly up. Just fly up to the ceiling of the room because it's such a wonderful feeling to be free from the force of gravity. It's like feeling high. And that's what it is. And I know I can do this while dreaming. Being in a dream and having the distinct view that I am dreaming. Being in a trance with clear thoughts.

During a seminar on fire-walking I first learned about this special trance of watchfulness, of alertness and vigilance. What I expected was to be led into an especially deep trance in order to be able to walk over the burning coals. But I was wrong. During seven hours of preparation we spent most of our time finding out what we felt to be right at the moment. In a trance of alertness and vigilance we learned to . . . be present at the present moment. In a trance of watchfulness we learned to . . . be aware of changing feelings. What about you? Would you be ready for fire-walking right now, being totally in the present? Are you aware of your inner sensations while you follow my stories?

I had gone to this seminar with a feeling of confidence, but then the teacher told us about the temperature of 700-1000 C., a temperature at which aluminum melts. These figures and the image of the melting aluminum gave me a shock in the direction of reality. Open your inner ears and eyes and notice what is happening! Wake up! What is it that frightens you most today? What about a life without fear? What are you feeling right now? Where are you with your thoughts? Take the first few steps walking into the present! What do you want to change by throwing it into the fire? These were the questions we were asking ourselves. And what is fear? A bodily sensation? An illusion? Slowly there came the idea that we are greater than our fear.

And then we went outdoors, stacked up an enormous pile of wood silently in meditation, filled the gaps with paper. There was now no doubt, the time of the fire was approaching. The teacher poured some petroleum all over and then lighted the whole wood-pile. A strong wind stirred up the flames—where are you by the way?—to make a very bright light licking out with its red and yellow tongues, sometimes changing into blue and green. The wind made the fire crackle. And we gave to the fire all the things we wanted to change: our egoism, our jealousy, our rigidity, our arrogance, . . . thus cleaning our emotional system. The fire didn't want to take my paper at first, the paper on which I had put down all my garbage. It's not so . . . easy to look at our mistakes we are so used to in a new way. It's not . . . so easy to change. It's not . . . so easy to change our belief system. Then we had to wait until the fire had burned down. The main thing we learned was: Pay 100% attention! And: Only you know if you are able to walk on fire without being hurt. When you have taken the first step, just go on naturally. I felt warm from the expectant curiosity of the others. I felt I was together with people ready for the leap. Ready for this leap out of the thinking patterns of our logic, ready for the leap in development. What if the impossible suddenly is possible? If I can solve this impossibility I can also solve other problems my mind used to judge as unsolvable. Finally we are ready. The teacher rakes the glowing fire to a long carpet of fire. We take off our shoes and stockings and chant a song. The first person walks over the glowing coals. We go on singing. Others follow. At some time I start across. It's very simple and natural and I feel a hot crunchy floor. Afterwards my feet feel good on the cold earth. We repeat crossing over the burning coals, running, dancing, having fun. I stamp my feet very vehemently, because I am curious. I want to test this theory about an air-cushion. There is no air-cushion. We can just walk on fire. In our happiness we say, "thank you" to the fire for this lesson. We can do what seemed impossible to us before.

We can alter our dreams, our dreams of reality, that is our belief system, and our dreams at night. In some parts of the world people do fire-walking as a religious ceremony right up to present times. From very ancient times up till now, people still have to . . . learn again and again that the spirit is the master of the body.

As fire-walking is a nice foot-reflex-zone-massage, too, it cleans the whole system. You can feel this after fire-walking, feeling just wonderful from top to toe. It's the same feeling you can have in lucid dreams . . . flying for example. You can . . . develop your normal dreams to lucidity. Others have done this before. You can follow as you follow when you see somebody walking over burning coals. It's possible in a higher state of awareness. You can train yourself in a conscious trance.

Where I live right now, I have a little glass crystal hanging in my window. And when the sun shines, I can see the colors of the rainbow on my carpet and at the same time on my desk. When I look at the crystal from a special angle, the bright white light of the sun is reflected in the seven colors: *violet, indigo, blue, green, yellow, orange, and red* depending on the direction I am moving. And sometimes by moving to and fro I can count the colors to check whether the glass crystal is well-made, well-done, if all the colors are there.

And do you remember counting to seven, inhaling right at the beginning of this group induction? Holding that breath up to seven and counting to seven exhaling? Or would you have forgotten if I hadn't reminded you? Do you remember too that I told you that this is good for purifying the system? And do you think . . . it's worth remembering for the future? At least this single topic, even though you might forget everything else I have told you. In Ericksonian therapy there is a hypothesis that amnesia increases the effectiveness of suggestions, so, if this belongs to your belief system, you can allow yourself to . . . forget in order to remember better on another level: You will be able to go back into this relaxed alert state whenever you want to do so in your everyday life as well as in your dream life. All you need do is count to seven again while breathing. And each time you do this consciously during waking or dreaming you will be able to . . . go back into this relaxed alert state more easily and quickly because it is a skill and, like any other skill, will improve with practice.

And now you can allow yourself to . . . go back to your normal everyday sleep, if you don't want to . . stay alert like this. If you want to stay awake like this, that's all right too. You will be able to do your everyday work with more pleasure and lucidity, have a better overall general view, be led by the bright, white light of clarity and understanding, the gift of our consciousness given to us to . . . use it even in dreams, and you are able to do more than one thing at a time even with open eyes . . .

29

Jeffrey Zeig: That Area of Comfort

COMMENTS

Jeff Zeig jumps right into his goal at the beginning of his induction and utilizes and broadens the "initial" feeling of comfort you are asked to find somewhere in your body. Notice how he lets our "initials" become an anchor for this feeling of comfort and how he manages the future pacing towards the "initial sensations" of trance allowing us to make contact with our deeper learnings.

INDUCTION

And if it's easier to just . . . close your eyes and begin the process of going down inside yourself. And, as you go inside yourself, I would like you to take this opportunity to discover that there can be a special area of comfort, a special area of comfort, that you can find. And, I would like you to be willing to explore easily inside and take the time to find that special area of comfort. And, you may find that area of comfort in the very bottom of your feet. And, you may find that area of comfort in the palm of your hands. And, you may find that area of comfort in back of your eye. And here or there it can be a strong feeling, that area of comfort.

And, it's just a matter of taking the time to go inside and explore, also realizing that any time you want to, you can feel free to make any of those small adjustments that maximize your own sense of comfort and well-being. For example, with your eyes closed, you can look up to the top of your head, take a deep breath, exhale fully, noticing that point at which you exhale fully—it's the point of most complete physiological relaxation. And there is that area of comfort.

And, I would like you to realize, that that area of comfort can have definite shape, definite form. And, I would like you to realize, that you can make the necessary adjustments to explore that shape, to explore the form of that area of comfort—that special place inside. And, you can accept your-self the awareness that that special area of comfort has definite shape, definite form, again recognizing how you can any time you want to make any of those small adjustments, that really maximize your own sense of comfort and well-being.

And, as you attend to that area of comfort, you may realize that not only does it have definite form, but that area of comfort also has real depth. There can be real depth now. And, that area of comfort not only has length and width, but you can nod off to the understanding, that that area of comfort has length, width, breadth: Again, and again, understanding, that any time you want to make those adjustments, you can, with your eyes closed, just look up to the top of your head, take an easy breath and let your-self really grow (sic)/go inside that area of comfort.

And, I would like you to also understand, that there can be color associated with that area of comfort, a special color. I would like you to understand, that there can be certain sensations that can be a part of that area of comfort. And, that you can put your finger on those colors—on those sensations. And, that with your feet on the floor you can stretch your own imagination to remember this area of comfort, that certain kind of relaxation, the kind you can have in tense moments, because in tense moments, do you want to be fidgeting, moving around after this or that or would you rather just look up, take that easy breath and remember always that area of comfort.

And, I would like you to also understand that you can have your initials on that area of comfort; perhaps you would like to embroider your initials; perhaps you would like to print your initials; perhaps you would like to draw your initials on that area of comfort, so that that area of comfort can become indelibly yours, part of the functioning, of the practice of your ability to bring together so many different learnings.

And, enjoy always the capacity of your own inner mind, your own unconscious mind to surprise you in many creative ways, almost as if you took time momentarily to go inside that area of comfort and those balanced sensations. And, remembering the process of how your unconscious mind can enjoy the practice of the process of really using those learnings constructively about the area of comfort.

Recognizing the importance of trust: Now you can trust your own inner mind. Recognizing the importance of allowing your attention to be come more intense; how you can let your inner mind experience some of those sensations, understandings can happen involuntarily.

And yes, there can be that pleasant confusion. And yes, there can be that ability to remember and forget. But the ability, that you can have to avoid resisting your own tendency to go inside that area of comfort—to experience the initial sensations, so that you can in a way quickly view and review some of those valuable learnings stored and restored inside your own inner mind, recognizing that you can thank yourself for that ability that you have to appreciate the growing changes.

And now, here I would like you to realize, that you can alert yourself to new possibilities; that you can open your eyes to continued learnings; that you can reorient yourself to the process of understanding; that you can awaken yourself to the capacity of your own inner mind to guide you.

And so, now again, you can use this opportunity to take one or two or three easy breaths. Take one or two or three easy breaths now, reorient yourself completely rested, refreshed, energetic, wide awake, all over.

30

David Cheek: An Aura of Protection

COMMENTS

David Cheek gives us in this induction a complex learning situation with (1) the utilization of self-hypnosis for healing and protection, (2) the experience of ideomotoric finger signals, (3) the establishing of "yes," "no," and "I-don't-want-to-answer" signals for a possible dialogue with our deeper self.

In the original induction we learned how to use automatic writing simultaneously. David Cheek has put this extra after the induction here in order not to overwhelm students just beginning.

INDUCTION

Self-hypnosis gives you an aura of protection against picking up troubles of other people. You also improve your immune responses every time you go into hypnosis for the purpose of relaxing. While you are doing this exercise you will be finding that you can choose finger movements for answers to questions. There are many experiences in life that you cannot possibly remember consciously. It is possible to discover important memories when you have unconscious finger signals to answer questions.

Hold a pen or a pencil between the fingers of your right hand. Your fingers will pull apart a little to drop what you are holding when your inner mind knows you are relaxing well enough to use hypnosis in a helpful way. We are all experts at using hypnosis the wrong way, like thinking, "Everything is going wrong; nobody loves me."

Next, I am going to ask you to take three deep breaths very slowly, in and out. Look up as high as you can toward that Yoga spot in the middle of your forehead each time you are breathing in. Let your eyes come down in their normal range as you breathe out. Do it now to get the idea of it.

Your brain waves go into an alpha rhythm each time you look up. This helps your inner mind to remember the feeling you have as you go into hypnosis or start to fall asleep. The reason for the deep breath is that your chest muscles and diaphragm tighten to expand your chest as you breathe in. They relax as you breathe out. These are the muscles you tighten up when you are angry, in pain or depressed. So you are not only controlling your muscles when you are breathing out; you are telling your mind to forget tension, anger, pain and depression. After the three deep breaths I will ask you to imagine you are looking at a candle about 10 feet away. You could fix your attention on any moving object like a fire in a fireplace or smoke rising from a cigarette in an ashtray. As Milton Erickson pointed out many years ago, we slip into hypnosis as we remember sequences of thought or activity. You slip into hypnosis remembering how the flame of the candle gets larger, smaller, shifts a little from side to side with the gentle movements of air in a room. Don't worry if you have trouble at first consciously seeing an imaginary candle. You will be doing it unconsciously at first, anyway.

Now, let's start. First the deep breath in with your eyes looking up. After the third breath let your eyes rest as you watch the movements of the candle flame.—Feel your shoulders letting go a little more tension with each breath out as you breathe normally. The rest of your body will relax unconsciously as you think of relaxing the upper part of your body. We know much more about the upper abdominal and chest muscles than we do about the lower part of our body.

As you watch that candle flame I am going to count slowly to ten. Think to yourself, "relax, relax" with each number as I count [counting is paced with the breathing, "one" on inhaling, "two" on exhaling, etc.]

Continue letting your body relax progressively. Some of you have dropped your pen already. I am going to ask you all to think this idea, "When I am twice as deep as I am right now I would like my index finger on my right hand to lift a little, as though a string were tied to my finger tip."

When it lifts, please give yourself another suggestion. I want you to use a familiar experience in order to learn that you can shut down sensations in an arm. Most of us have had the experience of sleeping on an arm long enough to make it feel sort of numb because the circulation has been diminished by the pressure. Think to yourself, "I want my left arm to become half as sensitive as it is right now. When that has occurred at a physiological level, my index finger will lift to let me know." This will be the beginning of your ability to know what is going on below conscious levels of thought. The finger will lift before you realize consciously that the arm is really less sensitive. That finger will become your "yes" finger after this. Some other finger on that same hand will represent a "no" answer, and finally I will have you select a finger to represent your unwillingness to know an answer to a question. That one I call your "I-don't-want-to-answer" finger. These signals will all be on the same hand. Then, if you want to change to using your other hand, the signals will have the same meaning.

[About 90 seconds of silence follows this suggestion in order to let some of the subjects realize their abilities. Those who are working at a slower tempo can listen back to the tape recording of this induction until they drop their pen or pencil and recognize that they, too, can diminish sensation in the suggested arm. The reader can try this, too.]

Now I think all of you are deep enough so that you can imagine yourself in front of a full length mirror, that you are standing there in front of the mirror. See the aura of light around you, the light that you have with you, that expresses your feelings right at this moment. First you see it on an unconscious level, and I'm going to ask your finger that says "yes," to lift, when that's clear in the deep part of your mind you can see the color. And as it lifts you bring that information upward, so that you can actually see it as a visual memory. Notice what color it is, there may be several colors. If you can see that, and I think, with a little practice with it you'll be able to do it—we will come back to this later on before we leave tomorrow. Then I would like to ask you to order the aura around you to be one of protection, that keeps you from taking on other people's worries, fears, guilts, when you are dealing with them, be this as a psychologist or as a physician or a dentist, that you remind yourself of that aura later, whenever you feel with somebody this is a problem—you will not do this with everybody—but when you feel that there is a particular problem person, that you press the thumb and index finger together on your left hand just as a sort of reminder, a sample for yourself to call on that aura of protection that is there and that you are going to be giving out energy, not taking it in, because psychically we can do this. We don't just absorb. We can send out energy. It's really basic to prayer. It's a basic concept that Edgar Cayce probably is most famous for finding that he could help people at a distance. The Christian Scientists attempt to do this with their reading. It doesn't always work, but it's an idea that I think is worth thinking about. If you are going to radiate to the people you work with your caring, your trust in their ability to get well. You don't care how they do it, but that you are going to radiate to them your faith in their ability to get well. They may not get well. People have their own way of doing things; we cannot always control it, but we can help it when there is readiness to be helped. That's what we want to call it. I think we should not be too anxious to try to do a specific type of therapy as though we are controlling the things. We should rather think how can we help people use their own resources in getting well, sometimes in spite of what we are doing. That we may be doing the wrong thing, but we radiate out to them our faith in their being able to do something good for themselves, for the people around them, related to them.

And as I count in a few moments to ten, I would like to ask you going deeper, just really totally relaxed, so that you are using your own power. If there were things that you have been troubled about or confused about, they may be assimilated and you kind of put things together for yourself, so that you are no longer troubled. [Somebody had sobbed.]

Now, I am going to count slowly from ten down to zero to have you come up from whatever level you have reached, to become totally alert with all the sensations back to normal on your body. Please keep your eyes closed until I reach the count of "one" and always smile as you come out of hypnosis. Smiling seems to make your whole body feel the way you would normally feel when something makes you smile. Ten—nine—eight—seven—six—five—four—three—two—one—zero.

Suggestions for Automatic Writing Practice*

This can be done during a group induction as worded above. It is usually more successful if done with an individual who has learned how to use ideomotor responses in answer to ques-

*Reprinted by permission of David B. Cheek from "Hypnosis and Ideomotor Techniques."

tions. Here is an outline of a way the instruction can be given after the subject is in a good medium trance state, about where an arm could be lifted a little with your fingers under the wrist of the subject. Keep on with deepening suggestions until you find that the arm remains uplifted after you have taken your fingers away (catalepsy).

If you would like to learn how to access unconscious information at home using automatic writing, this is a way you can do it. If you clasp your hands with the left thumb appearing on top and you are right handed as an adult, you may find that your left hand and arm will want to move. Some converted left-handed people have found a new freedom in writing when they shift back to their original handedness orientation before someone made them use their right hand.

"See if you can get the feeling of a strap under your wrist where my fingers have been lifting your arm. To do automatic writing you need to have that arm that you are writing with feel light enough so it can move freely over the paper without friction. Some people can imagine the strap as though it is a sling under their arm. Others do better imagining they are in a swimming pool, holding a rubber ball down below the surface. The ball will be pushing upward against the palm of their hand. As they relax the pressure, the ball will push their arm up toward the surface.

Now, get the feeling of thoughts being able to move from your mind down that arm to the hand and the fingers holding the pen. Your earliest memories probably are about your mother. I am going to ask that your unconscious mind write something about your mother. Don't think anything consciously—just let your inner mind start sending energy to your hand and be curious to see what happens. First let the movement be in the air. Later you can sit at a desk with a felt tip pen in your hand lightly resting in contact with a wide sheet of paper. You can have your eyes open but usually it works better with your eyes closed. Your unconscious mind is very economical. It usually does not leave spaces between words. It does not cross "ts" and it does not dot an "i."

About one person in five will be able to do automatic writing on the first effort. I point out the value of automatic writing in therapy because the patient or client can do work at home that can be not only instructive but can be associated with a feeling of relaxation without concern about office time and pressure.

VIII

FUTURE-PACE AND CONSOLIDATION OF LEARNING

Finishing a seminar with a group induction has already become a habit for some Ericksonians. That is true of for example Carol and Stephen Lankton, who are at the same time providing both a demonstration of techniques and a learning experience to complement and extend the training. Their book "Enchantment and Intervention in Family Therapy" closes with their Dual Group Induction "The Tapestry" from the Ericksonian Congress in 1983. Its intention is to "stimulate and facilitate learnings about the Ericksonian material" (Lankton & Lankton, 1986, p.307). Similarly, their induction included here rounded off the twelve-day International Advanced Training Seminar on Ericksonian Hypnotherapy of May, 1983, in Fuschl, Austria.

Future-pacing implies that the therapists learning there in the group will be oriented towards using what is learned in their future professional work. Bernhard Trenkle demonstrates this very skillfully by means of case histories in an induction that unfortunately had to be excluded owing to space limitations. The same happened with Joseph Barber's induction in which he encouraged us to continue the work that has already commenced further in our dreams. David Cheek presents us with a valuable key for our therapeutic travels. Virginia Satir teaches us her meditation method thus providing us with a tool to aid survival even in real catastrophes. Similarly Wilhelm Gerl recapitulates all we need to enter trance on our own. Finally, Bernhard Trenkle explains in detail the goals he and Gunther Schmidt envisaged for the closing group induction of their joint workshop.

31

Carol and Stephen Lankton: Climbing Squaw Peak

INDUCTION

C.: Well, our next topic . . . I'm reminded as we sit here in the middle of the mountains of Austria, mountains to the right and to the left, high mountains. Some days we can even see the mountains. Last night when we saw Peter's slides, some of you saw pictures of Squaw Peak. We were glad that Milton hadn't lived beside these mountains and said to climb these mountains, because they are much higher. Yet, a mountain is a mountain. We all know that. And you climb that mountain you live beside. That reminds us of a story that Robert Erickson told to us. Robert is one of Milton's sons. He said that, of course in growing up as any boy will do, he developed questions, difficulties, problems, about one thing and another, about girls, about school, about having enough money. And so, having a famous father, he would go straight away and ask his father: What shall I do? How shall I handle this problem?

S.: Without expecting that a trance will be developed.

C.: Or, at the very least, hoping the solution would be offered to him. The parent picked the solution made to order. But Robert said he was very disappointed because it didn't take him long to realize that his father had a very predictable response. And that response, when he would hear the question and the problem of his boy, before he had given any answer at all, he had a solution before the solution. And that solution would always be one word: "climb"! And Robert knew what that meant. And he knew that it was pointless to persevere and try to get his father to answer that question and help him solve that problem until he had done his part. And that part involved a long hard climb. So . . .

S.: Maybe we should take just a few minutes to elaborate on this theme, if that's all right, because a lot of people will be faced with children who come to them with questions. You never know consciously what question your unconscious is going to ask, but sooner or later you're bound to be faced with the question. The question may come from you as a person, it may come from your unconscious, it may come from your children, come from your clients. But questions abound. There are probably some questions lurking around here even now. And so, anticipation is something that everybody knows. And the desire to have somebody satisfy a need. Whenever we asked Dr. Erickson for something, in a seminar for example, where a lot of people had come, his response was always fairly predictable. At first he might say: That's a very good question. That's good that you have those questions. It would be a pity if you didn't have those questions. Those questions are an indication that you have a healthy nervous system and a quick mind.

C.: And your conscious mind would like to think that it would be so convenient if someone would just answer the question, give a solution.

S.: He might say: Yes, you really wonder about that, don't you?

C.: And that would deprive your unconscious from being able to provide you a unique solution in its own time, in its own place.

S.: At the end of the day, if not at the beginning of the day, or perhaps right at the moment when you asked the question he was bound to say: Have you ever climbed Squaw Peak? It's a very good experience. Climb Squaw Peak. Sunrise is a very good time. Perhaps you would like to see it at noon. Sunset is also very lovely.

C.: And midnight.

S.: Midnight is a very good time to climb Squaw Peak. So I climbed it at each of those times. And every time I climbed it, I'd remember something that he said to me. And remembering is something that is very unpredictable. You can ask a question and not remember. You can even remember something when you haven't asked a question. But inevitably in climbing Squaw Peak I'm sure the same thing happened to Robert that happened to me, happened to Carol. He said, and I quote: I had a man in my office one time, who couldn't even walk in a straight line.

C.: But he could climb a stairway.

S.: I was really curious about what it meant that he couldn't walk in a straight line. You hear about crooked little men with crooked little sticks who walked in crooked little streets. But the idea that a person couldn't walk in a straight line really intrigued me. And so I wasn't really understanding what the point was, when he said, he could climb a stairway. "And so I told him," he said: "You lift your leg up in the air and in the act of placing it down, go more deeply in a trance. And you inhale as you lift your right leg up, and placing it down, you'll be able to go more deeply into trance."

C.: And so, with each step you take, and the higher you go, simultaneously, paradoxically, the deeper you go into trance.

S.: Now I listened to the story, thinking okay, climbing stair steps perhaps could put this man in trance, but I didn't understand why he couldn't walk in a straight line. And Milton said: It was very mysterious that he could walk in a straight line climbing stairs, so I made sure that with every step he goes more deeply in trance.

C.: It doesn't much matter whether Robert could think about it consciously or whether it's your unconscious that responds to the stimulus of the stairway that leads up Squaw Peak. But time and time again, having asked a question or posed a problem, he would gather the things he needed to take with him on that climb. He would start out at the bottom of the mountain, take a deep breath, think about how far he would have to go once again, and wonder what you will learn there. And then he would climb, first one step and then another.

S.: These Erickson stories are so boring.

C.: Somebody on Squaw Peak would always have a transistor radio they took to keep them company. You could wonder why somebody would want to disturb the silence with that kind of music. [Radio music in the background]

S.: Every time I climbed Squaw Peak there would come a place where, twisting and twirling, going backwards and then higher, I'd finally come to a stairway of rock that I hadn't expected. And each time I'd take a step up this stairway, I'd go more deeply in trance. And I could ignore those other sounds around me. But what really surprised me was what would happen when I reached the top of Squaw Peak because I thought perhaps I would go into trance and remember something extremely important that Milton had said to me. He would always say: You climb Squaw Peak and have a new view of everything, a new view of your life. Review the events of your life. Talk your life over with me. Hear my words and be very satisfied with the answers that I give. And so, of course, I was going to expect a very nice trance where I would hear only that voice and see only that face. I wondered if I would talk out loud so that other people around me could hear me or whether I would keep totally silent. And I was surprised when I got to the top and, speaking of surprises . . .

C.: Robert told us that every time when he would get to the top of the mountain, he found that no matter what experience he had on the climb, and I doubt if he really thought about going in trance, but at the top of the mountain, he would just sit there, nevertheless, and fall into a natural kind of a trance that you experience when you have exerted yourself, when you have concentrated your attention inward. And, of course, with each climb up that mountain he would think about his problem in some way. And when a concern or a question is on your mind, your conscious mind may forget to think about it all the time, but perhaps your unconscious mind continues to think about it in one way or another way, consider it, consider solutions on an unconscious level. Your conscious mind can enjoy the scenery from time to time, and so he would think about those questions in one way or another on the way up the mountain, and at the top of the mountain just fall into a bit of a trance, looking out over the city, above everything. And the problems that seemed so important down there seemed very remote from the perspective of the mountain top. And he said he would just sit there, he didn't know for how long and consider that problem perhaps in a dream, perhaps in a symbolic way. And trying to find out, find an understanding of the total context, wondering what his father had intended him to learn. It reminds us of a somewhat similar situation.

S.: Of course there is no need to worry about what Dr. Erickson intended him to learn. But by contrast there is a story told . . .

C.: . . . in the Sufi tradition.

S.: In the city of Ghor a potentate came with his entourage and a large beast, an elephant.

C.: The city of Ghor was inhabited by blind men and women. It was a city for the sightless. And somewhere beyond Ghor in the desert he made a camp. He had with him the elephant that he used to attack and also to impress those that he encountered. Like fools several of the inhabitants of the city of Ghor, hearing the commotion, ran to try and find out what it was.

S.: Some of them foolishly relied on childhood methods of trying to excite themselves by scaring themselves. Others tried to ignore it while some of them thoughtfully and methodically decided to investigate this beast, this beast that had blocked their roadway.

C.: And in investigating it they each ran and they each began to explore a part, the part that they could immediately encounter. And so they explored and they came to their understandings.

S.: And speaking of understanding, when I'd leave Dr. Erickson's office—I of course didn't live near by, there was a lot of traveling involved in going home, and a lot of time. And time is relative.

C.: And what do you think about while you're engaged in that time consuming traveling?

S.: It's a very good way to come to some understandings about the time spent with Dr. Erickson. Time can seem like it was very short despite the fact that many days went by.

C.: And time can be a transition between what you learned and where you are going to use that learning.

S.: Sometimes you are driving in a car and having a nice conversation with somebody you'd like to talk to. And despite the fact that a lot of hours went by it seems like only moments. And so when a psychotic woman came to see Dr. Erickson and she said: I like to have my little fantasy trips by myself and I don't want to give them up. But other people bother me about that. He told her all about the way your unconscious mind can distort time for your own benefit. You can dream that you are falling out of bed and you awake and realize that you have only fallen a foot. But while you were dreaming it, it might have seemed like you were falling for hours and hours.

C.: And you are really entitled to enjoy those excursions into fantasy, those private places that you can visit.

S.: But there is no reason to allow that pleasure to get you in trouble with other people. So he suggested that at the onset of the desired trip into fantasy, that she go into trance very quickly and imagine that several hours have passed.

C.:	S.:
Two hours or two days or two weeks	Three weeks. A very enjoyable private fantasy, no need to do anything
And only two minutes may pass on the clock	
	and your conscious mind can think that you have been gone on a vacation for two or three weeks ten days
fourteen days	
	but your unconscious mind can alter your subjective experience of time so that only

two minutes of clock time have passed. In that way you can avoid getting in trouble with other people

And she was delighted with that adaptation, so she could continue to go as deeply into those secret recesses of her imagination.

as she desired

and still be safe

and she came back again and said: Now you have been able to help me with my desire to withdraw from people and you have been able to help me with my fantasies.

I've been having these episodes. What could you suggest to help me with my episodes? And he suggested that the minute you begin one of those psychotic episodes, you go into trance very quickly and put your psychotic episode in a small envelope and mail it. And he suggested that it get mailed to his office. And you might suggest to clients that they mail it to the North Pole because I wouldn't want to get a package of these psychotic episodes.

And sending it away

it just floats elsewhere and you can come out of trance quickly and be perfectly normal. And for the next several years, she would simply drop into trance and place the difficulty in an envelope and mail it to Dr. Erickson. And she checked 20 years later and found out that he had a whole packet of her Manila envelopes.

And he packed them away with care.

And that's time distortion. In riding an airplane home or even when I drove back to the home when I was staying nearby the workshop I would go into trance and review the experiences of the workshop.

You might begin by staring comfortably out of the window watching the scenery, the unrelated scenery passing by and it just passes by

effortlessly while you sit there effortlessly
relaxed on the seat, comfortable, and who can
really say with your conscious mind at what
precise moment you go into trance?

Even after teaching a long workshop, when I
sit down on the airplane seat and I really have
no desire to think about anything, even when
there is a lot of work to be done . . .

And even though a part of you still can see the scenery
and see the other people . . .

sometimes there is a strain on my face and
I'm about to cry from the effort or feeling.

your unconscious mind is so much more
interested . . .

Other times no movement in my face muscles
at all.

in your memories, your expectations . . .

And my conscious mind begins to

and emotions.

think about an idea, something I wanted to
remember, something that I wanted to do when
I get back home. But your unconscious mind,
as if responding to posthypnotic suggestion and
a need to relax after a long ride . . .

And I would even hear the sound of the
voice of the stewardess or the steward or the
flight attendant say: "For those of you that
don't know, your seat belt is operated by a
small metal buckle . . ."

Because the sound of the engine can
just allow you a comfortable isolation from all
of those irrelevant noises and allow you to
really consider

all of the learnings

the personal ways you are going to use them.

And sometimes just counting a
variety of things that were learned is a way
of reviewing them. There are numbers that

may come to mind: one, an idea of something learned in the first days of the workshop. And you probably couldn't just say how you go about learning something and remembering something that was learned. Two.

You may have learned it around, or including a certain emotion.

You may have learned it while in conflict or more relaxed. You may have learned it consciously and you know very well that you know it.

And you may have learned it unconsciously and enjoy discovering just one or some

Three.

small indicator of that unconscious learning

Four. And another idea may come to mind, and just letting go.

symbolized by an image, knowing that in the same way the horses on a merry-go-round go around and around and come back again, that those learnings are stored in your unconscious and

Five, six and other ideas come to mind.

you can be sure that they come back around and will be available to you.

All those images, all those ideas, at the conscious level are likely to symbolize some learning of a more complex nature of unconscious association. There's something you can't really put words to. The learnings eventually begin to come to mind and sometimes you think that you are remembering something you learned at the workshop and really it was something you knew all along. I frequently find that I say something that I think Dr. Erickson would really agree with, something I never heard him say. Later, listening to the audiotape, I found out that he really said it to me. And I thought it was my idea. Because you allow something that you hear to become your own idea in your own way when it's useful to you. Eight, nine, ten more ideas come to mind. But I would be asleep and I wouldn't even realize the plane had taken off. And I might be somewhere over Denver, the Atlantic Ocean but I was comfortable and safe in trance.

And just floating there in the air

How nice to leave the driving to somebody else.

above everything, secure in your own memories.

Eleven, twelve, thirteen more ideas. And my unconscious would make associations about where I am going

Fourteen.

to use those ideas.

Fifteen.

I sometimes dreamed about the clients with whom I intended to make application of those ideas.

And sometimes you think about how you are going to make application of those ideas in your personal life and how the applications you make in your personal life will ultimately influence the way you influence your clients. Sixteen. Seventeen. So many ideas.

And so much personal life. A lot of talk about the pressure from outside of yourself.

And your clients bring a pressure as they bring problems to you, placing their trust in you to help them find the answers their unconscious stores for them.

And the dissociation of the trance itself or rather the dissociation created by going into the trance yourself can be a very helpful device to insulate your sensitive mind temporarily from the pressures of other people.

And when you notice those little muscle movements of your fingers twitching even on that airplane

you can enjoy intensifying the trance and your
ability to dissociate from everything around you
and allowing that hand to float comfortably into
the air or even up to your face.

[somebody weeping]

Little children experience pressures from a variety of sources. Sometimes a child has to endure the manipulation of a parent.

And sometimes a child has to endure the
absence of a parent, their under-involvement.
And each knows a certain kind of pressure from
your personal history.

And what child doesn't want to show love to a parent? And what child is not willing to reduce the stress that unconsciously you experience the parent being under and goes to great length sometimes

to make every adjustment, withholding feelings,
to do anything in that child's small power

Modifying muscle tension that you carry with you for the rest of your life.

to bring the greatest amount of peace and harmony
into that family where he finds himself or
herself.

Every adult who has ever been a child ought to be very pleased with how, as a child, you showed a great deal of health, courage and flexibility in modifying your needs to grow into the person that you become in order to bring peace and harmony into the household, even when that peace and harmony meant that you acted up, even when it seemed as if you were causing trouble.

Your unconscious stores all those learnings in automatic
ways of responding that
would serve the purpose in the most
efficient manner.

The impulse to cause trouble in the family, to be different, is only the child's way of trying to serve the purpose of the parents in the most efficient manner.

And you really ought to be proud of your ability to have done that.

And thank that younger part of you
that was willing to learn and adapt and survive

despite the handicap you placed upon yourself.
Be very grateful with how strong the human animal is, that you have taken yourself so far.

How flexible you can depend on your
unconscious to be.

We want each of our patients to know that there's a good deal of strength in every one of them, in every person who walks into our office, despite placing behind you your aggressiveness.

No matter what the overlay of
neuroses that is logically developed
in the course of growing up . . .

Despite by placing behind you needs for sexuality.

. . . the core of the personality
that core of strength
of power . . .

Despite placing behind you the ability to recognize your sensations,

integrity

what you see and hear

remains unchanged
and undamaged

and millions of feelings and impulses

by life's experiences.

to really understand what you could be as a human being.

[tape changed]

One of my clients told me that he has been very sick and had spent the entire evening with the variety of symptoms of the illness, vomiting, having the need for the toilet, urinating, defecating. He had been perspiring during the entire night.

Tossing and turning in a restless manner,

he had been unable to really find a balance.

And he came in to therapy the next day and he said: "It really surprises me that you can say the human being is positive and a delightful miracle. How could anyone like me? My outside might be attractive, but my insides are filled with all kinds of awful things. I spent the entire night reviewing those things." Now, the demands that the person makes . . . You shouldn't blame yourself for making demands.

And just like there are seasons in nature,
cycles, your unconscious creates a balance.
Sometimes in the process of creating a balance
you review any difficulties and pressures
and demands.

The need for immediate gratification is something each of us knows. And in knowing it, we learn to control it in a way that suits the

It's all a

individual as a person. Some people

natural part

have the desire to eat more than

of the cycle.

they should eat.
And it's good that you have that impulse to eat when you want to eat.

It's your unconscious way
of requesting that you gratify yourself.

And you have an unprecedented opportunity to employ a variety of techniques you've learned as an adult, not to harness and to suppress the impulse, but to direct it in a way that fits you as a person.

And so your conscious mind can consider
how you might best go about gratifying
a need or perhaps simply responding to that
need in a way that allows you a necessary
amount of stimulation, comfort and enjoyment.
Enjoyment and comfort are often
best appreciated

Now there's the child who,

following periods of discomfort
because it's a part of balance.

as a child, learns that he should speak for what he wants, the minute he wants something.

The very, very young child knows instinctively to cry loudly at the moment when a need is first noticed.

And we each have the ability to realize that our needs can be met in a group and that other people can be trusted.

You can even meet your needs by cooperating which implies temporarily postponing a need or diverting a need.

And it's very inflexible to express your need in the minute you feel your need.

But you consider a need. It deserves that attention, and your unconscious is able to consider the entire context, while your conscious mind is oriented to the situations of the moment and how that need is immediately noticed.

And it's a good idea to notice your need for immediate gratification, but if it's really important, and if you are really important as an individual, then give consideration, due consideration to how you express that need. You owe it to yourself to use all of your learnings that you have accumulated over your life time, feeling thinking, judging, being. I taught a workshop ten years ago, a friend of mine who lives in Phoenix was present. And he said: "You are not happy with the criticism you received, but your ideas were very good. And I bet you gave a lot of time to those ideas. Did you give any time to thinking about how you would present the ideas?" And I said: "It had not occurred to me." He said: "I bet if you had used the same thinking that went into the idea and thought about how you would present the idea, more people would be very happy with the presentation."

And so maybe in those times

And I learned a great deal from that comment.

when dissociated in trance,
travelling, your conscious mind remembers to think about how you are going to use your ideas while your unconscious continues to store the ideas.

Your ideas are valuable.

Or perhaps it's just the other way around, and you unconsciously select and plan how you are going to use your ideas and you can consciously enjoy thinking about what those ideas are.

So you can go back in the mind while you consciously don't even need to pay attention and identify those moments when you made a decision on how you'd express your ideas, made a decision on what manner you would express your impulses and review those decisions. You don't have to know everything, you don't have to remember the pain. But you can appreciate that your ideas and impulses were of such value that you used all of what you could of yourself at the time, and you might have only been a very young child at the time, because time is relative. You can review the decisions of the past

comfortably from a distance

and realize, that you can't change the decision in the past

and you can have a learning about how, why

but you can change the decision of the past in the future.

And sometimes all that it is necessary to do with the client is remind them.

you made that decision. Appreciate the wisdom of that decision then.
And know you can depend on that same wisdom to modify, make new decisions now.

And when you make a decision you ought to decide when the decision will be over and when you'll review it. When an adult makes a budget you review that budget after a period of months and make certain that it is appropriate for you, when times have changed. And when you manage your budget of impulses and ideas in order to help a parent, in order to help a brother

a child, a client, yourself,

you ought to review those decisions by recognizing a signal that you have given to yourself at the time the decision was made, a little alarm clock that goes off in the back of your mind that says: I decided to be depressed when I was seven or five, and I'm only to go to be depressed for ten years. Then I'll reexamine that decision when I'm sixteen or seventeen. And if you decide to be depressed at fifteen, seventeen, maybe ten years is another good time, and at twenty-seven, twenty-five, a little alarm clock goes off: It's time to change the tape in the back of the mind. You may say: I don't need to be depressed anymore. I think I'll be much more willing to show my feelings for ten years.

And that was a perfectly good decision then. And I can appreciate that part of me that made that decision and the wisdom. Many children made a decision to shut off feelings in the same way you turn off a water faucet.

And you turn on a new tape? and that will last for a given period of time.

And you made that decision for a perfectly good reason. It wouldn't be useful to have those tears then. When the signal comes to you now, think back, far back, from a comfortable distance at the present time.

Every experimenter knows that an experiment must be reviewed after a predetermined period of time.

You have a certain amount of maturity and wisdom now that the younger part of you never had a way of knowing about.

So if you make a decision now that you are

going to be close to somebody, love somebody,

That younger part didn't even know that
you were going to survive.

that you are going to remember the events of childhood,

But you did survive.

that you are going to ask for help when you need it.

And although you have an understanding of the
pain that younger part of you felt
then,

And you are not going to suppress your feelings until you have anxiety attacks.

you might want to reassure that younger part that you
are from his or her future.

And you are going to stop being manipulated by people who put pressure on you to take care of them.

It's never going to be that way again.

Also make a decision to review the decision, three months, three years, five days or every time you go into trance.

Any you might even be able to picture that
younger part of you, comfortably out in
front, and whatever pain you see behind that
younger child's decision,

Every time you are going to France, every time you put on your pants, every time you dance,

you might enjoy just transmitting to that younger child

every time you take a stance

a bit of the understanding,

your unconscious

reassurance

in standing there

and love

needs to represent you as a new person in a new moment.

that you know about that was unavailable,
back then to that child.

A good computer program

You might even picture yourself
inviting that child
into your arms,

reads the data

nurturing him or her

but it must be told from the

in a way that can

beginning when to stop reading that

bring a great sigh of relief.

data and go to

It's something the child
may have longed for

some other process or some other

for a very long time.

data.
And when making a decision in childhood to forget something you've done you need to also decide when you'll stop forgetting something you've done and reexamine the decision. When you make a decision in childhood that you'll always criticize yourself when something goes wrong rather than standing up to that grizzly bear of a father, you need to reexamine that decision

You need to criticize objectively
the wisdom of that decision.

at a predetermined time. When I'm not around that father anymore I'm not going to criticize myself, until I think it over carefully. Or when you go to school you may decide: you are not as intelligent or as friendly or as able, or your parents are not of the proper status and you can't get along with the other children.

You may even doubt your intellectual
ability to learn as quickly or as
thoroughly as the other children.

And in the trance decide to either change the decision or reexamine it some years later perhaps when you re-enter another learning institution.

Because things change

And as a child when a parent dies

over time

and you decide:

passes slowly.

I can give of myself to help the others overcome this difficulty. You ought to decide: I can give of myself for a while and I'll reexamine this decision.

Every child has to say goodbye
to the parents of the past.
It doesn't matter what your
relationship to the parent is
now, whether the parent is living
or dead.
But you say good-bye—and saying
goodbye doesn't mean giving away
those precious learnings and
memories, the love that was given
to you by that parent.

It means being willing to say "Hello" to a parent in a new way the next time you encounter them.

Even if you only encounter them the next time in your memory or in your dreams.

Or even if you only encounter them face to face next time.

You can appreciate the intention
of that parent,

And a child's idea of religion

and forgive the parent

needs to be reexamined because

for their mistakes and

you are not the same person you

inadequacies.

once were.

Your idea of religion needs to be examined in light of your deeper knowledge of human experience. And you are not really free to believe in something unless you are free to not believe in something.

And so to the extent that you have been free to doubt your religious and spiritual depth, know that you are also free, precisely because of that doubt to really entertain and invite a new understanding.

So many people waste the potential which they are given. It's a miracle that you are alive. It's a miracle that you breathe, a miracle that each of ourselves contains the ability to grow,

It's a miracle each time

to reproduce.

your unconscious goes about healing

It's a miracle that you can have

a small cut, a wound on

children.

your body somewhere.

It's a miracle that you can remember things.

But your unconscious does go about healing

And despite the frailty of the human creature,

those physical difficulties, and by the same token,

we can live comfortably on the planet's surface.

goes abut healing those psychological scars.

And with a good deal of defensive measures we can live slightly below the planet's surface,

It's ready to cooperate with your conscious mind

slightly below the water,

making a new arrangement,

in the reified atmosphere of mountain tops,

direct your learnings,

or even in space given proper defensive measures.

in a fashion suitable for
your own betterment.

But there is only a limited range in which the human organism can exist comfortably. And we ought to use the entirety of our potential to make people think that they are not still children, that they are not still students, and they are just waiting until they have a good idea.

Waiting until you know enough,
experience enough.

Waiting until they are given a brain, waiting until they stop procrastinating

But you have everything you need.
Now is a perfectly good time
to be happy.

to feel successful feelings. Dr. Erickson said: Too many people wait until after they have succeeded in order to feel successful.

But they are your feelings.
You are entitled to feel your success
even now.

You are not a rat in a laboratory. You don't need to wait until later to reinforce yourself for what you are learning to do.

You can use your feelings and success
as an aid in taking those steps to
comfortably achieve that success.

You may feel your successful feelings by a smile on the face,

even by the ability to allow a
tear to flow over your cheeks,

or a hand levitating, or just the knowledge that your heart beats. Your breathing automatically regulates your body temperature by using your circulatory system.

the balance of the digestion
that you don't even think
about consciously.

Even now there is a difficulty in

[somebody weeping]

your body being here, a cut, a sore

a scar

maybe a memory, and memorize the feeling of
that successful operation within yourself. It's your
feeling and you are entitled to have it.

And you can go back in time
and memorize the comfort before
you had that cut or scar.

While you are under way learning something, while
you are doing something, after you have completed

And you go back to

something, you can feel successful

that future

the entire time.

into that future when
you are not going to have
that scar anymore.
And memorize that comfort

You feel successful before you drive

and bring some of that

a car.

back into the present.

And you feel successful while you drive a car, after
you drive a car.

You can feel successful

You can feel successful while you

while you change your

change your room-mates, before you

clothes,

change your room-mates.

even in the mundane matters of

brushing your teeth
and grooming your body.
It's an excellent opportunity

You can feel successful while you remember something from the past

to appreciate the body.

that you failed miserably at the time. It's a good idea to fail and to fail so cleverly at something that it allows you to continue to grow and change.

And looking back at that
failure and the things you learned
from it, you wouldn't trade that
failure now for anything, even

You could have failed at much worse

though at the time you

things than you failed at.

didn't want to go through
it then.

And you can appreciate how it is that in failing in what you failed at then,

You became you.

you didn't choose something worse to fail at.

And you wouldn't be you if
you hadn't failed at exactly
the things that you failed at, in
the way you failed at them.

So along life's highway, in the collection of successes, collect the proper number of failures. And the next thing I know the stewardess already said: "Please keep your seat belt buckled while we taxi to the terminal.

"You'll have a few moments to collect your
possessions when we are safely at the
terminal. Please stay seated
until then.

"Allow women with children, the handicapped, and those making other connections to get off the plane first.

"We hope that you'll enjoy staying
in this city or when you are going
on to another destination. We wish
you a fine good day."

I had been in trance the whole time and missed the entire flight,

missed the meal.

I may be glad that I missed the

(laughter)

meal.

Now, the three blind men came back to the city.

The populace of the city were eager
to find out what they had discovered.
The first one said: "I know the true
story of what this beast is that is camped beyond our city."
He was the one who had held the ear
of the elephant. He said: "It's a broad
rough thing like a tapestry."

The other one said: "No, I disagree entirely," having grabbed what we know to be the trunk of the elephant: "It's a large serpent kind of thing that could twine itself around you and crush you."

And the third one disagreed entirely,
proclaiming that he was the one who
really had the truth. He had felt a leg
and he was convinced that the beast
was really a pillar, awful and strong in its
power and so, of course, all had imagined
something,

and each had used his feelings to understand it.

something incorrect. They each
knew a part, none of them knew the
whole. The created is not informed
about divinity. There is no way in this
science by means of the ordinary intellect.

And that's the Sufi story that we're reminded of

And they were left to consider the mystery
and to come to their own conclusions.

standing on top of Squaw Peak and looking over the city of Phoenix with the lights sparkling at night just like the slides that we were shown.

Robert said that it was time
to return to the city.
He didn't know how long he had
been there, often, times, but
he always had to go back to where he
lived and where he worked and even to where the problem was.

I climbed at sunrise it dawned on me.

And so Robert said that whenever he would return down the
mountain, sometimes he still considered
his problem, sometimes he found he had
forgotten about his problem. And he
said the thing that never changed was
that he always considered his problem
differently and when he did get around
to consulting about it again with his father,
he had a different question to ask than the
one that he had asked before the
instruction to climb.

Now Peter, climbing Squaw Peak, decided to go up the hard way.

He didn't take advantage of the path
because he thought Dr. Erickson literally
meant to climb.

But I walked up the path with Carol

We didn't see where the

and we got so confused

path was and had to

we climbed down.

slide down.

So you can go up and down the easy way or even go up and down the hard

Go up the easy way and

way.

down the hard way, or up the
hard way and down the easy way.

But you always have to come down.
You wouldn't want to stay up
there for very long.

It's very hot

and thirsty

and you have to take your clothes off if you stay there very long.

And the water at the bottom of the mountain that comes out of those little fountains is so cold and so refreshing, you can almost forget about your experience on the top of the mountain and become so engrossed in that water.

And that's really the problem and the reason you want to have photographs from the top of Squaw Peak because you can forget about the entire thing. I don't remember now more than just a little glimmer of lights that I saw in the background. And I remember that I found a little piece of metal hammered into the center of Squaw Peak that apparently is the tip-top.

An official center, at
the top most point.

Thinking about it though I do remember seeing a small lizard and a nice picture of my son with the sun behind him, and a picture of Carol with the sun behind her.

We can only imagine what it would
be like on the top of one of these mountains.

I heard the howl of coyotes. It sounded like a bunch of rowdy teenagers lurking somewhere around there. Now there is something lurking, so maybe there are some questions lurking in the back of your mind. But knowledge is lurking around here somewhere. Maybe we should take a short break to look for it.

Pacing	Mountains of Austria Squaw Peak
Questions	Robert's story of climbing Squaw Peak
Exploring a part	Sufi story
Time distortion	Travelling after Erickson's workshop (car)
Confusion by two voices touching	Client story (psychotic woman with "fantasy trips")
Dissociation beginning	Travelling after Erickson's workshop (airplane)
Deepening Expanding	Counting: reviewing things, having more ideas
Dissociation	Plane taking off
Regression	Child and parents Working on pressures and discomforts Client's story of illness Undamaged sensations Needs, trust
Therapy	New Decisions
	Expression
Progression	Reexamine the decisions, when growing
Integration	Balancing failures and successes
Amnesia by abruptly changing the subject	Plane landing
Integration	Sufi story
Confirming the change, lead back	Robert's story of climbing Squaw Peak
Future pacing	Squaw Peak, souvenirs
Pacing	Mountains of Austria

Figure 1. Basic structure for Carol and Stephen Lankton's Climbing Squaw Peak

32

David Cheek: Whenever You Drive a Car, Stay Alert

COMMENTS

In his induction, David Cheek gives us another instrument to use for therapy, self-therapy and broadening consciousness. It is a special method to bring up deep information. By reviewing sequences of activity first with ideomotor unconscious muscle movements without trying to remember things consciously, you may regain forgotten dreams, traumatic events and the mislaid key of your car! We acquired a practical implement for our everyday life and, for very special events, a serviceable key service. At the end David Cheek carefully makes sure that we stay our of hypnosis when we drive a car after leaving the workshop, something everybody should take care of who leads groups with hypnosis. This is a general recommendation, but for those who are experienced in trance David Cheek agrees that even driving cars at speed is possible while in hypnosis. It is far better to stay in a totally alert, awake state.

INDUCTION

How many of you have not been able to get finger signals? There are still two or three who have not.

[He asks one who has held up her hand whether she dropped her pencil during the group induction we did on the first day. She nods her head to indicate "yes."] Now, in order to drop your pencil your fingers holding the pencil had to pull apart just a little. That movement was unconscious. It is just a matter of a little practice before you can be sure your fingers are moving unconsciously to represent unconscious answers to questions. I would like the group now to go along with a simple hypnotic induction involving a review of sequential experiences, those going on here from the time we first met three days ago until the present moment.

Every time we review sequences of activity we go into hypnosis in the process. This was a discovery made more than 40 years ago by Milton Erickson. Instead of holding a pencil between your thumb and index finger please rest both hands on your lap and wonder which finger will lift for each of the moments I describe. There will be just three fingers involved and I would like to have all three be on one hand.

Close your eyes and let your inner mind go back to our first day. Manfred (Prior) is outlining what we will be doing. When you are recalling that moment your finger that will now become your "yes" symbol finger will lift as though a thread were tied to the tip of your finger. Each time you come to something you feel is very important to you your "no" finger will lift. When you have ended the review at the present moment your "I don't want to answer" finger will lift.

Do not try to remember anything consciously. This is an unconscious review. If you went over the entire three days three or four times you would begin to remember consciously what we were doing. This, however, is just an exercise in reviewing as well as establishing finger signals that could be used to discover information that is consciously unknown to you.

As you go along with the review you will be going progressively deeper. For most of our uses we can remain at a very light level of hypnosis while the movements of our fingers are accessing information that may be residing at very deep levels of memory. Repetitive reviewing allows the information to be raised to higher levels where it can be translated into spoken language.

Go back to the beginning now. Your "yes" finger will lift to let you know you are listening to Manfred. Your "no" finger will lift to indicate each important moment and your "I don't want to answer" finger will lift when you are back to the present moment. Hypnotic time moves very rapidly. You can in a few minutes review the entire 72-hour period. I will keep quiet while you do this. (Pause)

When your "I don't want to answer" finger lifts, you can open your eyes and be wide awake again feeling relaxed and comfortable. (It took approximately eight minutes for the group members to start opening their eyes and coming out of their hypnotic state. David Cheek then asked us to close our eyes and allow our unconscious mind to think about this request.) When ever you are at the controls of a moving vehicle I would like you to stay at a totally alert and awake state. When your inner mind is willing to accept this to protect your safety as well as the safety of others your "yes" finger will lift. If, for some reason your subconscious mind refuses to do this, your "I don't want to answer" finger will lift. If it lifts, I want to talk to you at the end of this meeting. It is very important to stay out of hypnosis when you are driving an automobile.

— 33 —

Virginia Satir: Morning Meditation

INDUCTION

This is the last morning of our conference. And I think, it's a special time. A special time because of all that has happened in the last four days. And I want to honor that in a meditation this morning.

For those of you, who were not here yesterday morning, I would just like to say a few words about meditation. It's a time, when I give full permission to myself for a concentrated space of time to just be with me. And I see it as a way of giving myself an opportunity to pull all my energy into one place, pull it from out here and bring it to me. I've then a more integrated core within myself. To do this five minutes, two minutes, one minute, 20 minutes, twice a day would be very helpful.

And one of the other things about meditation for me is, that it gives me a chance to separate myself from the rest of the world and to give myself a chance to see "me" in a perspective, in a way, I don't ordinarily see myself when I am so busy interacting. It's a time when I can bathe my insides. I can nurture myself making it possible for me to have strength for what I need to do. In the world today we need lots of strength to be able to use our wisdom and to find effective ways to make the changes that we have to make in the world. And changes can be made from a person that is in charge of himself and in touch with all his strength. The more we are integrated within ourselves the more relevant will be what we see and hear and what we say and do. And I would like to be able to have myself at my disposal at the highest level of my confidence. Meditation is one of the ways I achieve that.

Also in meditation there is a certain set of ideas that I have to reinforce myself with, that for me is a design to help me to become strong so that I can use myself more effectively. And that's the meditation that I use in variations all the time. There are many others, but this one is one I particularly like to use.

Now at this moment everyone is seated, I can see that. What I would like you to do now is very gently let your eyes close. And as your eyes close, just let yourself become aware of how quickly your eyelids followed your thoughts. You didn't scold them, you didn't promise them anything, you just had a thought to close your eyes, and they closed. Could it be, that we could be on such an intimate relationship with all the rest of our body that it would respond in the same way as our eyelids now? I think so, but yet I do not know how, totally.

Now, as we are seated here, our eyelids are closed. Now let us be in touch with our breathing. We do it all the time, in fact, if we stop, we would not be here. But this morning we will do it with an awareness of our breathing, noticing the rhythm of our breathing, how we take in the air, and then knowing, that we have this wonderful machinery that takes out of the air what we need. Perhaps there will be an awareness, a growing awareness, that in the taking of the breath some times we need to look at the kind of air that's there from which we breathe. And I know, it's on the mind of many of us at this point about what is in our air now from the accident in Russia. Maybe in this moment we can give our bodies extra strength to take out of the air that, which doesn't fit for our bodies and let it go out in some way, ask our bodies to be a companion and help to us to take in only that part of the air which is helpful.

And now, taking in the air and recognizing that it is out of the air we breathe, that we get our nurturing. Without it we cannot live another second. Life and breath are the same. As we pay attention to our breathing we must also be aware, that with all awareness we can send our breath to all the different parts of our body, that through the way we physically breathe, we can allow the breath to nurture ourselves.

And now, our eyes being closed, being in touch with our breathing, can we now become aware of the relaxed nature of our body. If there are any little tight places, we can let them relax and give ourselves over to relief, allowing the chair and the floor to support us, feel the feeling of the alertness of our body and at the same time the relaxation. It will be in the spirit and in the unconditional relaxation, that we will be able to do our best.

And now, our eyes are closed, we are in touch with our breathing; our body is relaxed, our mind is alert, and that we now, deep inside give ourselves a message of appreciation for us, that might sound something like: I appreciate me—meaning just that, not against anyone else or for anyone else, but simply an appreciation of me like one who would look at a beautiful painting or an art piece or something else that we deeply admire and appreciate and would want to take care of and want to be our best self in relation to. I appreciate me—and a fuller meaning of that would enable us to look for the best things for ourselves, that we would take the best care of ourselves and knowing deep down to the degree that we take care of ourselves we would not have to ask other people to do it. And that we, as we recognize that each person has the capacity of taking care of themselves would be willing to be lights to the other person, but in no way ask or demand that they do what we want. Inside the beautiful feeling we could have, as we become aware that we are the only one exactly like us in this whole world. And that every other human being is like us in some ways and different from us in some ways. Thus we are a unique being to be treasured, to be valued, to be discovered. And within that frame again feel what it feels like to honor ourselves by telling ourselves: I appreciate me.

And now, to move further to the place where we keep the treasure that is called by our name. As we move to that place, that very sacred place we notice our resources, our ability to see, to hear, to touch and taste and smell, to feel and to think, to move and to speak, we become aware that these resources are with us constantly and that, the umbrella over all these resources is our ability to choose, to choose out of all that we see and hear and feel and think. We exercise our most important resource, our ability to choose, to choose out of all that, which at this moment fits us well and let go that which no longer fits, blessing it, because once it did something for us. Now we give ourselves permission to develop that, which we need at this point, and in so doing know, that until the end of our lives we can continue this sorting process, letting go of that, which no longer fits, choosing what we have, which fits us well and taking the courage and the initiative to develop that, which we see we need, which we yet do not have and know that because of our resources we can do that. And now to remind ourselves of our resources, our relationship to the center of the earth, where the energy moves constantly and to become aware of that energy moving upward through our feet and legs and thighs into our torso, bringing with it the energy of groundedness, our ability to be reasonable and practical and to analyze, to be logical. And then to become aware of the energy from the heavens, as it moves down through our head and face and neck and arms and chest into our torso, bringing with it the energy of inspiration, of imagination, of sensing, and the realization, that here is, where our dreams come from. Because of our imagination and inspiration and sensing we can start to form that, which will make our dreams become a reality. As the energy of our inspiration and of our groundedness join in a beautiful union, they create still a third energy, the energy to move outward outside of us through our arms and hands, touching, being touched, physically, emotionally, mentally, and bringing back that energy to us inside, creating the energy of connectedness with other human beings.

Then to become aware that we always are in touch with our energy of inspiration and groundedness and that, where we are in the presence of others, we have the chance for directly connecting with those energies. Without the presence of others we have the memory of people close to us, from whom we draw energy. So at this moment becoming aware that for the rest of our lives we can know that we are part of the family of the planet, of the earth, of the whole universe through our connectedness with the center of the earth, the heavens and the people upon the earth outside of ourselves.

During these last days many wonderful inspiring informative things have happened. They have happened in such a way, so that everyone was free to look and to listen and to taste everything so much while at the same time giving ourselves permission to take out of all that richness that, which fits us well and to give ourselves permission to use it in our own special way.

Now this moment allow yourselves to remind yourselves again of an appreciation of yourself, and perhaps, as you do that, to deepen an appreciation for others; to remind yourself of your continuing developing resources and to remind yourselves that we are all in this universe.

In this seminar, I have been pleased and felt love and value from you; I in return have those feelings for you, I hope for you and for myself, that we move to light up the dark places of ourselves and the world, that we give ourselves permission to know, who we really are, so that the light of hope does not dim, even when our world is at a moment in time in chaos. My hope is at this time, that you give yourself a blessing and a message to grow.

Now let your beautiful eyes open and gently allow whatever sound or movement wants to come out of you as you come fully to this place. Then perhaps you will turn and greet people on your right or left. [pause] Thank you very much.

COMMENTS

Virginia Satir held this morning meditation during the terrible days directly after the Tschernobyl disaster when most people had not yet managed to comprehend the crucial significance of this unprecedented man-made catastrophe. Then she gave us such a deep confidence in our human potentialities that no panic occurred and the participants left the Symposion Family Therapy in Osnabrück indeed all the more ready to deal with things and take action. Therefore, I am particularly pleased to be able to include this very beneficial group induction, which connects us to our roots, and thus make it available to many more people. It is for me still a constant source of nourishment, both timely and timeless, formally well-formed and valid in content. This induction shows as clearly as possible that mention of contemporary incidents and the then prevailing conditions is absolutely necessary if other people are to be reached. How could we have sat there at all quiet and relaxed if this had been omitted!

The introductory personal words about what meditation means to Virginia Satir convey coherently the immediate significance of the moment and motivate the group. In a formal sense, they also productively occupy the time it necessarily takes for quietness to settle at the beginning of a large gathering.

The next step where we are requested to close our eyes is already used by Virginia Satir to draw our attention to our abilities, namely, how well our body follows our thoughts. When during the next section she turns to breathing, this is done by mentioning the previous steps once again and these are thus declared stages:

Stage One. We are sitting here;

Stage Two. We have closed our eyes;

Stage Three. Let us get into contact with breathing.

Here a fundamental human ability is again pointed out: taking those parts of the air that we need as nourishment. As we have this basic capacity it could also be possible for us to filter our injurious, nocuous constituents. Here a foundation stone is laid for trust in the human potential for development, and the request directed at our body to render this possible is an entreaty for existence, a petition to Life.

Breath can be guided into all areas of the body. This reference results in a natural transition to relaxation of the whole body.

Stage Four, the deepening of trance, is very skillfully obtained by Virginia Satir's repeating the previous steps before starting a new one. In the following *Stage Five*, the polarity between relaxed body and watchful mind, is used to achieve the deep inward balance that makes trance work feasible. In this we are exhorted to appreciate our own worthiness, our own valuable being. However difficult this may be, no one can escape the realization of being a unique person, the only one of this like being in the entire world, and this is in itself sufficient reason to value one's self in one's own uniqueness.

On continuing to progress to *Stage Six*, further resources are reached, here they are quite concretely recognized as our sensory perceptions. What particularly impresses and pleases me is Virginia Satir's insight into the usefulness of our most important resource, our basic ability to choose with regard to all these sensory-based perceptions. The time dimension is now brought into play. What we bid farewell to is worthy of respect: and what is still lacking we can still develop fully trusting in our basic ability of choice. In the section where we were occupied with breathing, Virginia Satir had set a seed for this fruit of meditation, aiming at contacting our resource of choice potential.

In the next part, *Stage Seven*, we are placed as a human in the polarized, universal energy field of earth and heaven, which meet perceptibly within our body. Virginia Satir is excellent at integrating these forces by smelting them to something new, to unison and alliance with other people. Through this she achieves not only a balanced flow of energy within our physical, corporal life but also a harmony at the level of understanding. In a future-oriented suggestion she helps us to experience how, through sharing in these forces, we are members of the great family of this world and of the entire Universe.

Now reorientation begins. This occurs very naturally through reviewing the previous days as Virginia Satir reminds us how we were able to use our resources during this period. Linguistically of note, is the literal repetition of our sensory perceptions, the resources named in the penultimate section (Stage Six). Then we are led further back through the region of self-esteem and self-value (Stage Five). Now this acceptance and recognition can be extended to other people. During the further return journey to the present, all hitherto mentioned aspects are brought in again combined artistically and yet naturally. In my opinion this trance induction of Virginia Satir entails extremely intensive work and striving to the effect that we may become wakeful and may begin to explore our genuine human potentialities.

34

Wilhelm Gerl: Finally It's Yours

COMMENTS

Wilhelm Gerl presents us with a farewell gift or a souvenir from his seminar in the form of a bird's eye view of a self hypnotism model. He hands this to us not in the form of a drab grey memorandum but prettily wrapped as a group induction.

INDUCTION

Once, at the end of a private seminar, a participant said, "I know I've learnt a lot, even though I can't say at the moment what it all is and how I shall actually use it—there was so much implicit. But I would have like (sic) to take something with me that will help when I sit down at home this evening or tomorrow and want to practice further more, like a step-by-step model I can use to orient myself and then know where I am now—and to what I should pay attention next."

I think this is a good idea and reply: "Right, what I'm going to show you still is not really new. Basically you know it already. And maybe you may also know that Milton Erickson said, 'You cannot learn about your unconscious mind with your conscious mind.' But nevertheless your conscious mind can give you valuable assistance. And you simply need it to set securely the frame within which you set about setting out to develop your self-hypnosis. You need its cooperation 'at the entrance to a trance' . . . and then its, well, benevolent support for returning pleasantly refreshed from the trance. It can play its part in the transformation and help actively 'whenever you need a translater (trance later)' . . . You understand?" Well so far, so good: what I want to (do) remind you of these completely easy steps, that are so natural that they may simply appear quite trivial like—letting them serve you easily for you to observe them. As soon as the sequence of steps is clear to you, it will serve you letting go into trance in any way—and always in a wholly personal way . . . You can feel full of well-being knowing full well you are always fully able to learn more further—furthermore all ways wholly in your own way and at the same time trying out the various possibilities that you become easily well-acquainted with.

Of course you have already agreed with yourself setting on a course for getting yourself ready setting a time for this learning now—and set your inner watch to give you a signal that is right to see to your return when it is right for you. In case there are other people at home, put a sign on your door with the note "Don't disturb! I am available again from . . ." (and state the exact time). Then you agree with yourself to set a signal that you get in case some happening happens to occur that requires a break. For instance, you can decide that your right or your left hand touch a part of your body and you breathe strongly, pleasantly before in case of need your eyes open.

Well now you have seen to a proper safe set-up and may now take up the time that is wholly there for me. And as you enter into trance as agreeably as possible and you want to return later just as easily, it's good for you to make sure right at the beginning that you really sit comfortably—or repose in some easy pose—and everything that otherwise only unnecessarily restricts is loosened up or put aside or taken off . . . You can really feel completely free to see that everything is put into its place, deposit there, until it's quite all right for you . . .

For you have maybe already developed some idea about this, it may be quite vague for what you would like to use this time for . . . you can leave it open and leave it quite (quiet) up to your intuitive knowledge to work further . . . and you can feel safe and secure in this knowledge for your being in contact with yourself and this complete entire knowledge, this entity, within which you will find it easy to contact this profound being deeper down within . . . into contact with something that needs nothing further than this time . . . and may show itself as assistance for learning, that is more deeply satisfying . . . And you take for yourself a few minutes clock time—and all the personal time for your unconscious, n o w . . . [2 minutes]

As you are sitting here (hear), you sometimes do not realize everything you are learning . . . But you can notice everything that you are aware of at the moment: of everything, of all that you can sense . . . of all that simply belongs to that . . . for you, simply experience, whatever may be sound, resound for you . . . and whatever may appear to you all of its own accord, entirely in its own way in, too. (Into) Like in (liking) our dreams: only when a dream has come to an end do we know what we have been dreaming—and afterwards, retrospectively, we discover single phases or steps of this happening that could just happen so simply . . .

So then, why not simply go and have another look and discover a helpful structure? Or observe the inner order of this happening . . . therefore it's good for many people if they get a view of the whole. One uses sketches, paper or a table—a second lets the happenings pass by and marks in turns the points that appear important—and which can then be noted more easily. This can, for instance, look as though you let a blank space, possibly something like a sheet of paper, appear in front of your inner eye . . . with an upper edge, a left-hand margin and a right-hand margin . . . and up top left is the starting point, and there you note down an idea, a phrase, that is at the first phase beginning the happening—for instance: "attentive," if it is about describing the way into a pleasant trance of middle depth . . . there someone needs full attention—and that is surely certain to be so for you devote yourself to that . . . Right, well, after the injunction "be attentive" has been well and truly carried out, we may look at the right-hand side of our plan to see what will now be the next thing. And which word is the right one here? And this is clear to us at once: what we need now is to be "concentrated" . . . so we go down one line lower and write down left once more "concentrated" . . . "concentrated" as the starting point for the next step . . . and this follows so naturally there, for to be "absorbed" is simply the other side of being concentrated, therefore this happens automatically . . .

Therefore we may go down one line lower down once again at once . . . and entirely easily let the word "absorbed" appear left . . . Right now what will well happen right next? This question is easily solved if you only attend somewhat to what is doing you good right now—as you are sitting here as comfortably as possible—as a mind and a body . . . feel quite free to let yourself relax even more and let go comfortably with each breath (breathe) in and breath (breathe) out—for it is quite clear that the right words for that could be "free" (or "detached" or "relaxed") . . . just look there where this is already right for you—and where you would like it to develop still further . . . And we can descend one line lower down again . . . and as soon as that's all right for you, when "free" (or "detached" or "relaxed") appears left, then just leave open what will happen further all on its own within the next minute . . . there's plenty of free space left to be right in the free place left . . . You may let yourself feel completely free to leave the choice up to your unconscious—and in the meantime you may be developing some idea of which word describes this state of mind all right for you—maybe very simply "open" is the right word? Then you can go down one more line lower down once more in and look to see how well "open" feels here in this place . . . and you yourself need not be curious, not to say open—it is enough when you are simply somewhat open minded so that you may continue further to learn with your intuitive (into a deep) wisdom more creative in this way further more in contact with your profound deep knowledge . . . and so it is indeed a deeper satisfying learning, within which you have access to all your knowledge, able to use it well—able to deepen it further . . .

Well, now, the last word that's right and properly sunk in now is the word "deepened" . . . ((i.e., engrossed, sunk in)). And there in front of your inner eye you have the possibility of picturing this whole plan again: From

attentive	to	concentrated
concentrated	to	absorbed
absorbed	to	free (detached, relaxed)
free (detached, relaxed)	to	open
open	to	deepened
deepened	to	. . .

And when you feel like it sometime you can draw or write down this picture—perhaps even more like your own experience—and then by chance discover how you have already used this all ready internal model quite automatically: during a good, really profound deep discussion with someone . . . while telling an animated anecdote—or at a pause or break in the induction of such a pleasurable and creative state, just as you like yourself . . .

And then of course it sometimes is an extra additional pleasure to listen to colleagues perhaps here working at a course—and hereby to know even more certainly where you are right now . . . or the joy of discovering one has when one reads an article in a book for the second time and it's like scales falling off one's eyes, a light being switched on . . . And you say, "Hello!" and you feel really lively—exactly as you may need now . . .

COMMENTS

Please notice the rich inventiveness as play with "left" and "right," so that both hemispheres take part in simultaneously experiencing and understanding the trance process. Also appreciate the skill involved in using the lines of an imaginary sheet of paper to let us "go down," descend more deeply. There are no limits to what everyday things can be used by an ingenious hypnotherapist.

35

Gunther Schmidt and Bernhard Trenkle: Final Fare-well Trance

COMMENTS

As the last induction of this book it is my pleasure to present the dual integration trance of "the two dissimilar brothers who work so well together," Gunther Schmidt and Bernhard Trenkle. Bernhard Trenkle's detailed commentary draws attention to the otherwise possibly unnoticed, earnest intentions, concealed references and word-play full of puns that the authors have woven together as a strong meshed safety net for the whole group. It is surely no accident that Bernhard Trenkle, who jazzes up his MEGaphon(e) [the German Milton Erickson Gesellschaft (M.E.G.) newsletter] with therapeutic jokes, ends this induction, the seminar and, also, the practical part of this book by retailing a humorous, though perhaps somewhat crude, anecdote.

INDUCTION

G.	B.
That was a coming and a going. And whoever wants to can go out. And just like one can go out, one can like going in, according to wherever one wants to go in on a conscious or an unconscious plane,[1]	
	just as one can sit down relaxed and easy and can remember the last round, or the last round but one,
or the last round but two, and this memory can be used to simply allow oneself to look in what way one can let oneself go in today in a pleasant way accompanied by sounds into other experiences,	

into trance experiences[2]

and just as Marianne had not
at all known that it is an experience if she can now sit
down quite quietly—[1]

So one learns without cease
never finished with ease

And hears outside the banging
of the car door. And how today
in contrast to workdays no
lorries passing—[3]

All the things one must miss in
a trance that one allows oneself on a Sunday—

how many people today simply
sit there, those who can treat
themselves after working, work
well-done, just sit there . . .

So like how on one beautiful
evening, a restful evening, one
simply looks back over the past
day's trip one has taken—simply lets it pass by like an internal film one looks at, all
the pictures, memories, feelings
that are connected with this trip

And it will last a certain
time until an inner peace and
calm,—and until one simply
need not think of anything.
And whether one can think back
to Monday and to the arrival

and to Wednesday and to the
arrival
and to Friday[3]

and to Tuesday

and to all the many new themes
and stimulating suggestions and
interesting ideas

and to the familiar themes
and well-known suggestions
and ideas

and, completely concentrated,
think about all the forgotten

to be able to orient oneself
completely towards
what one wants to begin with
today and what one can do with
all the days that are still
given to one.

just as some inner attitude may
have changed

And you are all so different in
your very own potentialities
for practical learning in all
your very own experiences and
associations, so that I wonder in
what various ways each and every
one of you here will take your
own and will make this possible
step by step from what is for
you today the appropriate form
of trance.

you can simply allow yourself

And one can on the conscious
plane take part or simply let
it be. And one can so easily
find it's slightly hard or a hard
trial and it can hardly be trying
to be tempted hard to let oneself try and deal lightly with it[4]

and what will your unconscious
offer you next?
pleasant
ways sitting swimming[5]

move on move

suggestions, where one can
leave everything behind

Sunday

And the weather has changed—

in one direction and in the
other direction. Simply sit there—

And the use of symbols in
your own way

to integrate more and more

and dive in and dive out, submerge and emerge

to an appropriate, fitting

more and more

stroke by stroke
stroke by stroke.
breath by breath

submerge and emerge

stroke and (sic) stroke[6]

pleasant temperature
this feeling of being borne up
and how difficult it was then
to learn how to swim, and how
safely, fully automatically,
warmly, pleasantly stroke on freely[5]

stroke by stroke
now you can swim.[6,7]
And isn't it interesting to be
able to perhaps also realize
consciously once again that we
are now free of all possible,
all manner of skeptical thoughts
that one has often otherwise thus
said: ((quietly and quickly)) Oh,
it won't work, and poor talents,
bad show, and what's really the
matter with me and O God, this is
so strenuous! And I shall never
be able to integrate this in a
completely playful way

peace full peace
stroke by stroke
bit by bit
piece by piece

and be able to integrate this
in an entirely appropriate and
suitable way for oneself whatever one would like to take out
of this whole great offer, this,
a sack full of presents.[8]

Or to imagine how a space tra-
veller,—how grave and serious
a weighty matter this training
is, weightlessness for
resisting gravity—how weighty
and gravely arduous it is to[9]

learn—per ardua ad astra—

and some know that perhaps—
that a plane can simulate
weightlessness and pretend to
resist the downward pull of

gravity. And in all the short
time it must learn to deal with
that and then when the plane
flattens out again, this total
weight, this unbelievable
weightiness

that gives one on the other
hand safety, this familiar form
of orienting

and the longing for that at
last to be there longer for
once for a while to be really
able to hover and float, suspended in space, fully poised,
lightened, at ease with all the
knowledge and the gained skill
and be still able to move
completely freely[10]

quite simply be able to float
and hover with lightness, simply
gliding. What great internal
freedom on a neutral plane, simply
be able to hover craftily and
float to wherever one want
to float.[10]

And like an astronaut who from
his perspective is able to take
a general survey and make a vast
overall prospect, with the
overview can look down onto
things, can see the magnificent
colors from above[11]

and completely different relationships and connections

he must then always bear in
mind the individual skills,
the mathematical training and
the many physical things he has
learnt about guiding missiles,
piloting planes, steering
rockets and about this and[12]
that, many buttons and
switches—

and all the many confusing details, that were so confusing that one sometimes thought, "I shall perhaps never have the prospect and get a whole clear view overview"

errors in the prospectus, mistakes in the manual, misunderstandings with the master or the boss, the doubts: Have I understood that properly, haven't I understood that?[12]

And the joy on recognizing on the conscious or unconscious plane

being able to simply float, hover fully poised, suspended

And one notices how something gradually integrates itself bit by bit, piece by piece, move on move, growing together—developing

and all the things that lie behind one

to one harmonious entity

to be able to simply hover, well poised, and be able to trust the acquired knowledge and above all the colleagues

floating, hover, over firm ground

with the colleagues who are right now doing the work while one can just simply float well—poised, easily confident that everything is all right and in order. That whenever anything unforeseen happens, one can rely on and draw on all knowledge already (all ready) obtained, fully automatically

And as one floats so can one, lightly poised and hovering, carry out whether one prefers to in a grave and weighty manner or in a light and easy manner or whether one oscillates between weighty and lighter matters, to all the harmoniously evolved experience that one has had develop so gradually comprehend, rely and depend upon being able to fall back upon again.

What an enormous experience that must be therefore for there is for one when one has prepared oneself for years to . . . always the longing again and then 30 seconds of floating easy weightlessness, free of the load, the heavy downward pull of gravity, at long last finally longer floats stable (floats able) in every situation, easily poised in every position

to have the prospective, pleasant prospect, entire survey, allround view over view

from above, entirely free

just like in a semi-nars (near's) first class-room with a long meta-phor (far) may (farm) be able to let this survey, view over view, gradually become more and more

And I don't know whether up there above if one had the vast entire survey over view, the whole prospect, one thinks of certain connections and relationships, may be about a story heard in a philosophy or history lesson or about a meditation course, that thought of course may be coming here[13]

or memories of a symbol or of symbols (cymbals!)

How one thinks such things or matters may be integrated more and more

or memories of deeper trance
experiences in other settings

this entirely three-dimensional
experience

where entirely in your own
middle you do what is right at
the moment[16]

or four-dimensional experience

just as though one's own inner
compass, the outcome of inner
wisdom comes out of oneself
what it does for one

so that, forth-with, the three
dimensions in space out to get
a fourth, time, when at the
moment of intense enjoyment
time stands still likewise one
is fully there without current
interests, without needs, within oneself, well poised and
freely floating

simply here and now this confidence in the feeling here
and now this here and now
familiar feeling

without having to think of the
entire knowledge and be able to
trust confidently whenever this
will prove necessary like
driving a car

trusting that this here and
now familiar experience and
what does it mean to everyone
of us here and now let trusty
familiar experiences simply develop

And this story from meditation,[14]
this story of the two brothers[15]

from these two dissimilar, very different
brothers who worked together
cooperating both

and his story and the other's

so differently and yet still
cooperatively

and these two brothers who ran
a ranch or farm together
(farmed together).

And can that be that one can

both be different and still cooperate? Both either or as well
as either as also or? Or both
as well as also either or either
and or—
or what?

And often new methods of
cultivating, tilling, and sowing
till when two brothers work
together so until one brother
has more time

and the other has less time

to care for things, to read
books, attend, furthermore, furtherance courses and, of course,
the other then, the willingness
to take up new impulses and
ideas

so that each in his own place
can reap something fruitful and
ripely enriching for the whole[16]

and harvest festival, that's
Thanksgiving, always a time,
thinking back till the time of
tilling the field all ready

to the time also of resting, of
looking back, of looking together,

time of care, whether the
weather may be willing

time of hope that it will be
may well be if one needs it

and then in that time after
the harvest festival and
Thanksgiving, then these two dissimilar
brothers who were so different

and yet still had cooperated
and worked together in puzzling
out their brains in their
conscious thinking

about the year and the harvest

and over justice and righteous-
ness and the appropriateness of

the different contributions
and the other brother

and so one brother

the one who had a wife and children had thought over and back over the year and the harvest

and the other brother who was in another situation in his life and had thought over and had simply rightaway let emerge up out of his unconscious whatever at the moment his organism held to be right and proper and thought over in his own proper way

when the married brother thought: we have shared the corn, the potatoes and all the fruit fifty-fifty

this pleasant feeling of warmth that can develop

and that is not right and proper, fifty-fifty. My God, when I think of how often my brother was longer out on the fields. I was already at home because the family was waiting. Or early in the morning he was already out on the fields while I was still lying in bed with my wife. And at the weekends we went for a drive with the children and my brother was always there. Fifty-fifty is not right and proper.

And as for the other brother as he was sitting there in his chair and was allowing himself completely different feelings in his bodily plane at the physical level

parallel, please,

heaviness, weight, warmth and

sometimes lightness and ease
whatever was pleasant for him
and thus in a very clear plane
was having thoughts: "Fifty-
fifty—that's not right and
proper."

but still not able to sleep

and therefore the married one
got up and carried a good part
of his harvest into the barn
of his brother

and the other was always still
thinking about that, "Fifty-fifty,
that's not right, not at all in
order for he has so many proper
needs, so much I do not need at
all, fifty-fifty

My God, when I think about I
am alone and single, he has a
wife, he has children

I need not even the half. Fair-
ness and fitness is not only an
arithmetic question"

now then he got up and then a
good portion of his corn
(cereal) and his potatoes and
his fruit were borne by him (serially)
into the barn of his married
brother

So that both different brothers
had in completely different ways
obviously done almost the same
thing. And one had borne a part
of his takings into the barn of
the other and the other taken a
part of his takings into the barn
of the foremost secretly by night

and in the morning both barns
full
that was confusing

full strange and wonderful
worthy of attention is also what
interesting associations can
appear floating weightlessly
and which feelings can be

so such an astronaut
such an astronaut can while he
is floating above simply

offered to one there by
and how much battle are you
able to battle on with this
knowledge when something is integrating itself and it does not
yet want at the moment, too,
it does not want to allow and let
all the feelings and the esteem
and this understanding all the
longing for that and express the
past
for all the feelings are offers
out from our unconscious that
can remind us on a conscious
plane what we are all ready, already always knew and wanted
and are now able to rediscover, find, it again
able to find oneself again
can put oneself gradually together more now with measure
with feeling and thinking together
entirely all right all in order whatever comes

draw, rely, fall back upon
So that one can even sometimes
prefer and bring forward
some of what one did earlier
here and there occasionally
just simply again, maybe, even
sometimes with mistakes—simply
to make and take again in a playful way so that one know that
one can still do it well, be

at the height of competence

suspended in space
And floating freely

and the feelings of the astronauts may be different, maybe
the one concentrates on working
on something

and the other simply is occupied with his own self and in
oneself

and yet at all times be able to
know whenever that becomes necessary immediately and fully
well concentrated on all that
well tilled and gleaned after
long labor, on all that familiar knowledge
all resources

good at it. To make mistakes in
an artistic manner is not always
so simple. And how important it
is to know that one can still do
well, be able to make the old
mistakes from time to time, so[17]
that one need not integrate everything always.

And why has that boss or
master written for one of his
colleagues in the book as dedication: make many mistakes
and learn from them?[17]

And what has the person who has
had this written for him in the
book drawn on knowledge and
gained in insight for himself?
And so much need is still there
also, of course, always to know
already, in advance, what one has
all ready integrated and how will
it all be readily approached and
interesting, intriguing it is to
be surprised sometimes, like
this friend of mine who was presented with all the different
onions, bulbs, corms and other
sorts of flower seed
then
and presented with
symbols for so many[18]

then
at the end of the studies
symbols

and the confusion about the
many bags, white bags without
labels

colored bags
and not to know what could
all be in there and to think:
"Ah, now I've properly got it
really categorized, and then
again the question—Maybe
there may be far more still
inside than I can see

only the instructions,
only the instructions,
when, where and how these bulbs
are to be planted

and how are they then to be cared for

no hint, no name, simply just have to wait

and not to know whether everything in the consciously controlled way will really germinate

and these months where absolutely nothing can happen

where it looked simply as though there was nothing there at all and what can one month mean!

Although then the friend who had given all these bulb presents had somehow reckoned with the impatience somewhat and therefore included snowdrops so that sometime already after a somewhat shorter time something would become visible

also for conscious thinking

then, month for month, the larger plants, interesting colorful flowers of the most varied forms and different types

magnificent flowers, masterpieces, wonders of nature

and still the gratitude also for the first snowdrops

that wanted to calm down and sooth the conscious thinking in their impatience there and in spite of that this uncertainty of conscious thinking what of all the bulbs and what of the seeds will germinate, those seeds sown 'nd you'd seeduring (sic!) their sowing and how they're germinating. Which of them will germinate and which not yet? And what perhaps not all—straightaway

And accept the weather, for they're
many things, that one cannot
control, and sometimes an
astronaut really can and may
end the flight in the regular
way, for instance,[19]

and can observe the weather,
how, for instance, the plants can
be nourished within instants
even by rain and animal motion—
manure—and develop with slight
movements—[20]

Moving and getting into motion
all ready having to prepare for
the landing

Movement and motion bring
blessings, motion on land well
being a blessing

Having to prepare oneself for
landing in a completely certain
and sure ways and means
no longer be able to float so
freely and

and sometimes
some see drab
landscapes seemingly scant
and bare and when the rain
comes with the wind's new
movements, so much new stuff
blooms and blossoms a fresh
spring so

completely concentrated on
one's own knowledge and abilities and certain interests and
motives and needs so naturally
a good landing on course.
And of course must fasten one's
safety belt, buckle down to
activate one's own knowledge

And fasten safety belt buckle
down in order to put the last
pieces together gather together piece for piece makes
peace
and each puzzle piece pieced
together furnishes a further
puzzling piece move by move

in all quietness and peace
and calm be all ready prepared

whether the weather still with
a stroke of Donner and Blitzen

stroke on stroke
breath by breath
furnishing a moving
furniture move on so the
breath taking landing can
be accomplished[21]

will move on peacefully furnishing a more breath taking
your own place
independently and
moving on

and one can rely on the colleagues and every one whether he
or she, also when in the same
room the entirely individual
impressions, one's own
completely private impression
may remain forever conscious
or unconscious like remembered.

And piece by piece it can do
very much that conscious thinking cannot always foresee, just
like this girl who had been on
a sinking ship swam 20 km, and
when she finally arrived on the
shore, safe and sure and full
of new experiences, even though
they were also not always
pleasant, asked in surprise:
What, I am supposed to have
swam that? 20 km. And the
others said, "yes." And asked, "How
did you manage that, little
girl?" And she said, "I just did
by saying simply now I'll swim
just one more stroke and then
another stroke and stroke
again a stroke by stroke,
breath by breath[22]

back

bit by bit
to the shore
standing sure on both legs
move on move
breath by breath
to the sure
clear, refreshed,
fully oriented

to the shores of
consciousness.
Take everything with you
that you want
And breath by breath
move by move and ([simultaneously knocking rhythmically])
Step by step

[Noises and laughter of participants
Someone says: "What did you say: about a
pause or—sure—shores?"—loud yawns]

There's a very interesting
story that fits in . . .

[Very loud laughter from participants.
someone says: That reminds me of a story]

It's not the right weather,[23]
but there was once really a
drought, a very long period of
drought and they really went to
church and prayed for rain and
sang "Cry when the rain falls"[24] and
did everything they could, and
they even set fire to things,
because they thought, "Perhaps
it will make clouds and then
it will rain." Nothing could be
done. The whole harvest was
endangered, until at last the
oldest man in the place said
"There's nothing else to be
done. I must do it." Then he
sat in the middle of the
village market place and said,
"Bring me that horse and a dead rat!"
Then he took the reins and bound the
rat's fore (four) paws together
and somehow, somewhere there up above,
clouds gathered and it began to pour
with rain. And then they asked him,
"Well, come now, tell us how on earth did
you manage that?"

And he said "Well, don't you know the
saying "It never reins but what it paws?"
(It never rains but what it pours.)

([more loud laughs from participants])

Are we all awake again?

And as a German friend
of mine said: "Cry when rain falls and
coal (Kohl) comes!"

This is one of the quickest
re-induction techniques—when some-one does this
sort of shocking thing![25]

Have a good trip home!

COMMENTARY
by Bernhard Trenkle

1. Some participants had to leave early, others had already prepared to leave and return here to the group room to take part in the Final Farewell Trance. "To go in," with the double meaning: entering the group room, going into trance after the beginning, and perhaps leave before the end, while this demonstrates once more how to accept behavior and utilize it instead of letting oneself be disturbed.
2. Reminder about previous "rounds" (trance inductions and learning units). Remembering former trance experiences and associative meshing assist and accelerate the present trance and simultaneous associative memories from previous learning units prepare for the coming learning integration.
3. Further special words from the trance inductions and learning units of the seminar in connection with suggestions and symbols for relaxation (Sunday, time after work) 11.-13. refer to an earlier group trance, where play upon words like the following was employed: there are people who work on Wednesday and have Thursday as a free day, so that for them the Wednesday is a Tuesday [Transl. Note: i.e. work-days: as also the pronunciation and meaning in German] and the Thursday a Friday . . . [Note: pronunciation and meaning in German = freeday]. From 15. on: Orientation towards the goal: What will every person do completely individually with the abundant variety offered?
4. Induction of "soft," easier confusion with the use of puns: light-heavy (Note: also means easy-difficult in German).
5. Symbolic permission to go deeper into or again come up somewhat more from trance. (Fractional induction) Simultaneously reminding about a previous trance induction where work was done using the image of a swimmer who dives down and surfaces up.
6. Seeding for coming swimmer story, where a small girl from a sinking ship swam an

incredible distance in cold water and then managed to reach the shore and reports she had always only thought of the next stroke, stroke on stroke and stroke by stroke . . .

7. Strengthening feeling of well-being (pleasant water temperature) . . . Building up learning attitudes and transition from lack of confidence when learning to swim to trust and automatized pattern of behavior.
8. Connecting: just as it was then when learning to swim, first lack of confidence, doubt and scepsis and then the transition to fully automatized playful control, so will it be with the learning material of this seminar . . .
9. Continuation of the theme . . . Floating free of weight versus great heaviness and weight—an indirect offer of dissociation, of leaving the body and/or feeling great weight . . . at the same time once again symbols for fractionated trance: weightless, away from the earth (to go deeper) versus feeling heavy, the force of gravity (returning to earth) . . . and naturally parallel to this the whole time: learning, conscious learning, unconscious learning, and everything can become increasingly automatic and integrated.
10. Transition to prolonged feeling of weightlessness after all the long practicing and training, longing to be able to be suspended in space freely floating over a longer period of time—thus indirectly building up motivation to let oneself drop and leave go . . .
11. To have a general survey, an overview, perspective (over the earth and, in the other meaning, over what has been learnt) the words "Semi-nar" ("Seminar," pronounced "semi-nah," is here a German pun meaning both "seminar" and "partly near") and "Metaphern" ("Metaphern," pronounced "meta-fern," is here a German pun signifying "metaphor" and also "over, beyond, above-distant, far, away") were written on the blackboard by a participant during a pause. In this context they allow association of many meanings: preparation for leave-taking; semi-near, meta-far: is the standing aloof still distant? Semi-near, meta-far as steps towards is the standing aloof still distant? Semi-near, meta-far as steps towards letting oneself descend and go more deeply. Symbol for the fact that we have also learned from the participants and return again increasingly more towards the end of the seminar to the same shared plane—semi-near and meta-far.
12. Connecting with other learning and existential experiences of every participant concerned.
13. Further deepening.
14. onwards: This story of the Two Different Brothers: the seminar lasted 7½ days. After this trance the participants go home and then, full of new ideas and impulses, meet the partner and colleagues at work, for example. This story is aimed at acknowledging the partner and colleagues with their differences and their contributions and at reducing competition. What has been "sown" should have favorable conditions for germinating and growing and should become fruitful for the closer fields of relationship and with reference to the further environment.

15. Abrupt return to the theme before this story, whereby amnesia for the two-brothers story is facilitated (so-called structured amnesia).
16. Some participants react to this tale with tears, others attempt to suppress showing they have been touched. Therefore: suggestions in the direction of accepting oneself and one's emotions and activating the resources one needs to that end . . .
17. Inviting and permitting making mistakes . . . waiving hindersome claims to perfection . . . surrendering troublesome perfectionistic pretensions.
18. onwards: Story about the gift of flowerbulbs (Transl. Note: in German bulb is the same word as onion: symbol of multiple layers, a multitude of meanings) as a symbol of ideas that have been sown and will at some unknown time blossom out [Footnote: a return of thanks to our friend, Dr. Harald Ullmann, who gave me (B.T.) the gift of many flower bulbs during my end-of-studies party.] Summons to patience, being able to wait and let things mature and ripen.
19. Back to the old astronauts again: accepting the fact that one cannot have everything under control, e.g., the weather, the clients etc.
20. Double meaning: rain and movement, thus combining and passing from the bulb theme to new/old: landing of the astronauts (symbol for gradual return from the flight of fancy and orientation to the walking state). Seeding of the final anecdote.
21. Integrating symbolism via puns: piece, peace, stroke, breath, moving. (It was the first seminar held in Gunther's new professional premises, Bernhard had recently moved from Heidelberg to Rottweil. Both moves had been topics during the seminar.)
22. Explanation of the idea "Zug um Zug" seeded earlier. (Transl. Note: -stroke for stroke—bit by bit—breath by breath—move on move, etc. are all included in the German multiple pun "Zug um Zug", even—train by train—draught by draught.)
23. The shocker at the end giving light relief makes the parting easier and wakes everyone up.
24. In this anecdote there was much play on words and several puns. In the original German text the old man asked for a saw and then sawed into his own leg. After the rain came, he explained, "Don't you remember the saying "Sich sägen bringt Regen" (Sawing yourself brings rain). The correct German saying is "Sich regen bringt Segen" (Moving, doing something brings blessings, i.e., positive results). "Sägen" and "Segen" are homophones, and both words rhyme with "Regen" and "sich regen" ("Rain" and "move").

    During most of the seminar week there had been magnificent late summer weather but it had just begun to rain outside, so this fortuitous fact was immediately put to use. Gunther then added a further pun: "Weine nicht wenn der Regen fällt". ("Don't cry when it rains") This was an allusion to a German pop song from the sixties, which had the same title. As "Regen" and "Reagan" are homophones, he attributed this remark to an American friend so the second meaning in German was "Don't cry if (Ronald) Reagan falls (from power, from office)"

25. I had actually intended to tell the story to wake people up and come to a definite, clear, final end, but then instead of saying "is one of the quickest re-orientation techniques" I said with an unconscious slip of the tongue, "re-induction techniques." As said before: it was a fine seminar . . .

— IX —

RE-ORIENTING

This section is addressed to the normal conscious mind of the reader in the logical, predominantly left hemispheric state and presents a (re-) orientation to the whole subject of "Hypnotherapeutic Group Inductions." First in this section is a general survey of terminology, function, possible applications, limitations and advantages and disadvantages of Hypnotic Group Inductions. Then comes a passage dealing with the historical development of this induction type. A comprehensive guide to "how to improve a group induction" follows next.

36

Survey of Group Hypnosis

ORIENTATION

Group hypnosis is a tool, not a therapy in its own right, and is used to help members of a group reach an altered state of consciousness, called "hypnotic" or "therapeutic trance." Recently Jeff Zeig has described six traditional definitions of hypnosis differing according to the underlying theory of personality. These objective approaches define hypnosis in terms of dissociation (Janet, Hilgard), as a role people are playing (Sabin and Coe), as motivated by a special task (Barber), as a state of enhanced suggestibility (Weitzenhoffer, Bernheim), as a regression in the service of ego (Gill, Brenman) or merely as a state of relaxation (Edmundston) (Zeig & Lankton, 1988 p. 355).

He goes on to view these six traditional positions as goals that can be established simultaneously, but that still do not constitute the essence of hypnosis, because the interactional variables are missing. He then proposes to treat hypnosis in the same way as we would treat "love," knowing about the primarily subjective experience. Following Erickson in that the theory of the therapist can distort the patient's reality, he claims that we should rather have multiple definitions depending on the point of view. The observer could talk about hypnosis as "a context for effective communication." The subject might experience "a state of focused awareness on whatever is immediately relevant, in which previously unrecognized psychological and physiological potentials are accessed to some avolitional extent." And the therapist might see it as "a dissociative responsiveness to injunction in a context that is defined as hypnosis" (Zeig, 1988, p.356f.).

As this book deals primarily with the practice of group hypnosis, we are most interested in the subjects' possible experiences such as "alteration in perception and/or memory," "increased control of physiological function," and "increased accessibility of unconscious processes" that characterize hypnosis (Barber in Zeig and Lankton, 1988 p.28). Jeff Zeig mentions "modified awareness, altered intensity, avolitional experience and/or avolitional response" as the main subjective experiences of a person under hypnosis (Zeig in Zeig and Lankton, 1988 p.358).

Of particular importance for hypnosis with groups seems to be the increased learning potential inherent in this particularly active learning state so often emphasized by Erickson. Here participants may access "those unconscious creative potentials a human has without knowing or using" (Peter 1983, p.348).

APPLICATION

As group hypnosis is an instrument, it is itself neutral, with regard to moral values; so how it is used is our responsibility. We can use it for negative or positive purposes. How and when to employ it is a matter of timing and training and the experience of the therapist. It can be employed in group psychotherapy and in other groups. Braun (1979) divides the possibilities of application into four areas:

1. *Groups related to physical health care* such as patient training groups, symptom-oriented groups, and support groups for families and health care personnel. Dentists and obstetricians may train their patients in pain control. Symptom-oriented groups may work towards helping and healing people with problems such as smoking, obesity, multiple sclerosis, arthritis and cancer. Braun names the support groups "Project Hope" and "Make Today Count" for the terminally ill, their families and the professionals who work with them.
2. *Groups for increasing productivity* in the area of school and university. Study habits, test-taking behavior, and motivational problems may be changed (Krippner, 1963, 1966, 1977).

   Stephen Gilligan uses group hypnosis "as a major tool in training hypnotherapists, especially in advanced workshops" (Gilligan, 1987, p. 334).
3. *Groups dealing with personal growth and encounter*

   In the encounter movement personal growth, self-actualization, and sensory awareness were the standards lending themselves well to facilitation via methods often leading to altered states of consciousness. In the future, a fruitful cooperation between users of Gestalt techniques and hypnosis is imaginable.
4. *Psychotherapy groups formed by diagnosis*

   There might be groups formed around a symptom such as alcoholism, drug addiction, phobia, psychosis and so on.

   I want to add a fifth category here: the wide field of *family therapy*. Families, too, are groups.

In this book "Forget the Pain" by Hans Riebensahm is an example of the first group, "Effective Learning" by Wilhelm Gerl of the second, "Ego Building through Imagery" by Jeff Zeig of the third, while the Autogenic Training inductions by U. Freund, N. Katz, and H. Klippstein can represent the fourth group and "The Black Eye" by Ernst Petzold and Wolfgang Herzog the fifth.

Group hypnosis is an adjustable tool. It can be used throughout the stages of group development, because there are significant parallels to the phases of hypnotic work, as Braun pointed out:

- In the information-gathering phase, hypnosis may be used to increase calmness and openness after some information has been shared.

- During the attempts to find one's place in the pecking order, hypnosis may be used to "help people look at the intra-psychic issues which are being expressed interpersonally" (Braun, 1979, p.484).
- When intimacy is established and people do not want to continue to work on their problems, hypnosis can bring out individual and group issues and help make them more pressing.
- In the phase of differentiation, often called the work phase, hypnosis may be used to give support for risk taking.
- Finally, in the termination phase, hypnosis may assist an appropriate working-through of the themes of leaving and loss.

LIMITATIONS, CONTRAINDICATIONS

As in individual hypnotherapy, the contraindications to group hypnosis are relative ones, relating to the therapist's interactive capabilities and experience. Group hypnosis should never be used by persons lacking appropriate professional (clinical) qualifications. One must be prepared to handle strong and often unexpected abreactions, especially with hysterics. Some authors mention the danger of precipitating fragile or inadequately defended personalities into a seriously disintegrated or fragmented state such as a psychotic episode (Karle & Boys, 1977). Others warn that borderlines may flee from therapy if they cannot handle the rapid intimacy and closeness that can develop with group hypnosis. Psychotics might further lose touch with reality (Braun, 1979). Whenever hypnosis is used to break down or through a person's resistances, psychopathology may increase. Erickson hypnotherapy expressly does not do this.

A therapist should pay attention to the fact that a group induction is not a way to enter into a conflict or even powerplay with a group or some members of a group, and should not aim at sweeping rubbish under the carpet instead of bringing it into the open to utilize it, solve it, integrate it.

INDIVIDUAL VERSUS GROUP HYPNOSIS

The main reason for therapy being done in groups at all is the saving of *time and money*. This is true for group hypnosis, too. However, the *task of the group therapist* is more complicated, because there are more things to be aware of than in an individual setting; he has to be aware of the phase of the group's development, the psychological state of each member and interactions. Also it is more difficult to get feedback from each member. His possibilities of registering the ongoing feedback information from all participants is limited.

The *induction* of the trance may be accomplished more effectively in the group setting because group contagion may be used very effectively to build up belief in the efficiency and reality of trance (Fox, 1977). Peers' positive experiences with hypnosis create a subtle tendency for the slower hypnotic subjects to improve. Gunther Schmidt (1985) talks about the influential context of the group, which allows many persons to get into trance more easily in a group situation that in a dyadic contact. The *process of hypnosis* is the same both in individual and group hypnosis. In groups the therapist's ability will decide whether all members reach the deeper phases of trance at the same time and then whether their energies and thoughts can be synchronized for solving the tasks at hand.

Stephen Gilligan reports that "the depth and quality of trance is, for some people, less than that experienced in an individual setting" (Gilligan, 1987, p. 335).

Most of the *hypnotic techniques* can be used with individuals as well as with groups. But in a group setting it is more difficult to have physical contact with each member, if this is desired. The therapist can move around then. It is more difficult, too, to register responses to minimal cues. Concerning the language, it is helpful to use positive expressions and open formulations, because the therapist cannot assist all members at the same time if deep problems are touched. When using hypnosis with groups the therapist must remember that defenses and critical thinking are reduced and unconscious processes and emotions are more easily available.

Some people, however, will feel more secure in a group than in a one-to-one-contact, in accordance with the belief that shared threat is half threat. There is also the advantage of "possible covered therapy," where someone feels the empathy of the group and is able to do or let his or her unconscious do his or her own inner work, but "save his face" in his or her expression (Prior, 1989). Usually the therapist is the person of trust in individual therapy, although even then the client may be afraid that the therapist may learn in trance things he or she may not be ready to reveal. In groups there is the legitimate concern that others in the group may become aware of too *private material*.

When strong *abreactions* can be expected, it is better to work with individual hypnosis. In the group it is a help when a co-therapist can accompany the patient in trouble to another room and care for him or her there. Working with the affect bridge (Watkins, 1963) i.e., visualizing the scene but not necessarily re-experiencing the attendant emotion, has been found valuable in a group setting (Serlin, 1970).

In individual as well as group hypnosis, therapeutic trance has been found particularly meaningful in quickly establishing strong *transference* relationships, sometimes a significant factor in certain kinds of therapeutic changes (Watkins, 1963). In a group there are more possible transference objects, and more possible countertransference objects for the therapist. Emotional facets relating to other group members can be revealed here first, perhaps those to significant persons in the patient's real environment afterwards.

In both individual and group settings, hypnosis speeds up the therapeutic process by facilitating getting into touch with important material and by utilizing unconscious resources for working through the material. When a group gathers around a critical variable, this is the attraction of the group (Yalom, 1975). Hypnosis will increase the empathy and the cohesiveness of the group. There may be better attendance than in individual hypnosis and also more peer pressure available to *effect change*. Task-oriented homogeneous groups have appeared most successful. Heterogeneous encounter groups have been found more effective in producing greater self-actualization of members than homogeneous groups (Braun, 1979).

HISTORY

What we call Group Induction or Group Trance now and what is a special form of art developed by Ericksonians as shown in this book, has been developing since ancient times. Other procedures in the past with other goals, philosophies, and theoretical background were the precursors.

In ancient times group hypnosis was integrated into people's life much more than nowadays as our ancestors were much more linked to their religion and their culture, and had more places for experiencing altered mental states. In the temples of Egypt priests practiced their healing communication, whereas people in Greco-Roman healing temples lay in sleep-like states to regain their sanity and receive advice from the Gods. The hypnotic state is still practiced in so-called primitive cultures throughout many parts of the world, for instance, by the Eskimos and by American Indians as part of their religious ceremonies and as a therapeutic tool of the medicine men. When we go to church today, we are usually unaware that we are undergoing a process of group hypnosis, because the healing professions have been separated from religion for some centuries.

Since the days of Anton Mesmer (1733-1815) the term "hypnosis" refers to a special form of treatment for illnesses. It is little known that Mesmer treated his patients in groups when his practice grew too large for individual treatment to be feasible. As Massermann describes it, "Mesmer's patients would form a circle, hold hands, feel overpowered by the 'magnetism,' fall into trances, have an intensive 'corrective emotional experience' and leave praising the system and spreading the Mesmeric gospel" (Greenberg, p. 4).

This collective method was often used clinically from Mesmer up to the time of Bernheim and Charcot—not to mention its use by stage hypnotists.

In the early 20th century Freud turned away from hypnosis and thus markedly influenced the further development of this therapeutic instrument. He wrote about groups and group process in "Totem and Tabu" (Freud, 1956), but he did not actually work with groups. His disciple Alfred Adler, however, invited patients into his own home, because in his experience displaying an individual's problems to others had a therapeutic effect. Two names of people who made a contribution to the development of group hypnosis are worthy of mention although they themselves never employed this term: E. Jacobson, whose method of Progressive Muscle Relaxation (1938) is still taught, and J. H. Schultz, who, inspired by Eastern Yoga science, developed Autogenic Training (1932), currently the relaxation technique usually imparted to groups of people. In his contribution to Marcuse's book "Hypnosis Throughout the World" published in 1964, Schultz writes about individuals who are taught and trained by a doctor in six sessions to create an autohypnotic state, whereas students at the university usually were trained in big groups to learn the Autogenic Training at that time. Today in Germany, Autogenic Training is the most popular form of group hypnosis, but this terminology is avoided. An organizer of adult education courses once told me that today a program without Autogenic Training is impossible. Another special form of group hypnosis, "hypnodrama," has been developed by J. L. Moreno and J. M. Enneis (1950). Here either the protagonist alone is under hypnosis having an interaction with the group members or many other participants are hypnotized along with the protagonist. Moreno and Enneis (1950) used the hypnosis "as a psychological starter for the warming-up process in that it frees the patient from many of his inhibiting barriers, and places him in a condition of readiness to rise to a state of greater spontaneity" (p. 12).

Rhode's book "Hypnosis," published in 1950, mirrors the concept of these earlier days: Mass hypnosis was an overcharge of the directive hypnotist. Rhodes states that through his direct induction technique of graduated control he was able to immobilize "all but two or three in a group of about thirty, and then put approximately half of them to sleep simultaneously" (Rhodes, 1950, p. 85). In those days it just seemed remarkable to be able to "control" such a large number of subjects at the same time. In 1955 the British Medical Association stated: "In suitable subjects, it (hypnosis) is an effective method of relieving pain in childbirth without altering the normal course of labour." Three years later the American Medical Association placed its qualified stamp of approval on the medical use of hypnosis.

The medical speciality that has given hypnosis the greatest attention is obstetrics. The work of Grantly Dick Read on painless childbirth stimulated interest in drugless approaches to the pain problem of labor and delivery. Read at first did not involve hypnotic suggestion in his methods, a position which he subsequently modified.

In 1961 when Kroger published his book "Childbirth with Hypnosis," he mentioned Joseph B. DeLee, who had advocated hypnosis as being the "only anesthetic without danger" 20 years previously. Thanks to his and others' efforts, suggestive procedures to mitigate childbirth pain became increasingly popular in the States during the subsequent years.

Kroger found ante-natal relaxation and group training classes in hypnosis of benefit to all patients in the final months of pregnancy. "These are usually twice-monthly sessions of about two hours each" (Kroger, 1961, p. 73). This author has delivered several hundred mothers using either pure hypnosis or a combination of hypnosis and chemo-anesthesia. Twenty to 25 percent were carried through the stages of labor without analgesia or anesthesia. Fifty percent of all his patients required only minimal amounts of sedation. Participation in the hypnosis classes was voluntary, of course. Good hypnotic subjects were chosen to demonstrate, for example, glove anesthesia, and then the entire class was invited to participate in order to learn how to gain relief from discomfort and pain in childbirth. The method included learning from a model, direct suggestions, and posthypnotic suggestions, combined with personal office visits and relaxation exercises for inducing self-hypnosis at home.

Most well known are some hypnotic scales that serve as a test in a non-therapeutic situation. In Martin Orne's laboratory for Experimental Psychiatry, Ronald Shor and Emily Orne (1962) have modified the individually administered Stanford Hypnotic Susceptibility Scale (Weitzenhoffer & Hilgard, 1959) to a standardized group scale of hypnotizability for groups of unlimited size. In this research tool 11 hypnotic instructions are given in a direct manner followed by a self-report scoring. Findings indicate "that the adapted scale is an effective predicator of subsequent hypnotic depth" (Shor & Orne, E. 1963, p. 39). "The test today is still the most widely used assessment procedure for initial determination of hypnotic skill" (Orne, M. 1989, personal communication).

There was a consistent further development by Ronald Shor, adapting the Harvard Group

Scale by small steps to the Inventory of Self-Hypnosis (Shor, 1978), where subjects under the supervision of an experienced and responsible professional themselves read the instructions that induce hypnosis, give themselves 12 suggestions, and rate their own performances. It is designed to teach subjects self-hypnosis and can be used as a first hypnotic induction. Versions of these scales have been administered to many thousands of people throughout the world. In 1967, W. J. Ousby's general book about hypnosis was published, reporting the results of over 20 years of therapeutic work with groups in Australia, New Zealand, South Africa, Rhodesia, Kenya, and Britain. He was convinced that groups of ten to 20 people can be instructed in hypnotherapeutic techniques, and in this way learn to help themselves. For him hypnotherapeutic techniques include "relaxation, auto suggestion, self hypnosis and hetero hypnosis" (Ousby, 1984, p. 89), and he saw hypnosis as a natural healing agent to be used especially in the Preventive Health Service.

As far back as 1948, Ousby carried out a mass hypnotic session in New Zealand over the radio, "broadcasting suggestions of general relaxation and of general mental and physical welfare." As proved by a letter from the radio station to him, many people wrote reporting beneficial results. As hypnosis is contraindicated in situations where you have to keep your eyes open, there would be concern about this today because of the people who might be driving cars while listening.

Although there has been a lot of literature dealing with individual hypnosis, I. A. Greenberg's 1977 book "Group Hypnotherapy and Hypnodrama" was the first about Group Hypnosis. Contained in this book is a reprint of I. H. Perline's brief survey, first published in 1968. Perline writes that for problems such as enuresis, weight control, tension and anxiety, alcoholism and schizophrenia, group hypnotherapy was found to be an effective treatment method. From this account it is not easy to discern how group hypnosis was carried out except that most of the work "is of a didactic and directive nature" (Perline in Greenberg, p. 34). In the study of Peberdy working with patients suffering from morbid tension, "the major suggestions have been of confidence and relaxation given with indications of post-hypnotic continuance and reinforcement" (Perline in Greenberg, p. 30). L. K. Supple, who worked with Moreno's hypnodrama techniques, reported that his patients each revealed much deeper levels of trance than in psychodrama.

L. Wollman worked with more than 500 overweight or underweight patients and a significant weight loss or gain was reported in over 90 percent of the cases. "Hypnotic suggestions were given in a directive manner to diminish or increase by any chosen fraction the food intake of the previous week" (Perline in Greenberg, p. 32). Groups of five were found to be most effective. It was not successful when those patients who wanted to lose weight were mixed with those desiring to gain weight.

Astonishing results are reported by Illovsky, who worked with big groups of schizophrenics (150 patients). At the end of a year, 60 percent of the patients could be released from the hospital, those remaining were improved. Of interest, too, is the fact that the results from groups where tape recordings of the therapist's voice were employed, were the same as those groups having direct personal hypnosis. The rate of improvement is reported to be in direct proportion to the depth of trance achieved.

These astonishing results could not be replicated by the group hypnotherapist I. A. Greenberg, who worked with psychotics for many years and who had hoped for a similar miracle. However, in spite of his failures with many psychotics, he still found the group hypnotherapy sessions useful, especially for the non-psychotic patients. Greenberg (1977) also developed a new possibility for utilizing the group hypnosis setting: "I simply found myself doing individual hypnotherapy in a group setting of from four to ten patients per session" (p. xiii).

Two chapters in Greenberg's book describe how group hypnotherapy was practiced by W. T. Reardon. This psychiatrist treated acute anxiety, neurotic depression, emotional disturbances, child problems, alcoholism, obesity, smoking, insomnia, nail-biting, bed wetting, stuttering, marital and family problems, and migraine headache by simply teaching his patients relaxation in ways similar to Jacobson's Progressive Relaxation and Schultz's Autogenic Training. His belief was: "You do everything better when you are relaxed whether it be physical, mental or emotional" (Greenberg, 1977, p. 27). Having learned how to enter this special form of trance the group was given a post-hypnotic suggestion to re-enter this state quickly and deeply and do self hypnosis at home. The patients left supplied with their special homework and learned how to use this new "do it yourself" tool to solve their problems.

According to Ivañov (Greenberg, 1977, p. 84) group hypnosis, or better, "collective hypnosis" has been used in the USSR since 1904. He cited a report by Vjasemskii who worked with alcoholics at that time. As there was no crisis in the field of Soviet hypnology and as the ideological background emphasizes the collective awareness of a group, hypnosis has been used in a wide variety of settings: in neuropsychiatric dispensaries for psychic disorders, borderline conditions and chronic alcoholism, in specialized therapeutic departments for neurosis, in tuberculosis sanatoria and in general hospitals for purely neurological disorders.

Many investigations were being carried out in Russia at a time when hypnosis was still considered in the West as being pseudo-scientific or even mystical. These were based on Pavlov's fundamental concept of hypnosis as a partial sleep. His disciple Birman found the active, wakeful zones in the cerebral cortex constitute the physiological correlates of rapport. During the first quarter of the 20th century, the general belief was that the degree of suggestibility depended on the depth of the hypnotic sleep, so much of the research concentrated upon methods of deepening the hypnotic state. Afterwards, experimental data showed that therapeutic suggestions were effective at all depths of hypnosis, including the lightest. In 1966, after having examined the conditions that increase the effectiveness of suggestions in collective hypnosis, Libich formulated the following requirements: "1. Suggestion should be sufficiently broadly framed that each patient can select from it that which he needs for himself. 2. The general suggestion should touch on typical features of the disease which are to some extent common to all the members of the group. 3. Suggestions should be expressed in concrete imagery, but should only outline—as if to hint at—the decision which should then be taken by the patient" (Greenberg, 1977, p. 92).

Ivanov also pointed out that hypnotherapeutic sessions were always embedded in a more complex therapy plan including individual sessions with the therapist to compensate for the disadvantages of group methods such as greater distance between the therapist and the subject. The group sessions themselves follow a treatment pattern in which the uniformity in the conditions is emphasized: First the conscious ego is addressed giving explanations in a preliminary talk and discussing the illness. The right attitude toward the illness is defined and clear instructions are given. When the quiet benevolent atmosphere within the group has calmed the members, this prelude gives way to actual hypnosis.

Another Russian author, Lebedinskii, agrees that in the USSR therapy through hypnosis is carried out both individually or with groups of patients. Emphasizing the advantages of group hypnosis, Lebedinskii (1964) mentions V. M. Bekhterev as a strong supporter of group hypnosis and comes to the conclusion: "In a group susceptibility to hypnosis as well as suggestibility, both in the hypnotic and in the wakeful state is generally heightened" (p. 246). In a similar way the effectiveness of suggestion can be heightened: "To the suggestive influence of the doctor is added the interacting influence of other patients" (p. 257). He then reports another form of practice not mentioned before: "While working with the group, the doctor also comes up to each patient, and quietly, so that he alone will hear, makes a suggestion designed for him alone" (p. 257).

Only recently has the concept of direct inductions and suggestions begun to develop towards its contrary, i.e., indirect induction techniques and indirect suggestions, e.g. using Ericksonian approaches with images and stories such as those shown in this book.

In the British Hypnotherapeutic Handbook of 1987, there is an example of group hypnosis using guided imagery of a sandy beach. The suggestions of systematically described progressive relaxation, the "core of such an induction" (Karle & Boys, p. 267), are still formulated in a direct manner. Concerning the specification of the image the authors declare that a group induction can be "as specific as an individual induction, but on occasion it is easier and more satisfactory to use a highly permissive approach, which allows individual members to choose their own imagery" (p. 267). If a particular image is chosen employing as much detail and sense data as possible is proposed.

The "mind games" developed by Masters and Houston (1984), still give instructions directly. They require a very high level of hypnotic experience and cannot be used for beginners. If I understand them correctly, the authors invite non-professionals to lead groups for these mind games. With this they are taking a great risk, in my opinion.

A wide-reaching possibility to utilize group inductions was brought to awareness by Daniel Araoz who worked in New York with adolescents on resolving frustration in a constructive way. "Adolescents who have been found guilty of violent behavior are asked in group therapy to visualize their anger inside as a wild beast that they must learn to tame. Each is encouraged to become very familiar with his/her beast, with its living habits, its food, etc. They should give the beast a name. The suggestion is to control the beast so it can help them, work for them, rather than get them into trouble" (1989, personal communication).

Using hypnosis in family therapy seems to be a special area, where group inductions can be used successfully, and this may be a hint for the future. Michele Ritterman (1983) developed a concept, where the symptomatic state is considered "as partly a destructive utilization of trance capacities, in which the symptom bearer is carrying out some reconciliation of seemingly irreconcilable suggestions from another person or social context, a family context and/ or his or her own context of mind" (p. 37). To pattern the therapeutic counterinduction "to help family members to work in nonintrusive concert with each other" (p. 119) it is necessary to actually observe clear-cut inductive events in the family.

Utilizing, too, what the family is already doing, the Lanktons (1986) work with different types of Dual Inductions naturally, for example, also using family members as "secret" cohypnotists, as it could be shown in section VI also by Ernst Petzold and Wolfgang Herzog.

Another form of group trance induction with families is mentioned by Gunther Schmidt and Bernhard Trenkle. They ask the family questions they do not want to have answered immediately. This is a form of guided fantasy to direct attention to certain problem areas or particular resources. They (1985) also describe another integration of systemic family therapy and Ericksonian techniques whereby their comments and interventions are given at the very end of the session in the form of a trance induction for the family (p. 24).

Daniel Araoz and Esther Negley-Parker (1988) used five New Hypnosis "master-techniques" such as "Change Process" or "Past Accomplishments" in family therapy, leading the entire family into trance together. The authors give examples of how to phrase an induction, but they say: "One cannot 'prepare' this type of speech, depending on the specific goal of each family, the words you use will change" (p. 32).

Another far-reaching possibility for using group inductions in the future is the use of cassettes, where the wording is necessarily preplanned. In 1988, an Ericksonian approach using a standardized form of induction was reported. Haim Omer and his colleagues (Lankton & Zeig, 1988) investigated the use of a tape-recorded hypnotic intervention—Barber's Rapid Induction Analgesia (RIA) (Barber, 1977)—in three different gynecological-obstetric settings involving three different levels of stress and of potential for clash between hypnotic instructions and subject's experiences. They found that an automated treatment seems to be less effective in situations of high stress during labor, when personal reassurance was needed and even less so in situations of high potential for clash. In this study the automated treatment could not be compared with individualized treatment.

The Hypnotic Cassettes by Carol Erickson, Thomas Condon, Steven Feinberg et al. in the States, and by Hans Riebensahm, Ortwin Meiss, Lutz Mehlhorn in West Germany show that general goals can be aimed at such as "Natural Self Confidence," "Deep Self Appreciation," "Strengthening of the Inner Healing Forces," "Transformation of Anxiety into Composure," Lutz Mehlhorn, who had previously developed a subliminal program, believes his hypnotic cassettes are even more effective. In addition to the techniques contained in this book there are others, e.g., a third voice (Triple Induction), natural sounds, music (C. Erickson et al.) and a special technique of recording for a more stereophonic hearing experience (Mehlhorn, 1989, personal communication).

Estabrooks and Gross (1961) have talked about the real future of hypnosis "as an aid to the human mind . . . in the education and guidance of normal youngsters, who can benefit from its employ all the way from elementary school through college." As Stanley Krippner (Greenberg, 1977), who has worked with both individuals and groups with elementary and secondary school pupils and with college students, has pointed out, group hypnosis has long been an educational tool: "Classroom teachers attempt to relax their pupils before they begin a difficult assignment or an examination. High school athletic coaches motivate their teams by delivering 'pep talks.' College professors capture their students' attention with colorful language and visual aids. All are using techniques of hypnosis" (p. 123). So far this has been done more or less unconsciously, but this may change soon. The author emphasizes that "clinical reports indicate the possible utility of hypnosis in ameliorating students' study problems, improving concentration, reducing test anxiety, increasing motivation, and facilitating the learning of specific language skills" (p. 133).

HOW TO IMPROVE A GROUP INDUCTION

Group Inductions follow the same principles as individual inductions, although with some modifications. We have incorporated the five-step paradigm of the induction process by Erickson and Rossi (1980) and include the preceding step that Michele Ritterman (1983) added to the model of establishing an intense rapport, which Erickson also regarded as essential. We also include the steps Jeffrey Zeig pointed out to be in an induction. First some general hints:

- Remember that a cooperative atmosphere between the Group Induction leader and the group is crucial.
- Feel responsible for the outer conditions (the door remains closed throughout, the telephone ignored, i.e., possibly disturbing external influences avoided as far as can be determined in advance).
- Create a frame of safety and transparency by giving information about what to expect (content, theme, time frame) and about the nature of hypnosis. Allow everybody to participate in the experience to whatever extent and in whichever way they wish.
- Frame trance as a general context for secure exploration of the Self (Gilligan).
- Be sensitive and responsive to the "personality" of a given group (Gilligan).
- Keep the first induction with a group brief and simple (Gilligan).
- Understand yourself as an instrument, not as the creator of the group hypnosis. Each member of the group can allow the hypnotist to help an altered state of consciousness be reached. Every hypnosis is really an accepted self-hypnosis (Thompson). You only "elicit" hypnosis (Zeig, 1987).
- Keep your eyes open and co-experience with the group, i.e., allow yourself to go into trance yourself.
- Prepare the induction and be spontaneous, allow yourself to skip the plan (Lankton & Lankton, 1983).
- Accept whatever behavior the participants may show. There is no failure possible in the group's behavior.
- Respect resistance (reframe maybe . . .)
- Utilize the stimuli of the situation and the responses to both the situation itself and to the induction given to get positive outcomes.
- Be very careful with your language, because the unconscious takes messages literally in a

trance state and may choose personally important cues without considering the context. Use positive words, because the unconscious may not understand the logical operation of negation.

- Invite participants to talk to the therapist after the session, especially if any problems have occurred.

Phases of Grove Induction

In every group induction there are typical phases.

Phase I: *Warming Up*

Contact between group and therapist is established. Information and expectations are expressed and exchanged. Here it is important that the therapist, too, warms up and learns to feel full of well-being just like the group. The answer of the group, its response to the therapist, is required. This necessary interaction and feedback can be stimulated by questions, jokes, challenges, statements and allocation of tasks, e.g., the group should sit with an open position, an attitude of acceptance, thus simultaneously establishing a cue for future trance experience when the group is ready to react. During this phase the therapist tells the group members what awaits them and adapts to the situation through *pacing*. Description of non-contradictable things may also help toward a "yes-set", i.e., to a positive affirmatory attitude of acceptance to what is coming next.

Phase II: *Absorption in an Internal Experience*

The therapist guides the group towards directing focussed attention to the inside and perceiving what the individual member concretely sees, hears, and feels, until these experiences become automatic. In this way the group is directed toward the basic elements of every learning and by solely perceiving what is there will usually already be enjoying those relaxation processes that facilitate learning. For *leading* into a pleasant balanced state the therapist employs voice as instrument (e.g., deeper timbre, slower rhythm) as well as hypnotherapeutic language devices such as *implication, confusion* and *apparently causal relationships* to prepare the way for *dissociation.* A permissive manner is employed and manifold choice possibilities are left open in order to avoid arousing resistance.

Phase III: *Preparation of Concrete Learning Steps*

This third phase offers an appropriate opportunity for seeding the therapeutic goal, if not yet done, using metaphors, indirect suggestions or anecdotes. Seeding may take place at any time. Working with submodalities (the small elements within the visual, auditory and kinesthetic modalities, such as brightness, loudness, intensity or temperature) stimulates remembrance of actual skills and abilities based on concrete sensual data and/or allows the group to try out and train newly acquired skills. Thus a process of extending consciousness is initiated and old perceptual patterns disrupted. The therapist can augment this by using *pattern interruption*. Jeff Zeig mentions a neutral transition state between the induction and the utilization.

PHASE IV: *OPENING UP FOR NEW EXPERIENCES*

Techniques for deepening trance such as *implied directives*, *double binds*, *overload* and *confusion* are now indicated so the group members develop more trance experience. The therapist elicits *dissociation*, e.g., by inducing arm levitation or drawing attention to the fact that it is possible in a centered state to be on two or more levels of consciousness simultaneously, for instance, feeling particular emotions and being involved in the happenings during trance, while at the same time observing this and also being in contact with the real (external) environment. The therapist *ratifies* the trance by drawing attention to the changes that have already occurred.

PHASE V: *RESOURCES*

When the participants have become fully internally oriented and feelings, sensations, images or phrases emerge automatically and spontaneously, the energies needed for problem solving are available in this phase. The function of the therapist, increasing awareness, is to develop resources by utilizing possibilities of overstepping the present, e.g., by *time-distortion*. The resources of other times and places may be employed. The strengths and skills of the individual personal past and future become available via *regression* and *progression*, as may certain characteristics and abilities of suitable persons via *identification*. Supplementary to these, the therapist may relate stories and metaphors to remind the group of universally valid human knowledge assumably useful at a deeper level of consciousness.

PHASE VI: *THERAPY OR THE ACTUAL GOAL OF THE INDUCTION*

What was just an inkling after seeding, unfolds into its own full flower soon here and now. The most widely differing therapeutic techniques may be used to attain the desired changes: *reframing, symptom prescription, provocation, therapeutic double-binds, implied directives, work with submodalities, direct and indirect suggestions, metaphors and anecdotes, "parts" work, Gestalt therapy type dialogue, work on dreams, regression and progression*, just to mention a few. Particularly decisive here is the confident but nevertheless permissive, non-intrusive attitude of the therapist whose goal will be to lead from passive to active states, from helplessness to responsibility. Though suggestions and solutions may be offered, the actual deciding should always be left to the participant, for here, too, Erickson's fundamental principle still holds, "It's the patient who does the therapy" (Rosen, 1982, p. 89). It is difficult to check whether the therapy works during the group session. This is often only possible later on.

PHASE VII: *INTEGRATION*

Some time must necessarily elapse to allow the new experiences to settle and become consolidated, integrated within the frame of previous learning. Leaving time, giving possibilities for choices and aids to understanding and strengthening trust in the healing properties of the unconscious and/or a greater entity, a "higher instance," are the requisites of assistance here. The therapist may perhaps encourage the group to accept the drawbacks, the darker side of life, and give examples of how apparent bottlenecks often contain the greatest growth potential. Symbolic synthesis of opposites, symbolic approaches, solution of conflicts and reunification of what were previously separated (conscious-unconscious)—also on the physical plane (dissociated parts of the body)—can support the integration process.

PHASE VIII: *FUTURE-PACE AND CONSOLIDATION OF LEARNING*

Direct or *indirect posthypnotic suggestions* and *process instructions* may point out how transfer from the present work to future everyday reality may be achieved. Here it may prove beneficial to *anchor* the work in a particular bodily sensation, a sound or an image, a special attitude or a voluntary action. In order not to disturb the predominantly unconscious processing and transfer work, a permissive *prescription of amnesia* has proved suitable. Amnesia can be attained by *distraction, confusion, pattern interruption* and *swift, sudden changes*. This phase is often employed to foreshadow and prepare the end of the work.

PHASE IX: *RE-ORIENTING*

Both elegant and pleasing the need for symmetry *may be the end of trance reached as first begun*, giving one whole finished entire work that may continue to influence as in a work of art. In addition, a returning ritual, a certain ceremony, provides a safe anchor as assistance and proves that there is a key to the way out of the changed state of consciousness.

Single phases may be dispensed with. The warming-up phase, for instance, may prove superfluous with a familiar group. The reorienting phase can be reduced to a sole sentence if a group well versed in trance is expected to continue work in the same state. Phases may melt together in the artist's kitchen of productivity. Those of us who were perhaps first overwhelmed by all the details will surely find in trance always to express their own very personal messages according to the situation of the group and develop further incorporating all the new ideas that are waiting for us in the future.

If you prefer a solution before the solution, take Erickson's: "Climb"!

References

Araoz, D. L. (1989). Personal communication.

Araoz, D. L. & Negley-Parker, E. (1988). *The New Hypnosis in Family Therapy*. New York: Brunner/Mazel.

Bandler, R., & Grinder, J. (1980). *Metasprache und Psychotherapie*. Paderborn: Junfermann-Verlag.

Barber, J. (1977), Rapid induction analgesia: A clinical report. *American Journal of Clinical Hypnosis, 19*, 138–147.

Barber, J. (1988). The irony of the Ericksonian legend: The power of hypnosis. In J. K. Zeig (Ed.), *Developing Ericksonian therapy: State of the art* (pp. 22–29). New York: Brunner/Mazel.

Bateson, G. (1972). *Steps to an ecology of mind*. New York: Ballantine.

Benares, G. (1977). *Zen without zen masters*. Berkeley: And/Or Press.

Braun, B. G. (1979). Hypnosis in groups and group hypnotherapy. In: Burrows, G. & Dennerstein, L. (Eds.): *Handbook of hypnosis and psychosomatic medicine*. New York: Elsevier-North Holland Biomedical Press.

Carasso, R. L., Peded, O., Kleinhauz, M. & Yehuda, S. (1985). Treatment of cervical headache with hypnosis, suggestive therapy and relaxation techniques. *American Journal of Clinical Hypnosis, 27*(4), 216–218.

Cheek, D. B. (in preparation). Hypnosis and Ideomotor Techniques.

Ellenberger, H. F. (1985), *Die Entdeckung des Unbewußten*. Bern: Diogenes, Hans Huber.

Erickson, M. H., & Rossi, E. L. (1980). Two-level communication and the microdynamics of trance and suggestion. In E. L. Rossi (Ed.), *The collected papers of Milton H. Erickson, M. D. on hyponosis*. Volume 1: *The nature of hypnosis and suggestion* (pp. 430–451). New York: Irvington.

Erickson, M. H., Rossi, E. L. & Rossi, S. I. (1976). *Hypnotic realitities*. New York: Irvington.

Erickson, M. H. & Rossi, E. L. (1979). *Hypnotherapy: An exploratory casebook*. New York: Irvington.

Erickson, M. H. & Rossi, E. L. (1989) The February Man. New York: Brunner/Mazel.

Estabrooks, G. H. & Gross, N. E. (1961). *The future of the human mind*. New York: E. P. Dutton.

Farelly, F. (1974). *Provocative therapy*. Cupertino: Meta Publications.

Fox, J. (1977). The systematic use of hypnosis in individual and group psychotherapy. In: Greenberg, J. A. (Ed.) Group hypnotherapy and hypnodrama. Chicago: Nelson Hall.

Freud, S. (1956). *Totem and Tabu*. Hamburg: Fischer, Frankfurt.

Fuchs, K., Paldi, E., Abramovice, H., & Peretz, B. A. (1980). Treatment of hyperemesis gravidarum by hypnosis. *International Journal of Clinical & Experimental Hypnosis, 28*(4), 313–323.

Gackenbach, J. & Bosveld, J. (1989). *Control your dreams*. New York: Harper & Row.

Garfield, P. (1974). *Creative dreaming*. New York: Simon and Schuster.

Gilligan, S. G. (1987). *Therapeutic trances*. Brunner/Mazel: New York.

Gordon, D. (1986). *Therapeutische Metaphern*. Paderborn: Junfermann-Verlag.

Greenberg, I. A. (Ed.) (1977). *Group hypnotherapy and hypnodrama*. Chicago: Nelson Hall.

Hoffmann, B. (1981). *Handbuch des Autogenen Trainings*. München: Deutscher Taschenbuch Verlag.

Illovsky, J. (1962). Experiences with group hypnosis on schizophrenics. *J. Ment. Sci., 108*, 685–693.

Jeffrey, T. B., Jeffrey, L. K., Greuling, J. W., & Gentry, W. R. (1985). Evaluation of a brief group treatment package including hypnotic induction for maintenance of smoking cessation: A brief communication. *International Journal of Clinical and Experimental Hypnosis, 33*(2), 95–98.

Johnson, L. S., Johnson, D. L., Olson, M. R., & Newman, J. P. (1981). The uses of hypnotherapy with learning disabled children. *Journal of Clinical Psychology, 37*(2), 291–299.

Judd, F. K., Burrows, G. D., & Dennerstein, L. (1985). The dangers of hypnosis: a review. *Australian Journal of Clinical & Experimental Hypnosis, 13*(1), 1–15.

Karle, H. W. A. & Boys, J. H. (1987). *Hynpotherapy, a practical handbook*. London: Free Association Books.

Kelzer, K. (1988). *The sun and the shadow*. Virginia Beach: A.R.E. Press.

Klippstein, H. (1988). Hypnotherapy: A natural method of learning lucid dreaming. *Lucidity Letter, 7*(2), 79–88.

Krippner, S. (1963). Hypnosis and reading improvement among university students. *American Journal of Clinical Hypnosis, 5*, 187–193

Krippner, S. (1966). The use of hypnosis with elementary and secondary school children in a summer reading clinic. *American Journal of Clinical Hypnosis, 8*, 261–266.

Krippner, S. (1977). Individual hypnosis, group hypnosis, and the improvement of academic achievement. In J. A. Greenberg (Ed.), *Group hypnotherapy and hypnodrama*. Chicago: Nelson Hall.

Kroger, W. S. (1961). *Childbirth with hypnosis*. Hollywood: Melvin Powers Wilshire Book Company.

LaBerge, S. (1985), *Lucid Dreaming*. Los Angeles: Jeremy P. Tarcher.

Lake, D. (1984). The use of an initial handout for patients. *Australian Journal of Clinical and Experimental Hypnosis, 12*(1), 62–64.

Lankton, S. R. & Lankton, C. H. (1983). *The answer within: A clinical framework of Ericksonian Hypnotherapy*. New York: Brunner/Mazel.

Lankton, S. R. & Lankton, C. H. (1986). *Enchantment and intervention in family therapy*. New York: Brunner/Mazel.

Lankton, S. R. & Lankton, C. H. (1989) *Tales of enchantment: Goal-oriented metaphors for adults and children in therapy*. New York: Brunner/Mazel.

Lankton, S. R. & Zeig, J. K. (1988). *Research, comparisons and medical applications of Ericksonian techniques*. New York: Brunner/Mazel.

Lebedinskii, M. S. (1964). Hypnosis in the union of soviet socialist republics. In F. L. Marcuse (Ed.), *Hypnosis throughout the world*. Springfield, Illinois: Charles C. Thomas Publisher.

Masters, R. & Houston, J. (1984). *Phantasie Reisen*. München: Kösel.

Marcuse, F. L. (Ed.) (1964). *Hypnosis throughout the world*. Springfield, Illinois: Charles C. Thomas.

McCabe, M. P., et al. (1983). The role of sex of therapist and groups vs. individual therapy in treatment outcome using hypnosis with obese female patients: A research note. *Australian Journal of Clinical and Experimental Hypnosis, 11*(2), 107–109.

Minuchin, S. (1974). *Families and family therapy*. Cambridge: Harvard University Press.

Minuchin, S., Rosman, B. & Baker, L. (1978). *Psychosomatic families*. Cambridge: Harvard University Press.

Moreno, J. L. & Enneis, J. M. (1950). *Hypnodrama and psychodrama*. New York: Beacon House.

Ousby, J. W. (1984). *The theory and practice of hypnotism*. Wellingborough, Northamptonshire: Thorsons Publishers Limited.

Peter, B. (1983). Hypnotherapie. In R. J. Corsini (Hrsg.), *Handbuch der psychotherapie*. Beltz Verlag, Weinheim und Basel.

Peter, B. (1985). *Hypnose und hypnotherapie nach Milton H. Erickson*. Munchen: Peiffer.

Peter, B. (1988). Haben wir einen neuen Mesmer nötig? *Hypnose und Kognition, 5*(2), 87–96.

Peter, B. & Kraiker, C. (Eds.) (1989). Hypnose und das Unbewußte. *Hypnose und Kognition, 6*(1).

Peter, B. & Gerl, W. (1977). *Entspannung*. München: Mosaik Verlag.

Pilkington, J. M. & the Diagram Group. (1989). *Mind over matter*. London: Weidenfeld & Nicolson.
Prior, M. (1989). Personal communication.
Rhodes, R. H. (1950). *Hypnosis*. New York: Gramercy Publishing Company.
Ritterman, M. (1983). Using hypnosis in family therapy. San Francisco: Jossey-Bass.
Rosen, S. (Ed.) (1982). *My voice will go with you*. New York: Norton.
Rossi, E. L. (1986). *The psychobiology of mind-body healing: New concepts of therapeutic hypnosis*. New York: Norton.
Rossi, E. L. & Cheek, D. B. (1988). *Mind-body therapy*. New York: Norton.
Rossi, E. L. & Ryan, M. O. (Eds.) (1986). Mind-body communication in hypnosis. Vol. III. *The seminars, workshops and lectures of Milton H. Erickson*. New York: Irvington.
Scharfetter, Chr. (1986). *Schizophrene Menschen*. München: Psychologie Verlags Union.
von Schlippe, A. & Kriz, J. Hrsg. (1987). *Symposion Familientherapie Kontroverses-Gemeinsames* 1986, Osnabrück Verlag Wildberg: Mona Bögner-Kaufmann.
Schmidt, G. (1985). Gedanken zum Ericksonschen Ansatz aus einer Systemorientierten Perspektive. (31-57) In B. Peter, (Hrsg.) *Hypnose und Hypnotherapy nach Milton H. Erickson*, München: Pfeiffer.
Schultz, J. H. (1973). *Das Autogene Training*. Stuttgart: Thieme.
Scott, J. A. (1984). Hypnotherapy training for basket-ball: An experimental approach. *Medical Hypnoanalysis*, 6(3), 109–116.
Selvini Palazzoli, M., Boscolo, L., Cecchin, G. & Prata, G. (1977). *Paradoxon und Gegenparadoxon*. Stuttgart: Klett-Cotta.
Serlin, P. R. (1970). Techniques for the use of hypnosis in group psychotherapy. *American Journal of Clinical Hypnosis. 123*, 177–202.
Shor, R. E. (1978). *Inventory of self-hypnosis, form A*. Palo Alto: Consulting Psychologists Press.
Shor, R. E. & Orne, E. C. (1962). *The Harvard group scale of hypnotic susceptibility, form A*. Palo Alto: Consulting Psychologists Press.
Shor, R. E. & Orne, E. C. (1963). Norms on the Harvard group scale of hypnotic susceptibility, form A. *International Journal of Clinical and Experimental Hypnosis, XI*(1), 39–47.
Silverman, L. H., et al. (1982). *In search of oneness*. New York: International Universities Press.
Simon, R. (1985). Deeper, deeper, deeper . . . the family's hypnotic pull. *Family Therapy Networker*, 9(2), 20–26, 28, 69–71.
Tart, C. T. (1989). *Open mind, discriminating mind*. New York: Harper & Row.
Theoly, P. & Utecht, K. (1987). *Schöpferisch träumen*. Niedernhausen: Falken-Verlag.
Toomey, T. C. & Sanders, S. (1983). Group hypnotherapy as an active control strategy in chronic pain. *American Journal of Clinical Hypnosis*, *26*(1), 20–25.
Trenkle, B. & Schmidt, G. (1985). Ericksonsche Psychotherapie und Familientherapie: Möglichkeiten der Integration. *Hypnose und Kognition*, *2*(1), 5–26.
Walker, W. L., Collins, J. K. & Krass, J. (1982). Four hypnosis scripts from the Macquarie weight control programme. *Australian Journal of Clinical and Experimental Hypnosis*, *10*(2), 125–133.
Watkins, J. G. (1963). Transference aspects of the hypnotik relationship. In Kline, M. V. (Ed.), *Clinical Correlations of Experimental Hypnosis*. Springfield, Ill.: Charles C. Thomas.
Watzlawick, P. (1988). *Münchhausens Zopf oder Psychotherapie und "Wirklichkeit."* Bern, Stuttgart: Brunner/Mazel.
Weitzenhoffer, A. & Hilgard, E. P. (1959). Stanford Hypnotic Susceptibility Scale, Form A and B. Palo Alto: Consulting Psychologists Press.
Whitaker, C. (1982). Hypnosis and family depth therapy. In J. K. Zeig (Ed.), *Ericksonian approaches to hypnosis and psychotherapy*. New York: Brunner/Mazel.
Wilber, K. (1981). *Up from eden: A transpersonal view of human evolution*. Boston: Shambhala Publications.
Wilber, K. (1987). *Halbzeit der Evolution*. Scherz, Bern, München, Wien.
Wolberg, L. R. (1948). *Medical hypnosis*. New York: Grune and Stratton.

Yogananda, P. (1946). *Autobiography of a yogi.* Los Angeles: Self-Realization-Fellowship.
Yalom, I. D. (1975). *Theory and practice of group psychotherapy.* New York: Basic Books.
Yapko, M. D. (1981). The effect of matching primary representational system predicates on hypnotic relaxation. *American Journal of Clinical Hypnosis, 23*(3), 169–175.
Zeig, J. K. (Ed.) (1982). *Ericksonian approaches to hypnosis and psychotherapy.* New York: Brunner/Mazel.
Zeig, J. K. (Ed.) (1987). *The evolution of psychotherapy.* New York: Brunner/Mazel.
Zeig, J. K. (1988). An Ericksonian phenomenological approach to therapeutic hypnotic induction and symptom utilization. In J. K. Zeig & S. R. Lankton (Eds.), *Developing Ericksonian therapy.* (pp. 353–375). New York: Brunner/Mazel.